C. W. Passchier · R. A. J. Trouw   Microtectonics

Springer
Berlin
Heidelberg
New York
Barcelona
Budapest
Hong Kong
London
Milan
Paris
Singapore
Tokyo

C. W. Passchier · R. A. J. Trouw

Microtectonics

With 254 Figures

 Springer

PROF. DR. C. W. PASSCHIER
Universität Mainz
Institut für Geowissenschaften
55099 Mainz
Germany

PROF. DR. R. A. J. TROUW
Universidade Federal do Rio de Janeiro
Depto. de Geologia
CEP 21910-900 Rio de Janeiro
Brazil

2nd corrected reprint 1998

ISBN 3-540-58713-6 Springer-Verlag Berlin Heidelberg New York

CIP data applied for.

Die Deutsche Bibliothek - CIP-Einheitsaufnahme

Passschier, Cornelis W.:
Microtectonics / C. W. Passchier ; R. A. J. Trouw. - 2., corr. reprint. - Berlin ; Heidelberg ; New York ;
Barcelona ; Budapest ; Hong Kong ; London ; Milan ; Paris ; Singapore ; Tokyo : Springer, 1998
ISBN 3-540-58713-6

Springer-Verlag Berlin Heidelberg New York
a part of Springer Science+Business Media
springeronline.com

© Springer-Verlag Berlin Heidelberg 1996 / 1998
Printed in Germany

Typesetting: Storch GmbH, Wiesentheid

SPIN: 10971642   32/3111 – 5 4 Printed on acid free paper

To see a world in a grain of sand
and a heaven in a wild flower
hold infinity in the palm of your hand
and eternity in an hour

Wiliam Blake

To Henk Zwart

For his contribution to structural and metamorphic geology

Introduction

The origin of this book lies in a practical course in microtectonics started by Prof. Henk Zwart at Leiden University, the Netherlands, in the early 1960s. Both of us were students of Henk Zwart at the University of Leiden and later, as his assistants, charged with the organisation of this course. As such, we became enchanted by the many interesting thin sections of his collection which expanded over the years, as Henk extended his work from the Pyrenees to the Alps, the Scandinavian Caledonides and to many other places in the world. An explanatory text was elaborated and regularly updated by a number of assistants, including us, under Henk's supervision. This text, together with many thin sections of the collection, served as a core for the present book. In the early 1980s, the Geology Department of Leiden University was transferred to the University of Utrecht. The collection was transferred as well, and one of us (C.W.P) became responsible for its organisation and maintenance. A visit of R.A.J.T to Utrecht in 1991 with a number of didactic microstructures collected in South America triggered the final effort to build a manual for the study of microtectonics. Because of his contributions to science and his enthusiasm for microtectonics, we dedicate this book to Henk Zwart, who inspired us, taught us the principals of microtectonic analysis, and also furnished many crucial examples of microstructures.

Few geologists will be able to remember what their first impression was when they were confronted with a deformed rock under the microscope. That is unfortunate, because it inhibits experienced geologists from looking at geometries in thin section in an unbiased way. We commonly think that we 'see' dynamic recrystallisation, refolding and grain growth, while all we actually see are geometric patterns that may have formed in a number of different ways. In this book, we try to preserve some of the 'first encounter approach' with deformed rocks. Where possible, we present a description of the geometry of structures separately, followed by their state-of-the-art interpretation.

This book is meant for advanced undergraduate and graduate students, and is best used in combination with a practical course where thin sections can be studied and discussed. In our experience, a collection of 100–200 thin sections with examples from structures treated in our Chapters 3–7 are sufficient for such a course.

In Chapter 1 the 'philosophy' of how we think that microstructures can be understood is discussed, including their usefulness in tectonic studies. Chapter 2 gives a simplified, non-mathematical background in kinematics and rheology, meant to explain the terminology used in the interpretation of microstructures. Deformation on the grain scale and deformation mechanisms are treated in Chapter 3. Chapters 4 to 7 form the core of the book and deal with the most commonly observed microstructures. In Chapter 8 a brief outline is given of a new development in microtectonics which we called microgauges: structures that can be used to obtain quantitative data from deformed rocks. Chapter 9 describes a number of additional techniques other than optical microscopy. These techniques either use thin sections, or can be used in combination with optical microscopy to obtain additional data. The descriptions are short but should allow the reader to decide if his material can be studied using a technique with which he may not be familiar. Chapter 10 describes the problems involved with sampling and preparation of thin sections, including the problems of the interpretation of three-dimensional structures using two-dimensional sections. Chapter 11 is a selection of photographs meant as examples of common problems in microtectonics; the reader may use them as an exercise trying to interpret the structure; our interpretation is given at the end of the chapter. A glossary of commonly used terminology in microtectonics is given at the end of the book; the definitions in this glossary reflect our opinion on the meaning of the terminology as used at present.

Since this book mainly deals with interpretation of geometries, a large number of drawings and photographs are included. We decided to use only black and white photographs in order to obtain maximum contrast and to keep costs of the book down. In the figure captions, PPL and CPL mean plane polarised and crossed polarised light, respectively. Provenance of the photographed thin sections is given where known. For some thin sections in the old collection from Leiden, the provenance is unknown and these were marked as 'Leiden Collection'. The scale of the photographs is given as a width of view.

The following critical readers of the original manuscript helped considerably to improve the book with useful suggestions: Hans de Bresser, Bas den Brok, Paul Dirks, David Grey, Monica Heilbron, Renée Heilbronner, Ralph Hetzel, Kyu-ichi Kanagawa, Win Means, Uwe Ring, Herman van Roermund, Luiz Sergio Simões, Carol Simpson, Ron Vernon and Janos Urai. Bas den Brok provided data for Chapter 3.12 and drew the original of Fig. 3.32. Their help is gratefully acknowledged. Preparation of the manuscript was assisted by Anja Böhm, Magda Martens, Susanne Laws, Regina Summerer, Kerstin Thiel and Robert Bolhar, who are thanked for their efforts. Some of the photographs, samples and thin sections were kindly provided by Ralph Hetzel (Figs. 5.14, 7.45, 11.15), Paul Dirks (Figs. 7.51–54), Domingo Aerden (Fig. 11.10), Michel Arthaud (Fig. 6.23), Coen ten Brink (Fig. 9.11), Hanna Jordt-Evangelista (Fig. 7.21), Reinhardt Fuck (Fig. 11.14), Leo Kriegsman (Fig. 7.52), Gordon Lister (Fig. 4.24), Leo Minnigh (Fig. 6.24), Jin-Han Ree (Fig. 9.10), André Ribeiro (Fig. 11.2), Chris Schoneveld (Figs. 7.37, 11.16, and cover), Janos Urai (Fig. 6.2), Simon Wallis (Figs. 4.35, 7.35), Klaus Weber (Fig. 9.3) and Dirk Wiersma (Fig. 6.14a). Many other persons helped in one way or the other, either by furnishing samples with interesting microstructures that were integrated in our collections but not shown, or by discussing the meaning of microstructures. Their help is also gratefully acknowledged.

The Volkswagen Stiftung, the German Science Foundation (DFG), the Schürmann Fund, the Dutch Royal Academy of Sciences and the Brasilian Research Council (CNPq) provided funding for our research, the results of which have been used in this book; this support is gratefully acknowledged. R.A.J.T thanks the Brasilian Research Council (CNPq) for financing his stay at Utrecht University and the Department of Geology in Utrecht for its hospitality.

C. W. Passchier
R. A. J. Trouw

Contents

Abbreviations and Principal Symbols

A_k	kinematic dilatancy number
AVA diagram	Achsenverteilungsanalyse-Diagram
ccc	compressional crenulation cleavage
CIP	computer-integrated polarisation microscopy
CISH	cumulative incremental strain history
CPL	crossed polarised light
CRSS	critical resolved shear stress (τ_c)
ε	strain
$\dot{\varepsilon}$	strain rate
EDAX	energy dispersive X-ray analysis
FA	fabric attractor
GBAR	grain boundary area reduction
GBM recrystallisation	grain boundary migration recrystallisation
ISA	instantaneous stretching axis
L_r	reference lineation
LPO	lattice-preferred orientation
OCP	octachloropropane
ODF diagram	orientation distribution function diagram
PPL	plane polarised light
P-T diagram	pressure temperature diagram
PTt path	pressure temperature time path
R_f/φ	R_f: elliptic ratio of objects; φ angle of longest axis of elliptical shape with reference direction
σ	stress
$\sigma_1, \sigma_2, \sigma_3$	principal stress values
σ_n	normal stress
S	stretch
S_1, S_2, S_3	in Chapter 2: principal stretches or principal strain values (length of principal strain axes). In other chapters and in the literature also used as abbreviation for foliations
$\dot{S}$	stretching rate
S_i	internal foliation in a porphyroblast with inclusions
S_e	external foliation with respect to a porphyroblast with inclusions
S_r	reference foliation
sbc	shear band cleavage
SR recrystallisation	subgrain rotation recrystallisation
τ	shear stress
TTT diagram	time-temperature-transformation diagram
W_k	kinematic vorticity number
ω	angular velocity of material lines
X, Y, Z axes	principal axes of strain

1 A Framework of Microtectonic Studies

1.1 Introduction

From their first use in the last century, thin sections of rocks have been an important source of information for geologists. Many of the older textbooks on structural geology, however, did not treat microscopic aspects of structures, while petrologists would describe microscopic structures as, for example, lepidoblastic or nematoblastic without paying much attention to kinematic and dynamic implications. During the last decades, however, structural geologists learned to profit from the wealth of data that can be obtained from the geometry of structures studied in thin section, and metamorphic petrologists have appreciated the relation of structural evolution on the thin section scale and metamorphic processes.

Deformed rocks are one of the few direct sources of information available for the reconstruction of tectonic evolution. Nevertheless, observations on the geometry of structures in deformed rocks should be used with care; they are the end product of an often complex evolution and we can only hope to reconstruct this evolution if we correctly interpret the end stage. Simple geometries such as folds can be formed in many ways and it may seem hopeless to try and reconstruct a complex evolutionary sequence from geometrical information only. However, despite the simple geometry of our face, we can individually recognise most of the six billion people on our planet. It is likely that structures in rocks also contain a large amount of detail which we cannot (yet) recognise and interpret because we are not trained to do so, and partly because we do not know what to look for. It is interesting to page through old publications on microstructures, e.g. on inclusions in garnet or on porphyroclasts, to see how drawings evolved from simple to complex while understanding of the processes related to the development of these structures increased. At any time, some degree of misinterpretation of structural evolution is unavoidable and part of the normal process of increasing our understanding of the subject. This book is therefore a-state-of-the-art description of microstructures and their interpretation.

FABRIC, TEXTURE, MICROSTRUCTURE

In this book we mainly deal with *fabrics*. A fabric '... includes the complete spatial and geometrical configuration of all those components that make up a rock. It covers concepts such as *texture, structure* and crystallographic preferred orientation. ...' (Hobbs et al. 1976). The parts that make up a fabric, also known as *fabric elements,* should be penetratively and repeatedly developed throughout a volume of rock; a single fault in a volume of rock is not considered to be part of the fabric, but a large number of parallel foliation planes are. Fabric elements are therefore dependent on scale (cf. Fig. 2.6). A volume of rock may have a *random fabric*, i.e. a random distribution and orientation of its elements or, more commonly, a non-random fabric, including foliations and lineations.

In this book, we mainly deal with fabrics on microscopic scale, or *microfabrics*. Microfabric elements may include grain shape, grain boundaries, deformation lamellae, aggregates of grains with similar shape, and lattice preferred orientation.

In the non-geological literature about metals and ceramics, the term *texture* is generally used for lattice preferred orientation. On the other hand, most of the older textbooks on metamorphic petrology (e.g. Turner 1968; Miyashiro 1973; Best 1982; Williams et al. 1982; Bucher and Frey 1994) make a distinction between the **texture** and the **structure** of a metamorphic rock. In these texts, **texture** refers to the geometrical aspects of the component particles of a rock including size, shape and arrangement, whereas **structure** usually refers to the presence of compositional layering, folds, foliation, lineation, etc. In fact there is no clear difference between the two concepts and the subcommission on the systematics of metamorphic rocks of the IUGS recommends to substitute the term texture by *microstructure*. In this book, we use the terms microstructure and microfabric (see also Chap. 1.1) as synonyms.

Observations on the microstructure or *fabric* of a rock (Box p. 1), specifically in thin section, can be used in two major fields. They can be applied to thematic studies, to understand mechanisms of rock deformation and metamorphism; or they can be used to reconstruct the structural and metamorphic history of a volume of rock. Thin section studies are mostly in the latter field. Because such thin section studies can serve to reconstruct tectonic evolution, we use the term *microtectonics*.

This chapter is not only meant as a general introduction to the subject of microtectonics, but also serves as a definition of the framework within which we see studies in microtectonics. As such, it contains terminology that is explained only later in the text and in the Glossary. This chapter can be read before, but also in conjunction with, the other chapters.

In theory, one could expect that a sedimentary rock which is buried, deformed, metamorphosed and brought back to the surface should have the same mineral composition as the original sediment if perfect equilibrium conditions were to be attained at each stage. A simple fabric should be developed in such a case in response to gradual changes in the stress field and in metamorphic conditions. Fortunately for the geologist, who relies on structures and mineral assemblages in deformed rocks as a source of information, this is almost never the case. In most deformed rocks, structures with different style and orientation and minerals which represent different metamorphic grades *overprint* each other. This means that equilibrium is generally not attained at each stage: mineral assemblages representative of different metamorphic conditions may be 'frozen in' at different stages during burial and uplift. With overprint we mean that structures or mineral assemblages are superposed on each other and must therefore differ in age; this may be visible through crosscutting relations, overgrowth, or even differences in deformation intensity. In practice, however, *overprinting relations* can be difficult to establish. This book mainly serves to illustrate the possibilities of recognising overprinting relations in thin section and to determine the conditions at which they formed. The aim is then to translate overprinting relations in terms of *deformation phases* and *metamorphic events*.

Deformation phases are thought to be distinct periods of active deformation of rocks on a scale exceeding that of a single outcrop, possibly separated by time intervals with little or no deformation during which metamorphic conditions and orientation of the stress field may have changed (Chap. 1.2, 2.11). The concept was originally created in relation to groups of structures that can be separated in the field by over-

printing criteria (Chap. 1.2). Metamorphic events are episodes of metamorphism characterised by changes in mineral assemblage in a volume of rock. Such changes are thought to reflect changes in metamorphic conditions.

Once deformation phases and metamorphic events are defined, it is necessary to determine to what extent they correspond to *tectonic events* or *metamorphic cycles*, i.e. events on a larger scale such as those associated with plate motion or collision. Finally, *orogenies* (e.g. the Alpine orogeny) may encompass several tectonic events with associated metamorphic cycles. The following example illustrates this concept. In thin sections from several outcrops, a horizontal biotite foliation is overprinted by a steeply dipping chlorite foliation, and both are cut by brittle faults (Fig. 1.1). Based on these overprinting relations we could argue that a first 'deformation phase' with a component of vertical shortening formed a foliation under conditions suitable for growth of biotite; later, a second 'deformation phase' of oblique shortening was accompanied by chlorite growth under lower-grade metamorphic conditions. A third deformation phase affected both earlier structures at very low-grade or non-metamorphic conditions or at high strain rate, to cause brittle faulting. Time intervals of no-deformation activity are postulated between the deformation phases during which metamorphic conditions changed significantly while the volume of rock under consideration was 'passively' transported to another position in the crust. (e.g. by erosion and uplift). The deformation phases are accompanied by metamorphic events, which may lie

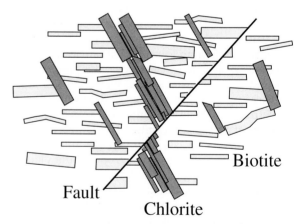

Fig. 1.1. Schematic diagram of a biotite foliation *(horizontal)*, a chlorite foliation *(inclined)* and a brittle fault. The sequence of overprinting relations is: biotite foliation-chlorite foliation-fault. The three structures may represent different deformation phases since they overprint each other, have different orientation and represent probably different metamorphic conditions

on the retrograde leg of a single metamorphic cycle (Chap. 1.3). The size of the area over which these deformation phases can be recognised should now be investigated and gradients in style and orientation monitored. Finally, the synchronous or diachronous nature of a deformation phase can be established by absolute dating of minerals associated with structures over a large area, or by crosscutting intrusions. Comparison with similar data on a larger scale, either from the literature or by carrying out further field and thin section research, can establish the regional significance of deformation phases with relation to tectonic events. Because such large-scale analysis is not part of the subjects covered in this book, we restrict ourselves to the establishment of overprinting relations, deformation phases and metamorphic events from data obtained in thin section. The following section gives an outline of some of the problems involved in establishing overprinting relations and deformation phases.

1.2 Establishing and Interpreting Deformation Phases

The concept of deformation phases has been used extensively in the geological literature in reconstruction of the structural evolution of rock units with complex deformation patterns (e.g. Ramsay 1967; Hobbs et al. 1976; Ramsay and Huber 1987; Marshak and Mitra 1988). The underlying idea is that permanent deformation in a volume of rock occurs when differential stresses (Chap. 2.11) are relatively high and that the orientation of the stress field may change between such periods of permanent deformation without visible effects on the rock fabric. The older fabric is not always smoothly erased or modified to a new fabric, since deformation in rocks is commonly partitioned (that is: concentrated in certain domains and less concentrated or absent in others); relics of older fabric elements may be locally preserved. A foliation that is shortened parallel to the foliation plane may develop folds, commonly with a new crenulation cleavage developing along the axial surface. The older foliation will be completely erased only at high strain or by recrystallisation and grain growth under favourable metamorphic circumstances (Box p. 88). Boudins and tight or isoclinal folds may be refolded but remain recognisable up to very high strain. Lattice-preferred orientation may be preserved in less deformed lenses up to high strain;

and porphyroblasts may preserve relics of older structures as long as the porphyroblast phase remains intact (Chap. 7.3–7.7).

Although the concept of deformation phases seems fairly simple and straightforward, there are some problems with its general application, as outlined below.

1. Overprinting relations may be produced by a single deformation phase. Non-coaxial progressive deformation (Chap. 2.5.2) may produce overprinting relations between structures without a major change in the large-scale orientation and magnitude of the stress field. Especially in mylonitic rocks developed in shear zones, it is common to find folds (often sheath folds) that deform the mylonitic foliation and which are clearly the result of the same deformation phase that produced the mylonitic foliation in the first place (Chap. 5.3.2); such folds can be formed at any time during progressive deformation (Fig. 1.2).

2. Subsequent deformation phases do not necessarily produce overprinting relations. Two subsequent deformation phases with a similar orientation of the stress field and a similar metamorphic grade may be indistinguishable in the final fabric. For example, a 2400-Ma-old hornblende foliation, formed under amphibolite facies conditions, could be overprinted by a 1600-Ma phase of amphibolite facies deformation in a stress field with approximately the same orientation. The result would be strengthening of the earlier foliation. In such cases, only detailed microprobe work or mineral dating may reveal the correct sequence of events.

3. Only the relative age of deformation phases can be established. Identical overprinting relations may

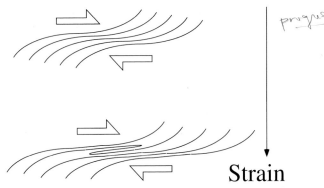

Fig. 1.2. Sequence of events in a shear zone to show how overprinting relations may form during a single phase of progressive deformation if some heterogeneity is present to cause folding

develop where an Archaean foliation is overprinted by a crenulation cleavage of Phanerozoic age, or in a thrust nappe within an interval of several hundred thousand years only. If metamorphic conditions are significantly different for two deformation phases, a minimum time separation can be established but otherwise absolute age dating is required.

4. The significance of deformation phases depends on the scale of observation. During development of a fold the axial planar foliation may be rotated to such an extend that a crenulation cleavage is locally formed, overprinting the earlier formed foliation (Williams 1972a). Such overprinting relations form during a single phase of deformation. The same effect may occur on a larger scale; consider a volume of rock in a thrust sheet that is transported over a ramp; the sudden changes in orientation of the rock volume when it moves up and over the ramp can induce overprinting relations. In this case, the final fabric will show separable deformation phases on thin section and outcrop scale, but these will be part of a single deformation phase on a regional scale.

5. Deformation phases may be diachronous. Deformation may affect volumes of rock in a progressive way, starting from one side and reaching the other end much later (Hobbs et al. 1976). As a consequence, an overprinting structure labelled D_2 may be older in a certain area than a D_1 fabric in another. A common setting for such an evolution may be in accretionary wedges, where undeformed rocks arrive at a subduction zone, and subsequently become incorporated in the wedge (Figs. 1.3, 7.57).

Because of the problems mentioned above and also because of the subjective nature of subdivision in sets of structures (e.g. Hobbs et al. 1976), some geologists have become reluctant to use the deformation phase concept any longer. However, we feel that the concept continues to be useful to classify structures in a sequential order, if used with care. Deformation phases refer only to the relative age of structures in a limited volume of rock, (commonly in the order of a few hundred km³) and are generally not equivalent to tectono-metamorphic events of regional significance. It is therefore necessary to determine the tectonic significance of local deformation phases. To establish deformation phases it is important to define sets of structures based on reliable overprinting criteria, such as a foliation (S_n) that has been folded (D_{n+1} folds), and not just on style, orientation, tightness of folds etc., which are criteria that may change from one outcrop to the next in structures of the same age. It is also important to take metamorphic conditions

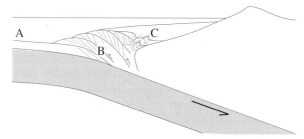

Fig. 1.3. Schematic representation of an active accretionary prism. At **A** no deformation is occurring whereas at **B** a first deformation phase D_1 is responsible for oceanward thrusting, probably accompanied by the development of foliations and folds in deep levels. While such D_1 structures develop at **B**, a second phase of deformation D_2 related to backthrusting is already overprinting D_1 structures at **C**

during deformation into consideration, since these are not subject to rapid change (Fig. 1.1). A final warning must be given for the extrapolation of phases from one area to another, or even from one outcrop to the next. The criteria for subdivision remain subjective in the sense that different workers may define a sequence of deformation phases in a different way, resulting in a variable number of phases for the same area. This, however, does not necessarily mean that one of these workers is right, and the others in error; it may just be a matter of different criteria for definition.

For all overprinting relations it is necessary to determine whether they could have formed during a single phase of deformation under similar metamorphic conditions. The following criteria may help to determine whether overprinting relations correspond to separate deformation phases:

a) Two overprinting structures composed of different mineral assemblages that represent a gap in metamorphic grade must belong to different deformation phases.

b) Foliations that overprint each other commonly represent deformation phases on thin section scale (Chap. 4.11.2), but exceptions such as oblique fabrics (Chap. 5.6.3) and shear band cleavages (Chap. 5.6.4) exist .

c) Overprinting folds with oblique axial surfaces represent different deformation phases. Care should be taken with refolded folds with parallel axes (Type III of Ramsay 1967), especially in the case of isoclinal folds since these may form during a single deformation phase (Fig. 1.2).

d) Shortened boudins are commonly formed by overprinting of two deformation phases (Passchier 1990a; Chap. 5.6.11).

e) Some structures preserved in porphyroblasts represent separate deformation phases (Chap. 7.3-7.5).
f) Intrusive veins or dykes can be important to separate phases of deformation and their associated foliations.

1.3 Deformation Phases and Metamorphic Events

A metamorphic evolution can be subdivided into *metamorphic events* defined by the growth of particular metamorphic minerals, in a way similar to the concept of deformation phases. Certain fabrics are indicative of growth sequences in metamorphic rocks (e.g. inclusions in porphyroblasts and reaction rims; Chap. 7.6.5 and 7.8) and relations between porphyroblasts and foliations commonly reveal the relative time sequence of their generation (Chap. 7.3-7.5). However, one must keep in mind that a metamorphic event is of an essentially different nature than a deformation phase. Whereas the latter is thought to reflect a period of deformation in between intervals of little or no deformation, the former normally reflects only the passing of critical PT values necessary for a chemical reaction to start and to produce one or more new minerals in the rock. Since deformation often has a catalysing effect on mineral reactions, many such metamorphic events are found to coincide approximately with deformation phases. In other words, many metamorphic minerals are found to have grown during specific deformation phases.

The metamorphic history of a volume of rock can be presented schematically in a *P-T diagram* as a curve, the *PTt-path* (pressure-temperature-time) (Fig. 1.4a; Daly et al. 1989). PTt-paths as shown in Fig. 1.4 have been theoretically predicted (e.g. England and Richardson 1977; England and Thompson 1984; Thompson and England 1984) and have been reconstructed in tectonic studies from data points that give P-T conditions at a certain time. Such data points can be obtained from metamorphic events (reactions between minerals reconstructed from geometric relations in thin section; Chap. 7.8) as compared with theoretically determined petrogenetic grids. They can also be calculated from the chemical composition of mineral pairs or associations in equilibrium, the so-called *geothermometers* and *geobarometers* (e.g. Spear and Selverstone 1983; Essene 1989; Spear et al. 1990). For example, in Fig. 1.4a, the deformation phases are separated in time and the metamorphic events

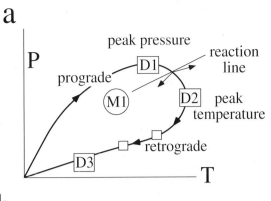

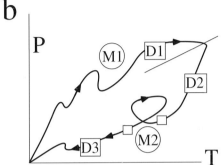

Fig. 1.4. a Data points in P-T space *(squares)* some of which are associated with deformation phases D_1 to D_3. A simple clockwise PTt path is postulated based on these data points, representing a single metamorphic cycle of prograde, peak and retrograde metamorphic conditions. The direction of the PTt path at peak metamorphic conditions is based on passage of a reaction line; however, other directions are also possible *(arrows)*. **b** In reality, the PTt path was probably more complex than what could be reconstructed with the available data points; during retrogression a new metamorphic cycle (*M1* and *M2*) may have been realised. Such complex paths can sometimes be recognised with detailed structural and petrological work

related with them are interpreted as points on a PTt-path associated with a single *metamorphic cycle* (M1) with peak pressure attained during D_1 and peak temperature during D_2. Data points are more common on the retrograde leg of PTt-paths than on the prograde leg, since the latter are usually destroyed by ongoing metamorphic reactions and deformation.

PTt-paths are usually clockwise but anticlockwise paths have also been reported (Harley 1989; Clarke et al. 1990). However, one should be aware that most published PTt-paths are based on few data points (usually less than five). Though metamorphic reactions may indicate in which direction a PTt-path was going (e.g. increasing temperature or decreasing pressure), many are based on the passage of a single reaction line and therefore the direction may vary by 180° (Fig. 1.4a). Although PTt-paths are usually presented as a single smooth curve representing a single metamorphic cycle, possible complex details in the shape of the PTt-path can rarely be resolved. Real PTt-paths may have complex shapes with several minor metamorphic cycles and subcycles which can only be reconstructed in rare cases, and then only through detailed combined structural and petrological studies (Fig. 1.4b; Kriegsman 1993; Zhang et al. 1994).

The PTt-path will generally be valid for only a relatively small volume of rock (at most a few km³), and different paths can often be reconstructed for different crustal units. The way in which these differ gives important information on the regional tectonic evolution. Where paths merge and continue together, rock volumes have been fixed with respect to each other (Figs. 7.57, 7.58). This can be the case if major sections of crustal material such as nappes or even terranes are juxtaposed along shear zones.

2 Flow and Deformation

2.1 Introduction

A hunter who investigates tracks in muddy ground near a waterhole may be able to reconstruct which animals arrived last, but older tracks will be partly erased or modified. A geologist faces similar problems to reconstruct the changes in shape that a volume of rock underwent in the course of geological time, since the end products, the rocks that are visible in outcrop, are the only direct data source. In many cases it is nevertheless possible to reconstruct at least part of the tectonic history of a rock from this final fabric. This chapter treats the change in shape of rocks and the methods that can be used to investigate and describe this change in shape. This is the field of *kinematics*, the study of the motion of particles in a material without regard to forces causing the motion. This approach is useful in geology, where usually very little information can be obtained concerning forces responsible for deformation. In order to keep the discussion simple, the treatment is centred on flow and deformation in two dimensions.

2.2 Terminology

Consider an experiment to simulate folding using viscous fluids in a shear rig. A layer of dark-coloured material is inserted in a matrix of light-coloured material with another viscosity and both are deformed together (Fig. 2.1). The experiment runs from 10.00 to 11.00 h, after which the dark layer has developed a folded shape. During the experiment, a particle P in one of the fluids is displaced with respect to the shear rig bottom and with respect to other particles. At any time, e.g. at 10.10 h, we can attribute to P a velocity and movement direction, visualised by an arrow or *velocity vector* (Fig. 2.1). If we follow P for a short time, e.g. for 5 s from 10.10 h, it traces a straight (albeit very short) line parallel to the velocity vector. This line is the *incremental displacement vector*. At another time, e.g. 10.40 h, the velocity vector and associated incremental displacement vector of P can be entirely different (e.g. related to the folding of the dark layer). This means that the *displacement path* followed by P to its final position at 11.00 h is traced by a large number of incremental displacement vectors, each corresponding to a particular velocity vector. The displacement path is also referred to as the *particle path*. We can also compare the positions of the particle P at 10.00 and 11.00 h, and join them by a vector, the *finite displacement vector* (Fig. 2.1). This vector carries no information on the displacement path of P.

If the behaviour of more than one particle is considered, the pattern of velocity vectors at a particular time is known as the *flow pattern*. The pattern of incremental displacement vectors is known as the *incremental deformation pattern*. The pattern of displacement paths is loosely referred to as the *deformation path* and the pattern of finite displacement vectors is the finite deformation pattern. The process of accumulation of deformation with time is known as *progressive deformation*, while *finite deformation* is the difference in geometry of the initial and final stages of a deformed aggregate.

2.3 Description and Reconstruction of Deformation

It is interesting to consider how we could accurately describe velocities and displacement of particles in the experiment of Fig. 2.1 using a film (Fig. 2.3). Intuitively, one would assume that the film gives a com-

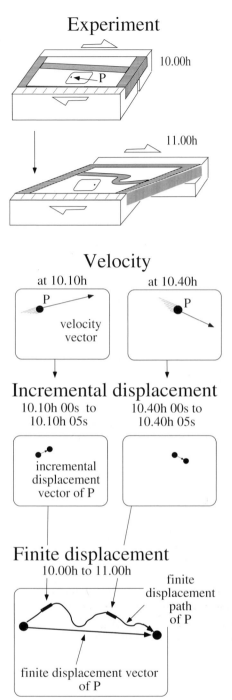

Fig. 2.1. Schematic presentation of the velocity, incremental displacement and finite displacement of a particle *P* in a deformation experiment in a shear box. Velocity of P at 10.10 h and 10.40 h can be illustrated as a velocity vector. If deformation proceeds over 5 seconds, the incremental displacement vector will be parallel to the velocity vector. The sequence of incremental displacement vectors gives the finite displacement path. The finite displacement vector is different and connects initial (10.00 h) and final (11.00 h) positions of P

plete and accurate picture of the experiment, and that no further problems occur in reconstruction of flow and deformation. However, such reconstruction is more difficult than it would seem. If we compare stages of the experiment that are far apart in time, e.g. at 10.00, 10.30 and 11.00 h, we can connect positions of particles by vectors which define the finite deformation pattern (Fig. 2.3 bottom). However, these finite deformation patterns carry no information on the history of the deformation, i.e. on the displacement paths of individual particles. Finite displacement paths have to be reconstructed from incremental deformation patterns; if we take two stages of the experiment that are close together in time, e.g. two subsequent images of the film (Fig. 2.3 top), these can be used to find the incremental deformation pattern. Finite displacement paths can be accurately reconstructed by adding all incremental deformation patterns; this is obviously impossible in practice; an approximation can be obtained by adding a selection of incremental deformation patterns, or a number of finite deformation patterns which represent short time periods. The flow pattern at particular stages of the deformation can be reconstructed from the incremental deformation patterns since these have the same shape.

2.4 Reference Frames

The flow, incremental and finite deformation patterns in Fig. 2.3 were produced with a camera fixed to an immobile part of the shear rig. The shear rig acts as a *reference frame.* However, the patterns would have a different shape if another reference frame was chosen. Figure 2.4 shows three possible arrangements for reconstruction of finite deformation patterns from two photographs taken at 10.10 and 10.50 h (Fig. 2.4a). For most studies of flow and deformation it is advantageous to choose a reference frame fixed to a particle in the centre of the domain to be studied, since this produces symmetric patterns around the central particle. An example is shown in Fig. 2.4d, where one particle (P) is chosen to overlap in both photographs, and the edges of the photographs are parallel; we have now defined a reference frame with orthogonal axes parallel to the sides of the photographs (and therefore to the side of the shear box), and with an origin on particle P. The patterns in Fig. 2.4b and c are not wrong, but less useful; they have additional translation and rotation components that have no signifi-

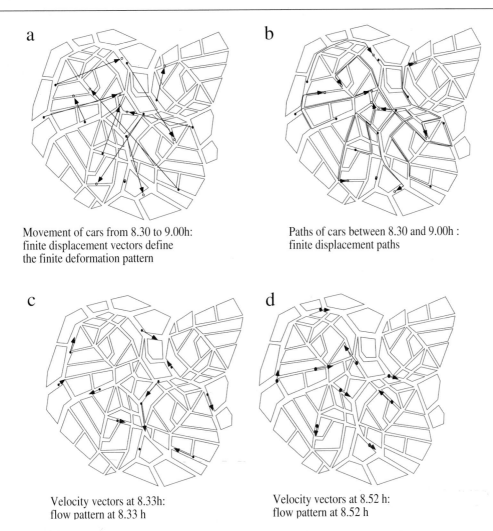

a

Movement of cars from 8.30 to 9.00h:
finite displacement vectors define
the finite deformation pattern

b

Paths of cars between 8.30 and 9.00h :
finite displacement paths

c

Velocity vectors at 8.33h:
flow pattern at 8.33 h

d

Velocity vectors at 8.52 h:
flow pattern at 8.52 h

Fig. 2.2a–d. Illustration of the concept of flow and displacement or deformation using cars in a town

TERMINOLOGY OF DEFORMATION AND FLOW; A TRAFFIC EXAMPLE

The difference between flow and deformation can be visualised by the example of cars in a town. If we compare the positions of all red cars in a town on aerial photographs at 8.30 and at 9.00 h, they will be vastly different; the difference in their initial and final positions can be described by *finite displacement vectors* (Fig. 2.2a). These describe the *finite deformation* pattern of the distribution of cars in the town. The finite deformation pattern carries no information on the *finite displacement paths,* the way by which the cars reached their 9.00-h position (Fig. 2.2b). The finite displacement paths depend on the velocity and movement direction of each individual car and its change with time. The velocity and movement direction of each car at 8.33 h, for example, can be described by a velocity vector (Fig. 2.2c). The combined field of all the velocity vectors of all cars is known as the *flow pattern* at 8.33 h (Fig. 2.2c). *Flow* of the car population therefore describes the pattern of their velocity vectors. At 8.52 h (Fig. 2.2d) the flow pattern will be entirely different from that at 8.33 h and the flow pattern is therefore described only for a specific moment, except if the cars always have the same direction and velocity. If we register the displacement of cars over 2 s, as a vector field starting at 8.33 h, this will be very similar to the velocity vector field at 8.33 h, but the vectors now illustrate displacement, not velocity. These vectors are *incremental displacement vectors* that describe the *incremental deformation pattern* of the distribution of cars in the town. The incremental deformation pattern is usually different from the finite deformation pattern. If we 'add' all incremental displacement vectors from 10.00 to 11.00 h, the sum will be the finite displacement paths (Fig. 2.2b).

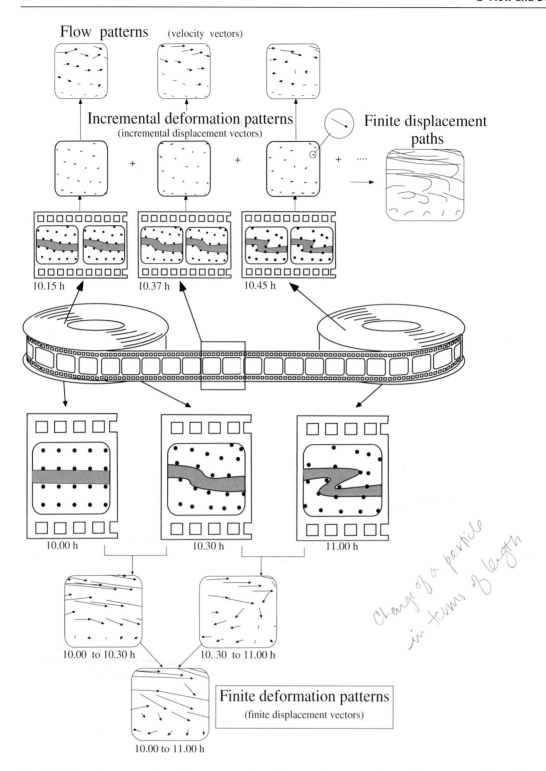

Fig. 2.3. Schematic presentation of the reconstruction of patterns of flow, incremental deformation and finite deformation based on a film of the experiment in Fig. 2.1. At the *top* is shown how incremental deformation patterns can be determined from adjacent images on the film: flow patterns and finite dis- placement paths can be constructed from these incremental deformation patterns. At the *bottom* is shown how finite deformation patterns can be constructed from images that are further separated in time. **Black dots** are marker particles in the material

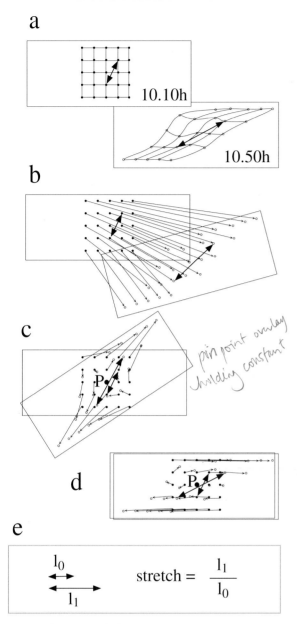

a

10.10h

10.50h

b

c

P

pin point overlay holding constant

d

P

e

$$l_0 \quad\quad \text{stretch} = \frac{l_1}{l_0}$$

l_1

Fig. 2.4a–e. Illustration of the influence of different reference frames on the finite deformation pattern for two stages in the experiment of Fig. 2.1. **a** Two photographic enlargements of the same segment of material at 10.10 and 10.50 h. *Arrows* indicate the distance between two particles in the two deformation stages. **b, c** and **d** show three different ways of constructing finite deformation patterns from the two images. In **b** no particle in both photographs is overlapping and the finite deformation pattern has a large component of translation. In **c** and **d** one particle (*P*) is chosen to overlap in both photographs. In **d,** the sides of the photographs are chosen parallel as well. Since the photographs were taken with sides parallel to sides of the shear box, **d** is selected as the most useful presentation of the finite deformation pattern in this case. **e** Illustration of the concept of stretch. l_o is original length; l_1 is final length

cance in the experimental setup described here, and therefore obscure the relative motion of the particles with respect to each other.

Flow and deformation patterns have certain factors that are independent of the reference frame in which they are described. For example, the relative finite displacement of two particles in Fig. 2.4 can be found from the distance between pairs of particles in both photographs. The final distance divided by the initial distance is known as the *stretch* of the line connecting the two particles (Fig. 2.4e); this stretch value does not change if another reference frame is chosen (cf. Fig. 2.4b, c and d). In the case of flow, *stretching rate* (stretch per time unit) is equally independent of reference frame.

2.5 Homogeneous and Inhomogeneous Flow and Deformation

2.5.1 Introduction

Usually, flow in a material is *inhomogeneous,* i.e. the flow pattern varies from place to place in the experiment and the result after some time is inhomogeneous deformation (e.g. Fig. 2.3). The development of folds and boudins in straight layering (Figs. 2.1, 2.3) and the displacement pattern of cars in a town (Fig. 2.2) are expressions of inhomogeneous deformation. However, the situation is not as complex as may be supposed from Fig. 2.2 since, contrary to cars, the velocities of neighbouring particles in an experiment or deforming rock are not independent.

Flow in nature is generally inhomogeneous and difficult to describe in numbers or simple phrases. However, if considered at specific scales (Fig. 2.6), flow may be approximately homogeneous with an identical flow pattern throughout a volume of material, wherever we choose the origin of the reference frame (Fig. 2.6a). The result after some time is homogeneous deformation.

Characteristic for homogeneous deformation is that straight and parallel marker grid lines remain straight and parallel, and that any circle is deformed into an ellipse. Homogeneous flow or deformation can (in two dimensions) be completely defined by just *four* numbers; they are *tensors* (Box p. 13). It is therefore attractive to try and describe natural flow and deformation as tensors. This is possible in many

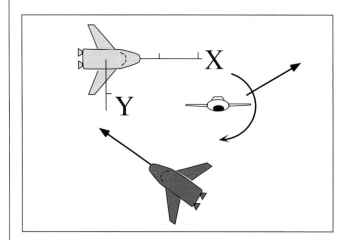

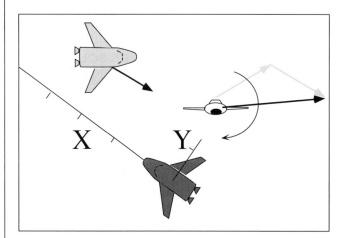

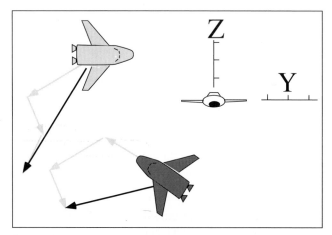

HOW TO USE REFERENCE FRAMES

The world in which we live can only be geometrically described if we use *reference frames*. A reference frame has an origin and a particular choice of *reference axes*. If a choice of reference frame is made, measurements are possible if we define a *coordinate system* within that reference frame such as scales on the axes and/or angles between lines and reference frame axes. Usually, we use a Cartesian coordinate system (named after René Descartes) with three orthogonal, straight axes and a metric scale.

In daily life we intuitively work with a reference frame fixed to the earth's surface and only rarely become confused, such as when we are in a train on a railway station next to another train; it can then be difficult to decide whether our train, the other train, or both are moving with respect to the platform. As another example, imagine three space shuttles moving with respect to each other (Fig. 2.5). The crew in each of the shuttles can choose the centre of its machine as the origin of a reference frame, choose Cartesian reference axes parallel to the symmetry axes of the shuttle and a metric scale as a coordinate system. The three shuttles use different reference frames and will therefore have different answers for velocity vectors of the other shuttles. Obviously none of them is wrong; each description is equally valid and no reference frame can be favoured with respect to another. Notice that the reference frames are shown to have a different orientation in each diagram of Fig. 2.5, because we see them from outside in our own, *external reference frame,* e.g. fixed to the earth.

Similar problems are faced when deciding how to describe flow and deformation in rocks. In experiments, we usually take the shear box as part of our reference frame, or the centre of the deforming sample. In microtectonics we tend to take parts of our sample as a reference frame. In the study of large-scale thrusting, however, it may be more useful to take the autochthonous basement as a reference frame, or, if no autochthonous basement can be found, a geographical frame such as a town or geographical North.

Fig. 2.5. Illustration of the concept of reference frames. If three space shuttles move with respect to each other in space, observers in each one can describe the velocities of the other two *(black arrows)* as observed through the windows; the reference frame is fixed to the observing shuttle in each case. The results are different but all correct. The *circular arrow* around the white shuttle *at right* indicates that it rotates around its axis in the reference frames for each of the other two shuttles. *Grey arrows* represent addition of velocity vectors in order to show how they relate

a

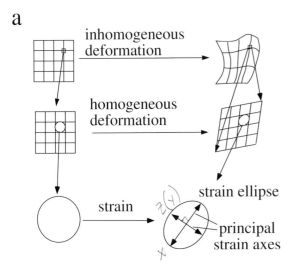

inhomogeneous
deformation

homogeneous
deformation

strain

strain ellipse

principal
strain axes

b

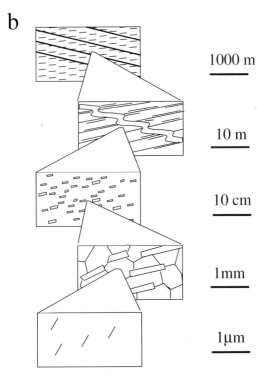

1000 m

10 m

10 cm

1mm

1μm

Fig. 2.6a,b. Illustration of the concepts of homogeneous and inhomogeneous deformation. **a** For homogeneous deformation, straight and parallel lines remain straight and parallel, and a circle deforms into an ellipse, the axes of which are finite strain axes. Inhomogeneous and homogenous deformation occur on different scales. **b** Five scales of observation in a rock. *From top to bottom* Layering and foliation on km scale – approximately homogeneous deformation; layering and foliation on a metre scale – inhomogeneous deformation; foliation on a cm scale – approximately homogeneous deformation; thin section scale – inhomogeneous deformation; crystal scale – approximately homogeneous deformation

TENSORS

All physical properties can be expressed in numbers, but different classes of such properties can be distinguished. Temperature and viscosity are independent of reference frame and can be described by a single number and a unit, e.g. 25 °C and 10^5 Pa s. They are *scalars*. Stress and homogeneous finite strain, incremental strain, finite deformation, incremental deformation and flow at a point need at least four mutually independent numbers to be described completely in two dimensions (nine numbers in three dimensions). They are *tensors*. For example, the curves for the flow type illustrated in Fig. 2.8a need at least four numbers for a complete description, e.g. amplitude (the same in both curves), elevation of the Ṡ-curve, elevation of the ω-curve, and orientation of one of the maxima or minima of one of the curves in space. We might choose another reference frame to describe the flow, but in all cases four numbers will be needed for a full description.

Homogeneous deformation can be expressed by two equations:

$$x' = ax+by$$
$$y' = cx+dy,$$

where (x', y') is the position of a particle in the deformed state, (x, y) in the undeformed state and a,b,c,d are four parameters describing the *deformation tensor*. Homogeneous flow can be described by similar equations that give the velocity components v_x an v_y in x and y direction for a particle at point x,y:

$$v_x = px+qy$$
$$v_y = rx+ty.$$

p,q,r,t are four parameters describing the *flow tensor*. Both tensors can be abbreviated by describing just their parameters in a *matrix* as follows:

$$\begin{pmatrix} a & b \\ c & d \end{pmatrix} \text{ and } \begin{pmatrix} p & q \\ r & t \end{pmatrix}$$

Multiplication of these matrices with the coordinates of a particle or a point in space gives the complete equations. Matrices are used instead of the full equations because they are easier to use in calculations.

cases, since deviation of flow from homogeneity is scale-dependent (Fig. 2.6b); in any rock there are usually parts and scales that can be considered to approach homogeneous flow behaviour for practical purposes (Fig. 2.6b).

2.5.2 Numerical Description of Homogeneous Flow and Deformation

Imagine a small part of the experiment in Fig. 2.1 that can be considered to deform by homogeneous flow (Fig. 2.7a). At 10.33 h, a regular pattern of velocity vec-

Homogeneous flow

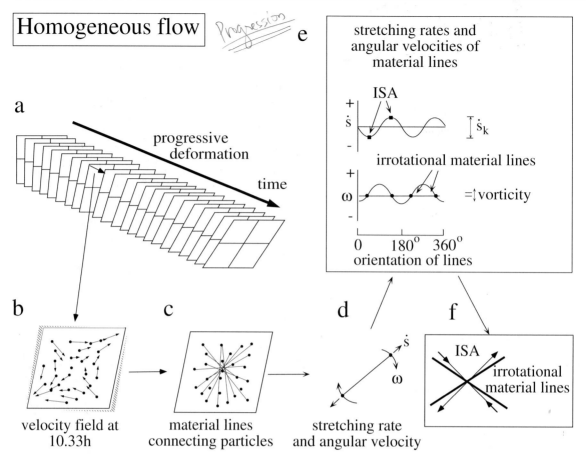

a progressive deformation

time

e stretching rates and angular velocities of material lines

b velocity field at 10.33h

c material lines connecting particles

d stretching rate and angular velocity

f ISA irrotational material lines

Fig. 2.7. a Sequence of stages in a deformation experiment (small part of the experiment of Fig. 2.1). Deformation is homogeneous. **b** Two subsequent stages are used to determine the velocity field at 10.33 h. **c** Marker points in the flow pattern can be connected by lines. **d** For each line a stretching rate ($\dot{S}$) and angular velocity (ω) are defined, which can **(e)** be plotted in curves against line orientation. In the curves, special directions can be distinguished such as the instantaneous stretching axes *(ISA)* and irrotational lines. The amplitude of the $\dot{S}$-curve is $\dot{S}_k$, a measure of the strain rate, and the elevation of the symmetry line of the ω-curve is a measure of the vorticity. Orientations of ISA and irrotational lines **(f)** can be found from the graphs

tors defines the flow pattern (Fig. 2.7b). How to describe such a flow pattern numerically? Imagine pairs of material points to be connected by straight lines or *material lines* (Fig. 2.7c), and register the *stretching rate* ($\dot{S}$) and *angular velocity* (ω) of these connecting lines (Fig. 2.7d). The stretching rate can be measured without problems, but in order to measure the angular velocity, a reference frame is needed; the edges of the shear box can be used as such. Stretching rate and angular velocity can be plotted against line orientation, since all parallel lines give identical values in homogeneous flow (Fig. 2.6a). Two regular curves result that have the same shape for any type of flow, but are shifted in a vertical sense for different flow types (Fig. 2.7e). The amplitude of the curves may also vary, but is always the same for both curves

in a single flow type. Maxima and minima always lie 45° apart. If the curves have another shape, flow is not homogeneous. It is now possible to define certain special characteristics of homogeneous flow, as follows (Figs. 2.7e,8):

1. Two lines exist along which stretching rate has its maximum and minimum value, the *instantaneous stretching axes (ISA)*. They are orthogonal in any flow type (Figs. 2.7f, 2.8).

2. If the stretching rate curve is symmetrically arranged with respect to the zero stretching rate axis, no area change is involved in the flow, and lines of zero stretching rate are orthogonal (Fig. 2.8); flow is *isochoric*. In the case of area increase, all material lines are given an extra positive stretching rate and the curve is shifted upwards; a deforming circle or

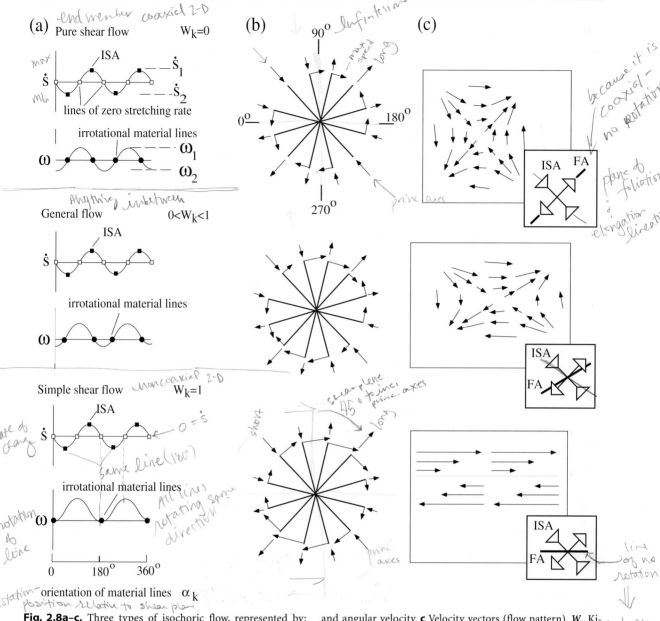

Fig. 2.8a–c. Three types of isochoric flow, represented by: **a** Graphs of stretching rate (Ṡ) and angular velocity of material lines (ω) against line orientation α_k. **b** Spatial distribution of material lines with ***arrows*** indicating sense of stretching rate and angular velocity. **c** Velocity vectors (flow pattern). W_k Kinematic vorticity number; ***ISA*** instantaneous stretching axes; ***FA*** fabric attractor (Chap. 2.9)

square increases in size in this case. If the curve is shifted downwards there is area decrease. A deforming circle or square decreases in size. In both cases, lines of zero stretching rate are not orthogonal.

3. If in a reference frame fixed to ISA the angular velocity curve is symmetrically arranged with respect to the zero angular velocity axis, no 'bulk rotation' is involved in the flow, and lines of zero angular velocity

(irrotational lines) are orthogonal. Flow is said to be *coaxial* because a pair of lines that is irrotational is parallel to the ISA (Fig. 2.8). This flow type is also known as *pure shear flow* and has an orthorhombic shape symmetry (Fig. 2.8 top). If all material lines are given an identical extra angular velocity, the angular velocity curve is shifted upwards (dextral rotation) or downwards (sinistral rotation). In both cases, flow is

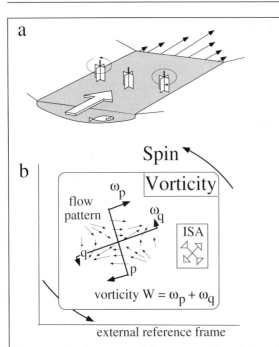

Fig. 2.9a,b. Illustration of the concept of vorticity and spin. **a** If the velocity of a river is fastest in the middle, paddle wheels inserted in the river will rotate in opposite direction at the sides, but will not rotate in the middle; they reflect the vorticity of flow in the river at three different sites. **b** Vorticity is defined as the sum of the angular velocity with respect to ISA of any pair of orthogonal material lines (such as *p* and *q*); additional rotation of ISA (and all the other lines and vectors) in an external reference frame is known as spin

VORTICITY AND SPIN

Vorticity is the 'amount of rotation' that a flow type possesses (Means et al. 1980). The concept of vorticity can be illustrated with the example of a river (Fig. 2.9a). In the centre, flow is faster than near the edges. If paddle wheels are inserted in the river along the sides, they will rotate either sinistrally or dextrally; the flow in these domains has a positive or negative vorticity. In the centre, a paddle wheel does not rotate; here the vorticity is zero. Rotation of material lines must be defined with respect to some reference frame (the edges of the river in Fig. 2.9a) and the same therefore applies to vorticity. In this book, we define vorticity as the summed angular velocity of any two orthogonal material lines in the flow with respect to the ISA (i.e. the ISA act as our reference frame; Fig. 2.9b). This means that vorticity is twice the angular velocity of the paddle wheels in Fig. 2.9a. If an external reference frame is used and ISA rotate in this external reference frame, the angular velocity of the ISA is referred to as *spin* (Fig. 2.9b; Lister and Williams 1983; Means 1994). Rotation of material lines in a randomly chosen external reference frame can therefore have components of spin and vorticity. Vorticity and spin can be shown as vectors parallel to the rotation axis of the orthogonal material line sets (the axes of the paddle wheels in Fig. 2.9a).

said to be *non-coaxial* since irrotational lines are no longer parallel to ISA (Fig. 2.8 centre). The deviation of the angular velocity curve from the axis is a measure of the rotational character of the flow, the *vorticity* (Figs. 2.7e,8; Box p. 16). A special case exists when the angular velocity curve is just touching the zero angular velocity axis and only one irrotational line exists; this flow type is known as *simple shear flow* (Fig. 2.8 bottom). All non-coaxial flows have a monoclinic symmetry.

Since flow can be visualised by two simple curves, it must be possible to describe flow using parameters of these curves such as their amplitude, the elevation of each of the curves with respect to the horizontal axis, and the orientation of special directions such as ISA in the chosen reference frame. This orientation can be expressed by the angle α_k between one of the ISA and the side of the shear box. The first three of these parameters are defined as (Fig. 2.8):

$$\dot{S}_k = \dot{S}_1 - \dot{S}_2 = \omega_1 - \omega_2$$
$$W_k = (\omega_1 + \omega_2)/\dot{S}_k$$
$$A_k = (\dot{S}_1 + \dot{S}_2)/\dot{S}_k .$$

$\dot{S}_k$ is a measure of the *strain rate* (the amplitude of the stretching rate curves in Fig. 2.7 and 2.8). W_k is known as the *kinematic vorticity number,* and A_k as the *kinematic dilatancy number.* W_k is a measure of the rotational quality of a flow type, while A_k is a measure of the rate at which a surface shrinks or expands with time. For example, simple shear flow without area change has $W_k = 1$ and $A_k = 0$. Pure shear flow has $W_k = 0$ and $A_k = 0$ (Fig. 2.8). All possible flow pattern geometries can be defined by just W_k or A_k, while $\dot{S}_k$ defines how fast deformation is accumulated for a particular flow type and α_k describes its orientation in an external reference frame.

VORTICITY AND KINEMATIC VORTICITY NUMBER

It may seem unnecessarily complicated to define a kinematic vorticity number W_k when we can also simply use vorticity. However, there is an obvious reason. W_k is *normalised* for strain rate and is therefore a dimensionless number. This makes W_k more suitable for comparison of flow types than vorticity. For example, imagine a river and a rock both flowing with identical flow patterns. Vorticity in the river is 0.2 s^{-1} at a strain rate of 0.3 s^{-1}. In the rock these values are respectively $4 \times 10^{-14} \text{ s}^{-1}$ and $6 \times 10^{-14} \text{ s}^{-1}$. In both cases, vorticity is vastly different. However, W_k is in both cases 0.67. The same principle applies for the kinematic dilatancy number A_k.

2.6 Deformation and Strain

Analogous to homogeneous flow, homogeneous deformation can be envisaged by the distribution patterns of *stretch* and *rotation* of a set of lines connecting marker particles (Fig. 2.10a–e). These values plot in two curves as for flow, but these are now asymmetric (Figs. 2.7e, 2.10d). It is also necessary to define if the stretch and rotation of a line are given for the position of the line at the onset of, or after the deformation. Here, we use the former definition. The maximum and minimum stretch values are known as the principal *stretches* or *principal strain values* S_1 and S_2. They occur along lines that are orthogonal before and after the deformation, the two *principal strain axes* (Fig. 2.10d,e). Since homogeneous deformation is a tensor, it can also be fully described by just four numbers. These are: (a) S_1 and S_2 which describe the *strain* or change in shape that is part of the homogeneous deformation (Chap. 8.2); (b) a number β_k describing the orientation of the principal strain axes in a reference frame at the onset of deformation, and (c) ρ_k, the rotation of the principal strain axes in the reference frame between the initial and the final state (Fig. 2.10e). Notice that *deformation* is normally composed of *strain* (which only describes a change in shape) and a *rotation* component ρ_k. Therefore, deformation and strain cannot be used as synonyms.

In homogeneous deformation, a circle is deformed into an ellipse (Figs. 2.6a, 2.10e). The shape of such an ellipse is a measure of the strain; the principal strain axes are the long and short axes of this ellipse. If the original circle has a radius 1, the ellipse is known as the *strain ellipse* and the length of the principal strain axes is S_1 and S_2 respectively.

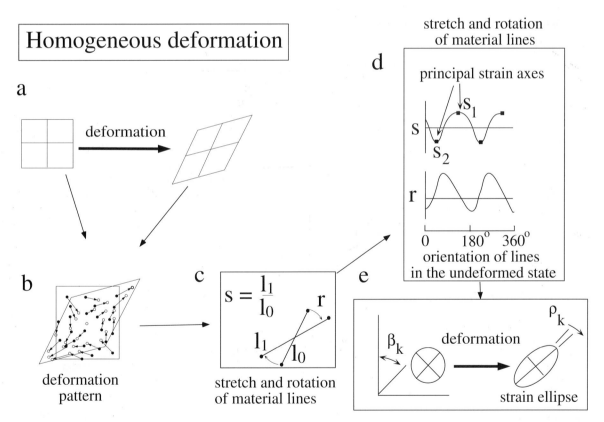

Fig. 2.10. a Two stages of the deformation sequence in Fig. 2.7a that are far apart in time can be used to reconstruct **b,** the deformation pattern. **c** Sets of marker points can be connected by material lines and the rotation *(r)* and stretch *(s)* of each line monitored. **d** These can be plotted against initial orientation of the lines. In the curves, principal strain axes can be distinguis- hed. **e** Finite deformation as deduced from these curves contains elements of strain and rotation (ρ_k). β_k defines the orientation of a material line in the undeformed state that is to become parallel to the long axis of the strain ellipse in the deformed state

2.7 Progressive and Finite Deformation

A homogeneous pattern of flow leads to accumulation of homogeneous deformation. Figure 2.11a shows how the total stretch and rotation of material lines with respect to each other can be identical in deformation states accumulated by pure shear flow and simple shear flow. Homogeneous finite deformation carries no information on the deformation path or on progressive deformation. However, the stretch and

rotation *history* of material lines does depend on the flow type by which it accumulated. This is illustrated in Fig. 2.11b by the stretch and rotation history of two lines in Fig. 2.11a. If the stretch behaviour of all material lines is studied, the difference in pattern is even more obvious (Fig. 2.11c); if deformation accumulates by pure shear flow, the orthorhombic symmetry of the flow pattern is reflected in the symmetry of the distribution of material lines with different deformation history (Fig. 2.11c). A pure shear deformation history where $W_k = 0$ is also known as 'coaxial progressive deformation'. Progressive deformation histories by flow types where $W_k \neq 0$ such as simple shear are referred to as 'non-coaxial progressive deforma-

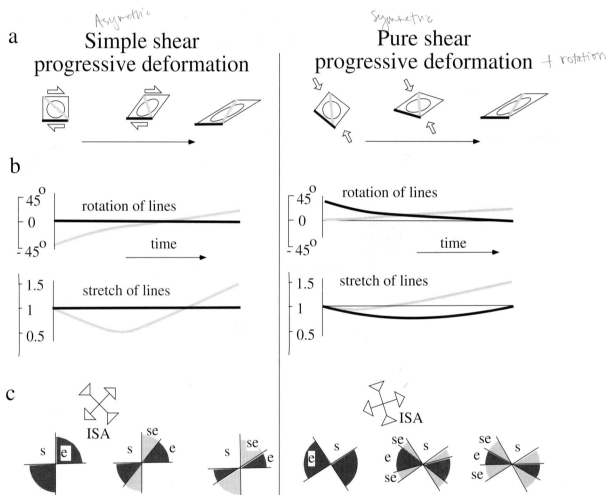

Fig. 2.11a–c. The effect of deformation history. **a** Two identical squares of material with two marker lines *(black and grey lines)* are deformed up to the same finite strain value in simple shear and pure shear progressive deformation respectively. The initial orientation of the squares is chosen such that the shape and orientation of deformed squares is identical. **b** The finite stretch and relative orientation of both marker lines is identical

in both cases, but the history of stretch and rotation of each line (illustrated by the *curves*) is different. **c** Circular diagrams show the distribution of all material lines in the squares of **a**. Ornamentation shows where lines are shortened *(s)*, extended *(e)* or first shortened, then extended *(se)* for each step of progressive deformation. The orientation of ISA is indicated

tion' and the resulting distribution of material line fields have a monoclinic symmetry (Fig. 2.11c). In most fluids, this difference in stretch history of lines is just a curiosity without practical value, but in rocks the difference is expressed in the rock fabric. If deformation is homogeneous on all scales it is not possible to detect effects of the progressive deformation path, but in the case of inhomogeneous deformation on some scales, as is common in deforming rocks (Fig. 2.6b), pure shear and simple shear progressive deformation can produce distinctive, different structures (e.g. Fig. 5.29). It is this monoclinic fabric symmetry which can be used to determine sense of shear (Chap. 5.5–5.7). It is therefore usually possible to obtain at least some information on the type of deformation path from a finite deformation fabric, although in nature it will not be possible to make an accurate reconstruction.

2.8 Flow and Deformation in Three Dimensions

The two-dimensional treatment of flow and deformation presented above can easily be expanded to a full three-dimensional description. If flow is homogeneous it can be represented in three dimensions as a tensor with nine components. Three of these define the stretching rates ($\dot{S}$) along three orthogonal ISA; three define the orientation of the vorticity vector and its magnitude; and three components describe the orientation of the flow pattern in space. This means that an endless variety of flow types is in principle possible. In the first part of Chapter 2, we discussed only those types of flow where the vorticity vector lies parallel to one of the ISA and stretching rate along this axis is zero, as in the shear boxes of Figs. 2.1 and 2.3. In such special flow types, the velocity vectors of flow are all normal to the vorticity vector, and flow can therefore be treated as two-dimensional and shown as a vector pattern in a single plane (Figs. 2.1, 2.3, 2.4, 2.7, 2.8). We restricted the presentation of flow types to these examples since they suffice to illustrate the principle, and may indeed represent some flow types that occur in nature, such as simple shear in ductile shear zones between rigid wall rocks. However, it is important to realise that flow is a three-dimensional phenomenon and that two-dimensional simplifications may be unsuitable to describe certain details correctly.

Homogeneous deformation in three dimensions is also expressed as a tensor with nine numbers. Three numbers define the principal stretches or principal strain values S_1, S_2 and S_3 along three orthogonal principal strain axes; three numbers describe the rotation of material lines coinciding with principal strain axes from the undeformed to the deformed state; and three numbers describe the orientation of the principal strain axes in space. Notice that, unlike flow, deformation compares an undeformed and a deformed state, and can therefore be described in several ways, depending on whether the reference frame is fixed to material lines in the undeformed or in the deformed state.

Three-dimensional strain is a component of three-dimensional deformation that can be described by three numbers such as the principal stretches S_1, S_2 and S_3. It is illustrated as a *strain ellipsoid*; principal strain axes are the three symmetry axes of this ellipsoid. They are usually referred to (from maximum to minimum) as the *X, Y and Z axes* of strain. As for flow, it is important to realise that deformation and strain are three-dimensional quantities, although we usually see two-dimensional cross sections in outcrop or thin section; for a full characterisation of strain, several orthogonal outcrop surfaces or thin sections should be studied. More details on flow and deformation can be found in Means et al. (1980), Means (1979, 1983), de Paor (1983) and Passchier (1987a, 1988a,b, 1991a).

2.9 Fabric Attractor

If the flow patterns of Fig. 2.8 work on a material for some time, material lines rotate towards an axis which coincides with the extending irrotational material line; this axis 'attracts' material lines in progressive deformation. In most types of three-dimensional homogeneous flow, a 'material line attractor' exists in the form of a line or (less commonly) a plane (Fig. 2.12). Since material lines rotate towards attractors, the long axes of the finite strain ellipse and most fabric elements in rocks will do the same. We therefore refer to these directions as the *fabric attractor* of the flow (Fig. 2.12). Even if flow is not homogeneous, fabric attractors may occur as contours in deforming materials, and fabric elements will approach them. This is the cause of the development of many foliations and lineations in deformed rocks.

a   b

Pure shear   Simple shear

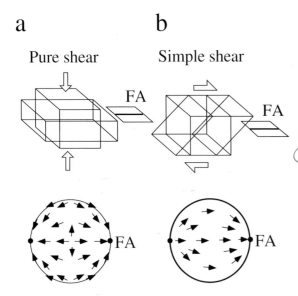

Fig. 2.12a,b. Concept of the fabric attractor. In both pure shear **(a)** and simple shear **(b)** deformation, material lines rotate towards and concentrate near an attractor direction, as shown in the stereograms. This line is the fabric attractor *(FA)*. Both foliations and lineations rotate permanently towards this attractor

2.10 Application to Rocks

The observations on flow and deformation presented above for experiments in a shear box are directly applicable to any surface within a deforming rock, although velocities in rocks are obviously very small. The homogeneous flow model allows us to predict what will happen if a rock undergoes progressive deformation by operation of particular flow types provided that it deforms as a continuum without faults on the scale of observation. Unfortunately, in rocks we lack the video camera and we have to make all reconstructions of finite deformation and the deformation path from the end-fabric in outcrop. If the initial configuration of the deformed material is known (e.g. lengths and angles in the case of fossils or minerals), it is possible to determine the magnitude and orientation of finite strain, but without supplementary information we can say little about the deformation path.

2.11 Stress and Deformation

Although in microstructural analysis it is usually only possible to reconstruct aspects of kinematics, it is useful to consider briefly how forces in rocks can lead to flow and deformation. A study of the relationship between forces and changes in shape is the study of *dynamics.*

Deformation of rocks is associated with forces in the earth's crust. It is advantageous to describe such forces independently of the size of the volume of material we are dealing with, i.e. using force per unit area (Nm^{-2}). Although we are used to think of forces in terms of simple numbers (scalars), they are in fact defined by size and direction, and can be drawn as vectors. In a continuum, the force-vector on a surface has a direction and size that are dependent on the orientation of that surface (Fig. 2.13a). Therefore, it is not possible to define the forces in a rock at a particular point by a single vector; each surface through the point has a different force vector associated with it. The relation between these values is expressed as the *stress* at that point in the material. Notice that stress is defined only for a particular point, since it is usually different from place to place in a material.

Like flow and deformation, stress is a tensor which, in three dimensions, needs nine numbers for its complete characterisation. However, since stress is taken to be symmetric in geological applications, six independent numbers are usually sufficient. Of these, three numbers describe the *principal stress values* along *principal stress axes* in three orthogonal directions, and three the spatial orientation of the principal stress axes. Principal stress values are expressed as σ_1 (largest), σ_2 and σ_3 (smallest). Principal stress axes are normal to the three surfaces on which they act (Fig. 2.13b). Stress is usually illustrated by a stress ellipsoid with principal stress axes as symmetry axes (Fig. 2.13b). Stress on a plane in a rock such as the contact of a pegmatite vein is a vector which can be resolved into components normal and parallel to the plane, known as *normal stress* (σ_n) and *shear stress* (τ) respectively (Fig. 2.13a).

It is useful in many applications to subdivide stress into a *mean stress* value ($\sigma_{mean} = (\sigma_1 + \sigma_2 + \sigma_3)/3$) and *differential stress* (usually defined as $\sigma_{diff} = \sigma_1-\sigma_3$, but $\sigma_1-\sigma_2$ or $\sigma_2-\sigma_3$ could also be regarded as differential stresses). The term *deviatoric stress* is also commonly used and is defined as $\sigma_{dev} = \sigma_n-\sigma_{mean}$; it describes how much the normal stress in any direction deviates from the mean stress. The differential or deviatoric stresses are the cause of permanent strain in rocks and are most important for geologists. However, notice that the directions of principal stress and strain *rarely* coincide. Stress axes may be parallel to flow-ISA, but only if the rock is mechanically isotropic, e.g. if it has the same strength in all directions; in practice, this is often not the case, especially not in rocks that have a foliation. Moreover, finite strain axes rotate away from ISA with progressive deformation if flow is non-coaxial.

The vertical normal stress on a horizontal surface at depth due to the weight of the overlying rock column equals ρgh, where ρ is the rock density, g the acceleration due to gravity and h the depth. For practical reasons, and because differential stresses are thought to be relatively small at great depth, stress is commonly treated as being isotropic, in which case ρgh defines a *lithostatic pressure*. Lithostatic pressure at a point is uniform in all directions by definition; if a differential stress is present, the term mean stress could be used instead of lithostatic pressure. If pores are open to the surface, a *fluid pressure* may exist in the pores of the rock that is 2.5–3 times smaller than a lithostatic pressure at the same depth. If the pores are partly closed, the fluid pressure may approach the magnitude of the lithostatic pressure or σ_3. In that case rocks may fracture, even at great depth (Etheridge 1983); this is one of the reasons for development of veins (including fibrous veins) in many metamorphic rocks (Chap. 6.2).

2.12 Rheology

Rheology is the science that deals with the quantitative response of rocks to stress. Only the main terminology is treated here as a background to the study of microstructures. Useful texts treating the subject are Poirier (1980) and Twiss and Moores (1992).

So far, only one possible range of deformation behaviour of rocks has been treated, i.e. permanent changes in shape achieved by ductile deformation. However, rocks can also display elastic behaviour in which changes in shape are completely recoverable, or brittle failure. Brittle behaviour is dependent on scale; if grains in a sandstone with a grain size of 1 mm fracture internally without development of faults that transect more than a few grains, the deformation on a metre scale is continuous and could be considered as ductile deformation. In this book, *brittle behaviour* means brittle fracturing on a grain scale or larger, and *ductile behaviour* means deforma-

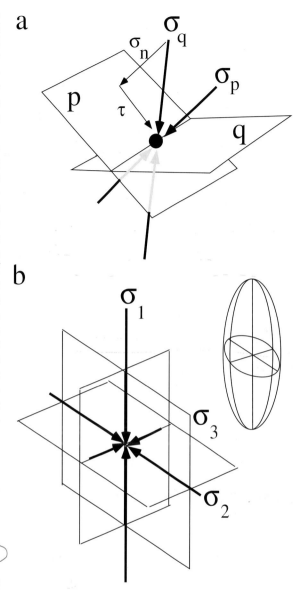

Fig. 2.13. a Illustration of the concept of stress. Surfaces *p* and *q* through a point in a rock under stress each have a different stress vector σ_p and σ_q associated with them. Each stress vector can be decomposed into a normal stress (σ_n) and a shear stress (τ) on the plane. **b** The complete stress state at the point is a tensor that can be represented by three orthogonal principal stress vectors which operate on three orthogonal surfaces. These principal stress vectors are symmetry axes of a stress ellipsoid as shown *at right*

tion without development of fractures on the grain scale.

All minerals and rocks can deform in both a brittle and a ductile way, and in general ductile deformation occurs at higher temperature and lithostatic pressure than brittle deformation, i.e. at deeper levels in the crust (Chap. 3.14). For ductile deformation, the rheology of rocks is usually described in terms of strain rate / stress relations. Stress is usually given as a shear stress (τ) or as a single 'differential stress value' ($\sigma_1 - \sigma_3$) since in experiments on rheology, symmetric stress tensors are imposed on the rock. There are several possible types of ductile rheological behaviour. Any rock will show elastic behaviour under mean stress by a small decrease in volume, and under differential stress by a small change in shape (usually less than 1%). Such an elastic strain is completely recoverable if the stress is released (Figs. 2.14a; 3.9). Mean stress increase in rocks will not lead to permanent deformation, even at very high values, unless the rock has a high porosity, or transformation to mineral phases with a higher density can take place. However, if elastic strain in response to differential stress exceeds a limit that the rock can support (the *yield strength*), ductile flow and accumulation of strain as described above can occur. Beyond this limit, rocks will deform permanently and if the differential stress

is released, only elastic strain will be recovered (Fig. 2.14a). The speed at which the rock changes shape permanently (the strain rate) increases with increasing differential stress, but the relationship between stress (σ) and strain rate ($\dot{\varepsilon}$) can be variable. If strain rate increases in a linear fashion with differential stress ($\dot{\varepsilon} \propto \sigma$), the rock is said to show linear or *Newtonian flow* behaviour. Most of the fluids that we know from daily use such as water, oil and honey are Newtonian. If strain rate increases exponentially with stress ($\dot{\varepsilon} \propto \sigma^n$), flow behaviour is said to be *non-Newtonian* or *power law* (Fig. 2.14b). Both types of flow are probably common in rocks. The stress exponent n is known as the strain-rate sensitivity of the flow stress and is 1 for Newtonian behaviour and higher than one for power-law behaviour, though not usually exceeding 5 for rocks. Although there are exceptions, Newtonian flow is thought to represent diffusion accommodated processes (including pressure solution; Chap. 3.3, 3.8), while power-law flow is typical of processes involving dislocation creep (Chap. 3.4). In simple cases, rocks show *steady state flow*, meaning that, if the differential stress is not

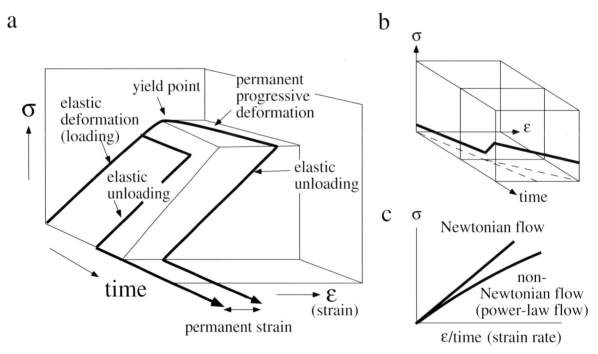

Fig. 2.14a,b. Illustration of some concepts of rheology in space, plotting differential stress *(σ)* and strain *(ε)* against time. **a** The *bold* curves illustrate loading and unloading of a sample in an experiment; when differential stress is applied, behaviour is first elastic till a yield point is reached, beyond which permanent deformation begins. When stress is released, the elastic strain is relaxed and permanent strain remains.

b Graph for permanent deformation in σ–ε–time space. Permanent deformation will proceed at a certain strain rate but if differential stress is increased, the strain rate will increase as well. **c** The way in which strain rate increases with stress can be linear (Newtonian flow) or exponential (non-Newtonian or power-law flow)

varied, they will deform at a constant strain rate. The ductile strength of rocks generally decreases with increasing depth in the crust if other factors do not change. Mean stress does not have much influence on the ductile rheology of rocks. However, grain size can under many circumstances be important (Chap. 3.9).

Most rocks do not show steady state flow during the entire deformation history because the fabric of the rock changes with progressive deformation. Both strain hardening and strain softening behaviour occur in rocks (Fig. 2.15). In Fig. 2.15 strain hardening and softening are indicated for constant strain rate, as may happen in an experiment. In nature, hardening may be a process of decreasing strain rate and increasing differential stress, and softening may be associated with strain rate increase and a drop in differential stress. Strain hardening may lead to brittle fracturing of the rock or cessation of deformation; softening may lead to localisation of the deformation in shear zones (Chap. 5.3.4).

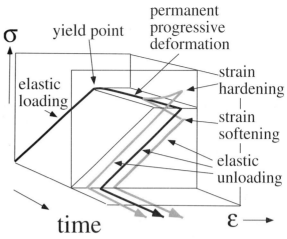

Fig. 2.15. Graph for permanent deformation in stress(σ)-strain (ε) – time space. If differential stress increases with time at constant strain rate of permanent deformation, the material is subject to strain hardening; if it decreases, it is subject to strain softening

3 Deformation Mechanisms

3.1 Introduction

Deformation in rocks is achieved by a large number of processes on the scale of individual grains. The actual processes involved depend on lithological controls such as mineralogy, composition of the intergranular fluid, grain size, lattice-preferred orientation, porosity and permeability; and on external controls such as temperature, lithostatic pressure, differential stress, fluid pressure and externally imposed strain rate. In this chapter, we will briefly introduce the most important rock deformation processes in a sequence from low temperature-high strain rate to high temperature-low stain rate. Grain-scale microstructures that are thought to be formed in response to these processes are highlighted, and it is shown how such microstructures can be used to identify deformation processes that have been operating. Structures visible within grains are known as *intracrystalline deformation structures*.

3.2 Cataclastic Flow

Cataclastic flow is essentially a brittle process that is achieved by mechanical fragmentation of rocks, and subsequent sliding and rotation of the fragments. Rocks deformed dominantly by cataclastic flow on the grain scale or larger are known as brittle fault rocks such as gouge, cataclasite and breccia (Figs. 3.1,5.2; Chap. 5.2). They occur along brittle fault zones that may show gradual or abrupt transition to the undeformed host material. During cataclastic flow, voids are created that may be filled with vein material precipitated from solution, which is subsequently involved in the cataclasis; as a result, most cataclasite and breccia contain abundant fragments of quartz or carbonate veins. Cataclastic flow usually occurs at

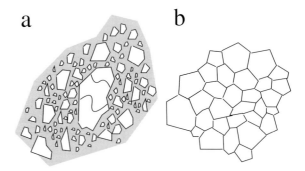

Fig. 3.1. a Cataclasite fabric – angular fragments of all sizes, some transecting grain boundaries, are embedded in a fine-grained matrix. **b** Recrystallised fabric – little variety in grain size

EVIDENCE FOR CATACLASTIC FLOW

Zones of cataclastic flow in thin section may be confused with shear zones that consist of dynamically recrystallised material (Figs. 3.22, 3.23). A cataclasite differs from a deformed and recrystallised rock by (1) a larger range in grain size, (2) the presence of grains that have angular outlines and straight sharp boundaries, and (3) the presence of polycrystalline rock fragments (Fig. 3.1; however, a deformed sandstone or sedimentary breccia may contain polycrystalline rock fragments, too, so care is needed). The constituent grains show no grain shape-preferred orientation if the host material consists of equant minerals such as quartz and feldspars. In some cases, cataclastic material is recrystallised after deformation, and distinction may then be impossible. Optical criteria are often insufficient for positive identification as cataclasite; only transmission electron microscope (TEM) investigation is conclusive in such cases (Chap. 9.6).

non- to low-grade metamorphic conditions, and at relatively high strain rates. The conditions also depend on the type of minerals involved (Chap. 3.12) and on fluid pressure; high fluid pressure promotes cataclastic flow and is responsible for the common occurrence of veins in cataclasite and breccia.

3.3 Pressure Solution

An important deformation mechanism in rocks that contain an intergranular fluid is pressure solution, i.e. the dissolution of grains at grain boundaries in a grain boundary fluid phase under high normal stress. Pressure solution is localised where grains are in contact along surfaces at a high angle to the instantaneous shortening direction, and where stress in the grain is high (Fig. 3.2). Selective pressure solution at grain contacts occurs because the solubility of a mineral in an aqueous fluid is higher where a crystal lattice is under high stress than at localities where stress is relatively low (Wheeler 1987a; Knipe 1989). Imagine a sandstone where grains are in contact (Fig. 3.2). Near contact points, the grain lattice is more strongly compressed than elsewhere; as a result, material will dissolve near the contact points and be redeposited at sites of low differential stress. The originally approximately spherical quartz grains will change shape although no actual deformation has taken place inside the grains (Fig. 3.2b).

Pressure solution may occur in a thin fluid film between grains in contact (Rutter 1976), or by dissolution undercutting of 'island structures' that are surrounded by fluid-filled channels, and which form a stress-supporting network between grains (Ray 1982; Spiers et al. 1990). The dissolved material can diffuse away from the sites of high solubility down a stress-induced chemical potential gradient to nearby sites of low solubility by stress-induced solution transfer, usually referred to as *solution transfer*. Redeposition of the dissolved material may occur at adjacent free grain boundaries that are in contact with the fluid,

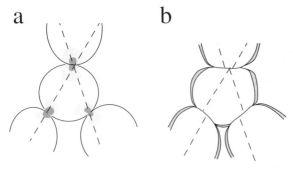

Fig. 3.2. a Grains surrounded by pore fluid, e.g. during diagenesis. At contact points, differential stresses are relatively high, as indicated by *shading*. **b** Pressure solution changes the shape of the grains. Material dissolved at the contact points is redeposited in adjacent pore spaces, indicated by *shading*. The marker grid in **a** is displaced in **b**

EVIDENCE FOR PRESSURE SOLUTION

Evidence for the action of pressure solution is the presence of truncated objects such as fossils, detrital grains, pebbles and idiomorphic phenocrysts (McClay 1977; Rutter 1983; Houseknecht 1986; Figs. 3.3, 3.4) and the displacement of layering on certain planes (Figs. 4.3, 4.20). In the latter case, however, the possibility of slip along the contact should also be considered; if the contact is indented, the displacement is most probably due to pressure solution (Fig. 4.20). Planes on which pressure solution occurred are commonly rich in opaque or micaceous material, which is left behind or deposited during the solution process (Figs. 3.3, 4.19). A spectacular example are *stylolites*, highly indented surfaces where material has been dissolved in an irregular way, allowing the wall rocks to interpenetrate. Stylolites occur mostly in limestone (Dunne and Hancock 1994).

The opposite process, deposition of material from solution, can be visible as new grains, fibrous vein fill or fibrous overgrowth of grains in strain shadows (Chap. 6). New grains grown from solution may be recognised by lack of intracrystalline deformation structures (Chap. 3.4), well-defined crystallographically determined crystal faces, and growth twins. New grown rims of material in optic continuity with older parts of a grain are also common but may be difficult to distinguish, except by cathodoluminescence (Chap. 9.2). Fluid inclusion trails (Chap. 9.3) can also reveal the presence of overgrowths.

such as occur at a high angle to the extensional ISA direction. Newly precipitated minerals can be different from consumed minerals; this effect is known as *incongruent pressure solution* (Beach 1979; McCaig 1987). Alternatively, the fluid with dissolved material can migrate by solution transfer over a larger distance and deposit material in other sites such as veins or strain shadows (Chap. 6), or even disappear out of the deforming rock volume[1]. Pressure solution and solution transfer of material is dominant at diagenetic to low-grade metamorphic conditions where fluids are abundant and deformation mechanisms favoured at higher temperatures, such as intragranular deformation, are relatively difficult. The effect of pressure solution is particularly clear in the development of differentiated crenulation cleavage at low to medium metamorphic grade, as explained in Chapter 4.9.3 (see also Bell and Cuff 1989). Further information on pressure solution can be found in Durney (1972); Elliott (1973); Gray and Durney (1979a); Rutter (1983); Groshong (1988) and den Brok (1992).

---

[1] Something to remember when drinking mineral water.

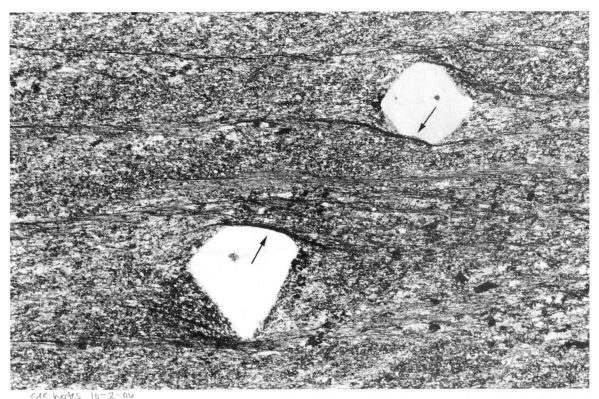

see notes 10-2-06

Fig. 3.3. Dissolution of single idiomorphic quartz crystals *(arrows)* in an ignimbrite. ***Dark horizontal seams*** consist of in- soluble material that became <u>concentrated</u> during dissolution. Leonora, Yilgarn Craton, Australia. Width of view 4 mm. PPL

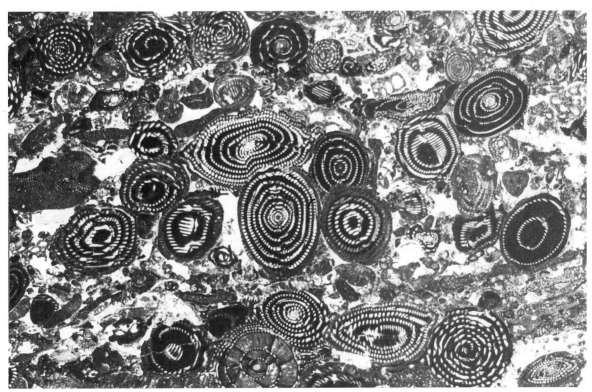

Fig. 3.4. *Alveolina* limestone showing evidence for stress-induced solution transfer during diagenetic compaction. The four fossils in the ***centre*** show indentation by dissolution and minor ductile deformation as a result of vertical shortening. Eastern Pyrenees, Spain. Width of view 21 mm. PPL

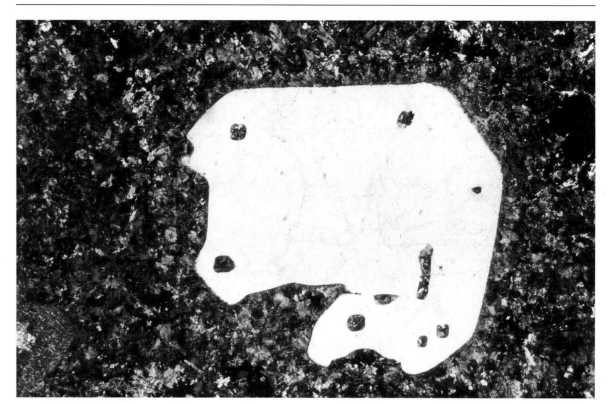

Fig. 3.5. Subhedral quartz crystal in an undeformed ignimbrite. Ornica, Southern Alps, Italy. Width of view 4 mm. CPL

Fig. 3.6. Quartz crystal flattened by intracrystalline deformation in a deformed ignimbrite. The crystal is boudinaged and the fragment on the *right hand side* shows deformation lamellae and undulose extinction. Argylla Formation, Mount Isa, Australia. Width of view 4 mm. CPL

3.4 Intracrystalline Deformation

Crystals normally contain *lattice defects,* most of which can be grouped into *point defects* and *line defects* (Fig. 3.7). Point defects are missing or extra lattice points (atoms or molecules) known respectively as *vacancies* and *interstitials* (Fig. 3.7a). Line defects may be due to an 'extra' half lattice plane in the crystal. The end of such a plane is known as an *edge dislocation* (Fig. 3.7b). Besides edge dislocations, *screw dislocations* exist where part of a crystal is displaced over one lattice distance and is therefore twisted (Fig. 3.7c). Edge and screw dislocations can be interconnected (Fig. 3.7d); they are end members of a range of possible dislocation types. Dislocations can also split into *partial dislocations,* separated by a strip of misfitted crystal lattice known as a *stacking fault.*

A dislocation is characterised by a *Burgers vector,* which indicates the direction and minimum amount of lattice displacement caused by the dislocation. The Burgers vector can be imagined by drawing a square circuit around the dislocation from atom to atom, with an equal number of atoms on each side of the square; in an intact crystal this circuit would be closed, but around a dislocation the loop is not closed – the missing part is the Burgers vector (Fig. 3.7d).

The shape of a crystal cannot be permanently changed by just squeezing it; the distance between lattice points can only be changed by a very small amount, leading to elastic deformation. If stress is released, the original shape is recovered. A permanent change in shape can only be achieved by a change in the relative positions of molecules or atoms. This happens by movement of lattice defects through a crystal, a process known as *intracrystalline deformation* (Figs. 3.5, 3.6; Poirier 1985; Hull 1975).

Consider the vacancies in Fig. 3.8. If neighbouring atoms occupy the vacancy sites, vacancies are moving through the crystal and the crystal may change shape permanently. Moving dislocations can also cause relative displacement of parts of a crystal lattice. Figure 3.9 shows how movement of a dislocation displaces parts of crystals without actually separating one part of the crystal from the other. Ductile deformation of rocks is to a large extent achieved

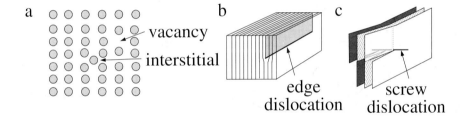

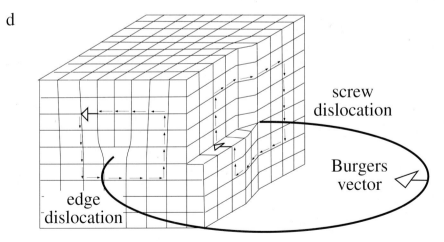

Fig. 3.7. a Lattice with two types of point defects. **b** Edge dislocation defined by the edge of a half-plane in a distorted crystal lattice. **c** Screw dislocation defined by a twisted lattice. **d** Dislocation with edge and screw dislocation regions in a crystal. A square itinerary of small arrows around the dislocation is used to find the Burgers vector of the dislocation, indicated by *open arrows*

see new text. addition to figure kind of 3.8

through the migration of dislocations and vacancies. Lattice defects can cause significant strain in crystals only if new defects are continuously created; this can happen at dislocation sources and vacancy sources within the crystal or at crystal boundaries.

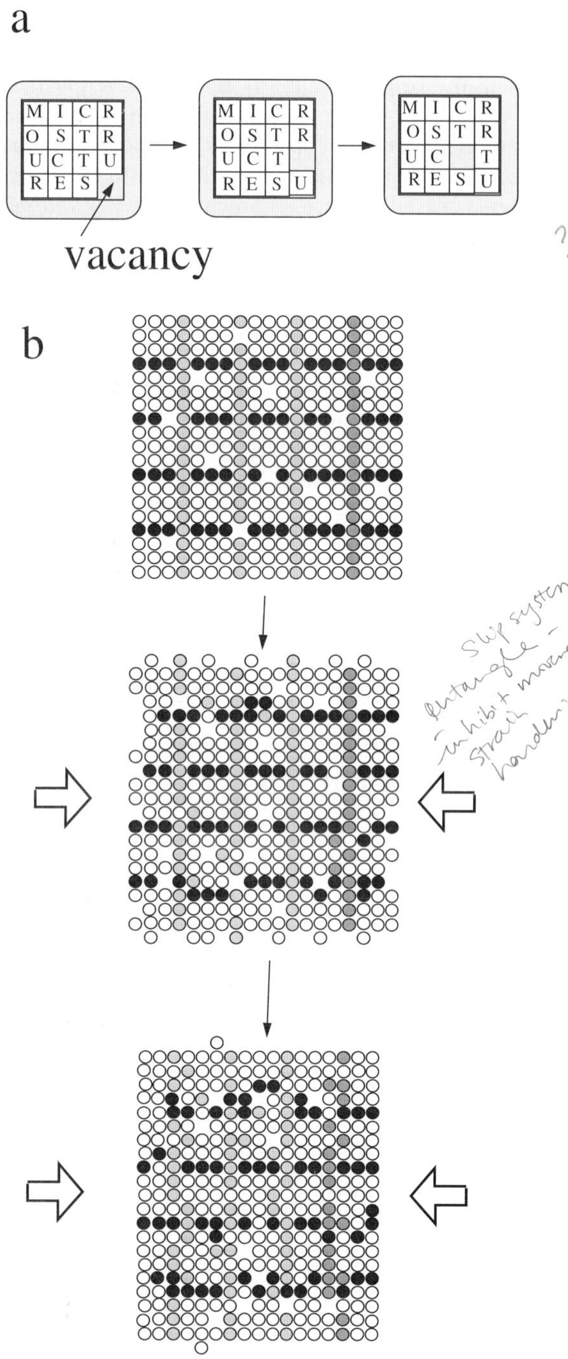

a

vacancy

b

Intracrystalline deformation by glide of dislocations alone is known as *dislocation glide*. Dislocations have a distinct orientation with respect to the crystal lattice and can move only in specific crystallographic planes and directions (Fig. 3.7d). A specific slip plane coupled with a slip direction (the Burgers vector) is known as a *slip system*. Slip systems for minerals are normally determined by TEM (Chap. 9.6). In most common rock-forming minerals such as quartz, olivine, feldspars and calcite, several slip systems of different orientation can be active (Chap. 4.15,4.16). The type of slip system that will be active in a crystal depends on the orientation and magnitude of the stress field in the grain and on the *critical resolved shear stress* (CRSS) τ_c for that slip system; τ_c must be exceeded on the slip system before the dislocation moves. The magnitude of τ_c depends strongly on temperature, and to a minor extent on other factors such as strain rate, differential stress and the chemical activity of certain components such as water that may influence the strength of specific bonds in a crystal. For each slip system this dependence is different. As a result, the types of dominant slip system that are active in a crystal change with metamorphic and deformation conditions (Chap. 4.15,4.16).

When different slip systems intersect in a crystal, migrating dislocations can become entangled and their further movement is obstructed. Such dislocation tangles can inhibit movement of other newly formed dislocations, which pile up behind the blocked ones. The crystal becomes difficult to deform and hardens. This process is referred to as *strain hardening*.

If we twist a piece of steel wire, it is difficult to bend it back into its original shape, and the wire becomes harder to deform upon renewed bending. Eventually the wire may snap; by bending the wire, we

Fig. 3.8. a The principle of movement of a vacancy. **b** Horizontal shortening of a crystal by displacement of vacancies

SLIP SYSTEM TERMINOLOGY

A slip system in a crystal is defined by a slip plane and a direction of slip (the Burgers vector) within this plane. These elements are usually indicated by Miller indices, giving first the plane and then the direction, e.g. (001)[010]. Instead of Miller indices, standard abbreviation letter symbols are used in some cases. Notice the shape of the brackets used; if a specific plane and direction are indicated this is done as (plane)[direction]. A set of symmetrically equivalent slip systems is indicated as {planes}<directions>. <f∩r> indicates the intersection line of f and r planes. If the Burgers vector does not correspond to a unit cell length, the length can be indicated with the indices, e.g. as {110}1/2<-110>.

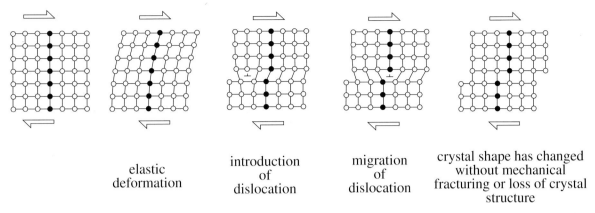

elastic
deformation

introduction
of
dislocation

migration
of
dislocation

crystal shape has changed
without mechanical
fracturing or loss of crystal
structure

Fig. 3.9. Deformation of a crystal by movement of an edge dis-location; the top half of the crystal is translated over one lattice unit to the **right** as a result of the passage of a single dislocation *from left to right.* View normal to the edge dislocation. One lattice plane is marked in **black** to show the relative displacement of the upper part of the crystal with respect to the lower part

have caused migration and entanglement of disloca-tions in the lattice of the metal crystals. Strain harde-ning occurs also in rocks, and can enhance brittle fail-ure. There are, however, mechanisms which work against strain hardening and allow ductile deforma-tion to continue. One important mechanism which allows dislocations to pass obstruction sites is the migration of vacancies to dislocation lines (Fig. 3.10); this effectively displaces the dislocation, and allows it to 'climb' over a blocked site. The mechanism of dis-location glide with climb of dislocations is known as *dislocation creep.*

An important effect of intracrystalline deforma-tion is the development of a *lattice-preferred orienta-tion* (LPO). Since dislocations move only in specific lattice planes, a rock deforming by movement of dis-

locations may develop a preferred orientation of the grains that make up the rock. The development and interpretation of lattice preferred orientation is dis-cussed in Chapter 4.12–4.16.

3.5 Twinning

Some minerals can deform by *deformation twinning* (or mechanical twinning) in addition to dislocation creep and glide (Jensen and Starkey 1985; Smith and Brown 1988; Burkhard 1993). Twinning can accommo-date only a limited amount of strain and always ope-

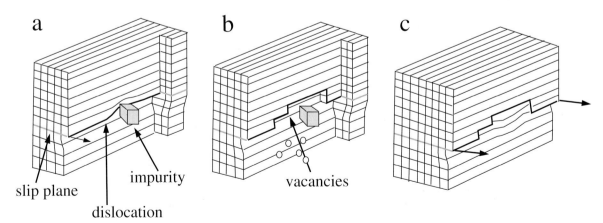

a

b

c

slip plane

impurity

dislocation

vacancies

Fig. 3.10. a Dislocation blocked by an impurity in the crystal. **b** Migration of vacancies to the dislocation plane can cause climb of the dislocation away from the obstruction. **c** After climb, the dislocation is no longer blocked and can pass the obstruction

EVIDENCE FOR INTRACRYSTALLINE DEFORMATION

Individual dislocations cannot be observed with an optical microscope. However, the effect of the presence of dislocations in a crystal lattice may be visible. A crystal lattice which contains a large number of similar dislocations can be slightly bent; as a result, the crystal does not extinguish homogeneously as observed with crossed polars; this effect is known as *undulose extinction* (Figs. 3.6, 3.11). Undulose extinction can be 'sweeping' when it occurs as large-scale, regular bending of the crystal due to the presence of dislocations, but can also be patchy and irregular, when it is associated with (microscopically invisible) small fractures and kinks besides dislocation tangles (Hirth and Tullis 1992). *Microkinks* occur as small isolated structures in quartz and feldspars. They are probably associated with cataclastic failure at sites of dislocation tangles (Tullis and Yund 1987) and are therefore indicative of dislocation glide. Another effect that is commonly observed in crystals deformed at low temperature by intracrystalline deformation are lamellae with a high optical relief which usually have a distinct preferred orientation, known as *deformation lamellae* (Figs. 3.6, 3.12). Deformation lamellae consist of dislocation tangles, small elongate subgrains, and arrays of very small solid or fluid inclusions that are only visible by TEM. Deformation lamellae are particularly common in quartz, where they usually have a sub-basal orientation. How deformation lamellae actually develop and how they should be interpreted is not well understood.

Finally, the presence of a lattice preferred orientation has been suggested as evidence for deformation by dislocation creep, although in some minerals (calcite) it can also form by deformation twinning. At elevated temperature, intracrystalline microstructures such as undulose extinction and deformation lamellae may be absent due to recovery or recrystallisation (see below). In this case, the presence of a strong lattice preferred orientation can be taken as evidence for dislocation creep.

EVIDENCE FOR DEFORMATION TWINNING

Deformation twins can commonly be distinguished from growth twins by their shape; deformation twins are commonly tapered, while growth twins are commonly straight and stepped (Figs. 3.13, 8.2, 8.3). Twins may be restricted to certain parts of a crystal. Growth twins are commonly bounded by zoning, while deformation twins can be concentrated at high strain sites such as the rim of crystals or sites where two crystals touch each other. In plagioclase, growth and deformation twins occur. Deformation twins commonly taper towards the crystal centre (Fig. 3.13; Chap. 3.12.4). In calcite, most twins are deformation twins which tend to taper towards the grain boundary (Chap. 8.5.1, 8.6.2; Fig. 8.2).

rates in specific crystallographic directions, so that additional pressure solution, dislocation creep or recrystallisation (see below) is needed to accommodate large strains. In general, twinning occurs in the lower temperature range of deformation (Chap. 3.12.3, 3.12.4). Twinning is most common in plagioclase and calcite, but has also been reported for microcline (Eggleton and Buseck 1980; White and Barnett 1990), biotite (Goodwin and Wenk 1990), kyanite and diopside (Raleigh 1965; Raleigh and Talbot 1967).

3.6 Recovery

$$\uparrow \Delta U \propto \uparrow \frac{\text{total length dislocation}}{V \text{ xtln material}} = \text{dislocation density}$$

Any crystal can be imagined to possess a certain amount of 'internal strain energy', which is at its minimum when the crystal lattice is free of dislocations. If we deform a crystal and induce dislocations, we increase this internal energy by local changes in the distance between atoms; the increase in internal energy is proportional to the increase in total length of dislocations per volume of crystalline material, also known as the *dislocation density*. Dislocations and dislocation tangles are formed in response to imposed differential stress. Other processes tend to shorten, order or destroy the dislocations. Vacancies can migrate towards dislocation tangles and straighten the blocked sections; bent dislocations can straighten; and dislocations can be arranged into networks. These processes can decrease the total dislocation length and hence the internal strain energy of crystals and will therefore operate following the thermodynamic principle to minimise total free energy in a system. During deformation, disordering and ordering mechanisms will compete while after deformation stops, ordering mechanisms progress towards an equilibrium situation with the shortest possible length of dislocations in the crystal lattice. We use the general term *recovery* to cover these ordering mechanisms.

Dislocations in a crystal can be grouped into regular planar networks as a result of recovery (Fig. 3.14). These networks are known as *subgrain walls* or *subgrain boundaries*. Such boundaries separate crystal fragments known as *subgrains,* which are slightly misoriented with respect to their neighbour subgrains or to the host grain (Fig. 3.15). The orientation of a subgrain boundary depends on the orientation of the slip system of the dislocations which accumulate in it (Trepied et al. 1980).

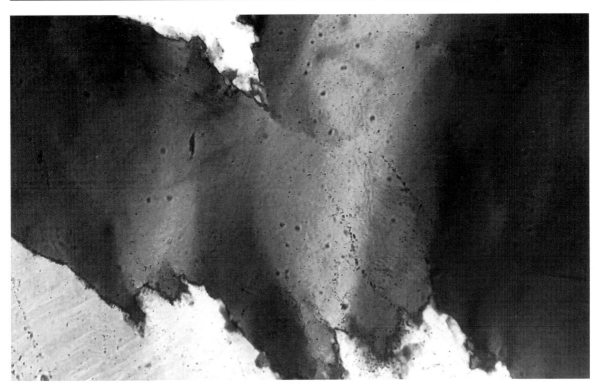

Fig. 3.11. Undulose extinction in quartz. Grain boundaries are irregular due to grain boundary migration. The grain at *lower left* has deformation lamellae. Micaschist, Orobic Alps. Width of view 0.6 mm. CPL

Fig. 3.12. Deformation lamellae in quartz (oblique). *Vertical planes* are trails of fluid inclusions. Mt Isa, Australia. Width of view 1.8 mm. CPL

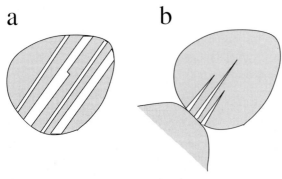

Fig. 3.13. a Growth twins in plagioclase with steps. **b** Deformation twins in plagioclase with tapering edges, nucleated on a high stress site at the edge of the crystal

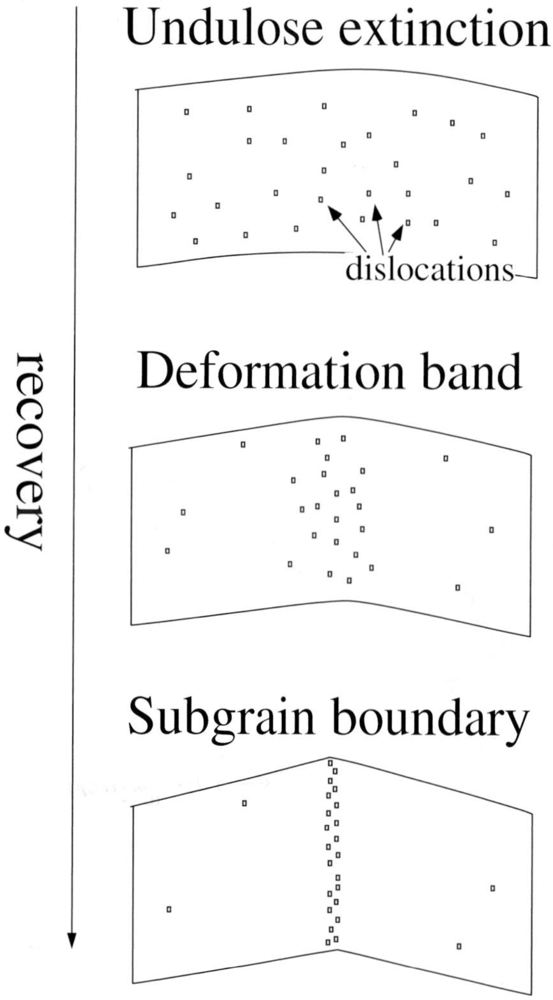

Undulose extinction

Deformation band

Subgrain boundary

recovery

dislocations

Fig. 3.14. Schematic illustration of the recovery process. Dislocations distributed over the crystal give rise to undulose extinction. Recovery causes concentration of dislocations in deformation bands and eventually in a subgrain boundary (tiltwall)

EVIDENCE FOR RECOVERY

In response to recovery, dislocations tend to concentrate in planar zones in the crystal, decreasing dislocation density in other parts. In thin section, this results in the occurrence of zones in the crystal which have approximately uniform extinction, and which grade over a small distance into other similar crystal sectors with a slightly different orientation. These transition zones are known as *deformation bands* (Fig. 3.14). They can be regarded as a transitional stage between undulose extinction and subgrain boundaries.

Subgrains (Figs. 3.15, 4.25) can be recognised as parts of a crystal which are separated from adjacent parts by discrete, sharp, low relief boundaries. The crystal lattice orientation changes slightly from one subgrain to the next, usually less than 5° (FitzGerald et al. 1983; White and Mawer 1988). Subgrains can be equant or elongate (Fig. 4.25). In many cases, subgrain walls laterally merge into deformation bands or high-angle grain boundaries (Fig. 3.16).

It is also important to notice that recovery in bent crystals as described above is only one of the possible mechanisms to form subgrains; alternative, though possibly less common, mechanisms are sideways migration of kink band boundaries, the reduction of misorientation of grain boundaries and impingement of migrating grain boundaries (Means and Ree 1988).

Fracturing, rotation and sealing by growth from solution may also play a role in the development of some subgrains in quartz (den Brok 1992). If crystals are separated into strongly undulose subgrains of slightly different orientation but with fuzzy boundaries, and if such crystals contain fractures, the 'subgrain' structure may be due to submicroscopic cataclasis of the grains (Tullis et al. 1990); such subgrain-like structures and even undulose extinction can form by dense networks of small fractures. Only TEM work can show the true nature of the structure in this case.

A subgrain boundary can be imagined as a plane separating two crystal fragments that have rotated slightly with respect to each other; such boundaries can therefore be classified according to the orientation of the rotation axis. Subgrain boundaries with rotation axes parallel and normal to the boundary are known as *tiltwalls* and *twistwalls* respectively. A tiltwall is shown in Fig. 3.14 and consists of an array of edge dislocations with the same Burgers vector. A twistwall consists of two intersecting sets of screw dislocations with different Burgers vectors. *Complex walls* have an oblique rotation axis and consist of networks of dislocations having two or more different Burgers vectors.

Fig. 3.15. Subgrains in quartz (horizontal), oblique to trails of fluid inclusions *(vertical).* Quartzite, Mt Isa, Australia. Width of view 1.8 mm. CPL

Fig. 3.16. Typical fabric of dynamic recrystallisation in quartz. Relics of large old quartz grains with undulose extinction and elongate subgrains pass laterally into domains of small, dynamically recrystallised grains. St Barthélemy, Pyrenees, France. Width of view 1.8 mm. CPL

3.7 Recrystallisation

3.7.1 Grain Boundary Migration Recrystallisation

Besides recovery, another process can contribute towards a reduction of dislocation density in deformed crystals. Imagine two neighbouring deformed crystals, one with high and one with low dislocation density (Fig. 3.17a). Atoms along the grain boundary in the crystal with high dislocation density can be displaced slightly so that they fit to the lattice of the crystal with low dislocation density. This results in local displacement of the grain boundary and growth of the less deformed crystal at the cost of its more deformed neighbour (Fig. 3.17a, inset). The process reduces the internal free energy of the crystalline aggregate involved, and is known as *grain boundary migration*. The grain boundary may bulge into the crystal with high dislocation density and form new, independent crystals (Fig. 3.17a); this process is known as *bulging*. It is also possible, though probably less common in rocks (Drury and Urai 1990) that a small dislocation-free core nucleates inside a strongly deformed grain with high density of dislocation tangles, and grows at the cost of the old crystal (Fig. 3.17a). Both processes, isolated nucleation and bulging of existing grain boundaries, lead to reorganisation of crystalline material; 'old grains' with high dislocation density are replaced by 'new grains'. This process is known as *recrystallisation* and more specifically as *grain boundary migration recrystallisation* (abbreviated GBM recrystallisation; Gottstein and Mecking 1985; Urai et al. 1986). There is not necessarily any change in chemical composition between old and recrystallised grains. However, in some minerals such as feldspar, small differences in composition may develop.

3.7.2 Subgrain Rotation Recrystallisation

A special recrystallisation process occurs when dislocations are continuously added to subgrain boundaries. This happens only if dislocations are relatively free to climb from one lattice plane to another. The process is known as climb-accommodated disloca-

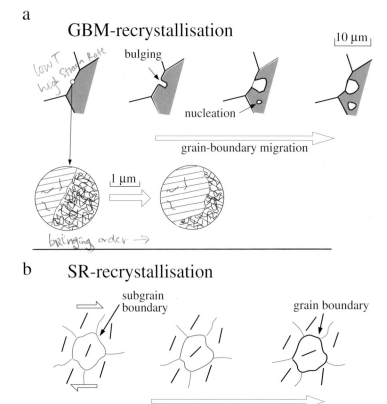

Fig. 3.17a,b. Two mechanisms of dynamic recrystallisation. **a** Grain boundary migration (GBM) recrystallisation. If two neighbouring grains have different dislocation density, the grain boundary may start to bulge into the grain with the highest density (*inset; grey straight lines* in crystals indicate crystal lattice planes). On the scale of individual grains, the grain with higher dislocation density (*shaded*) is consumed by bulging of the less deformed grain; the bulge eventually develops into an independent grain. Spontaneous nucleation and growth of new grains with low dislocation density is also possible. **b** Subgrain rotation (SR) recrystallisation. Rotation of a subgrain in response to migration of dislocations into subgrain walls during progressive deformation can cause development of high angle grain boundaries and thus of new grains. *Bars* in the subgrains indicate lattice orientation

EVIDENCE FOR DYNAMIC RECRYSTALLISATION

Evidence for dynamic recrystallisation is usually more difficult to find than evidence for deformation or recovery. Two types of characteristic microstructures can be distinguished: partially and completely recrystallised fabrics.

In partially recrystallised fabrics a bimodal grain size distribution is characteristic, with aggregates of small grains of approximately uniform size between large grains with undulose extinction and with subgrains of the same size as the small grains (Figs. 3.16, 3.19, 3.22, 3.23); such small grains are probably new grains formed by dynamic recrystallisation. The uniform size of new grains is due to deformation and recrystallisation at a specific differential stress (Chap. 8.6.1).

A completely recrystallised fabric may be difficult to distinguish from a non-recrystallised equigranular fabric. However, in an aggregate of grains formed by complete dynamic recrystallisation, the grains will show evidence of internal deformation, a lattice-preferred orientation (Chap. 4.13) and a relatively uniform grain size (Fig. 3.24).

Evidence for GBM recrystallisation is the presence of highly irregular grain boundaries (Figs. 3.19, 3.20). SR recrystallisation is characterised by a gradual transition of aggregates of subgrains to aggregates of new grains with approximately the same size, and by subgrain boundaries which pass laterally into grain boundaries (Fig. 3.21). A special lattice-preferred orientation may occur in recrystallised aggregates in the form of *orientation family* of grains, which may derive from large single parent grains that were completely erased by SR recrystallisation.

In the TEM, GBM recrystallisation is characterised by grains with a strongly variable dislocation density, while for SR recrystallisation all grains have approximately similar dislocation density (Tullis et al. 1990).

Jessell (1987) proposed microstructures that can be used to recognise grain boundary migration and to establish the migration direction of a grain boundary. Grains of a second mineral such as micas can pin a grain boundary and cause 'pinning', 'window' or 'dragging' microstructures (Fig. 3.18). If a grain is almost completely replaced by a neighbour, 'left-over' grains, all with identical orientation may indicate the presence of an originally larger grain (Urai 1983; Jessell 1986; Fig. 3.18).

An aggregate of small, dynamically recrystallised grains around a crystal core with the same mineral composition is known as a *core-and-mantle structure*, provided that evidence (as mentioned above) exists that the structure developed by dynamic recrystallisation of the core mineral along its rim (Chap. 3.13; White 1976; Figs. 3.22, 5.19–5.22, 11.1). If the mantle is extremely fine-grained and the mechanism by which it formed is uncertain, the term *mortar structure* has been used instead (Spry 1969). However, this term has a genetic implication as "mechanically crushed rock" and its use is therefore not recommended.

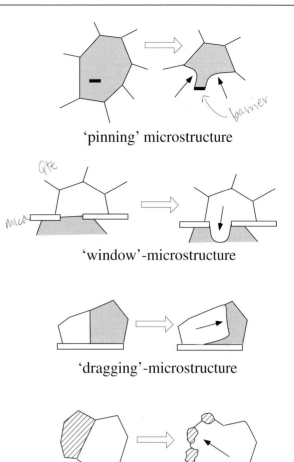

Fig. 3.18. Four microstructures which indicate movement direction of a migrating grain boundary during dynamic recrystallisation (after Jessell 1987). **Solid arrows** indicate the movement direction of the grain boundary by growth of the light grain into the shaded grain. Further explanation in text

tion creep. In such cases, the angle between the crystal lattice on both sides of the subgrain boundary increases until gradually the subgrain can no longer be classified as part of the same grain (Fig. 3.17b); a new grain has developed by progressive misorientation of subgrains or *subgrain rotation*. This process is known as *subgrain rotation-recrystallisation* (abbreviated SR recrystallisation). GBM and SR recrystallisation are both important processes in recrystallisation of materials during deformation, known as *dynamic recrystallisation* (Figs. 3.16, 3.20–3.24). GBM recrystallisation may take over from SR recrystallisation after a certain amount of rotation of former subgrains (Lloyd and Freeman 1991, 1994).

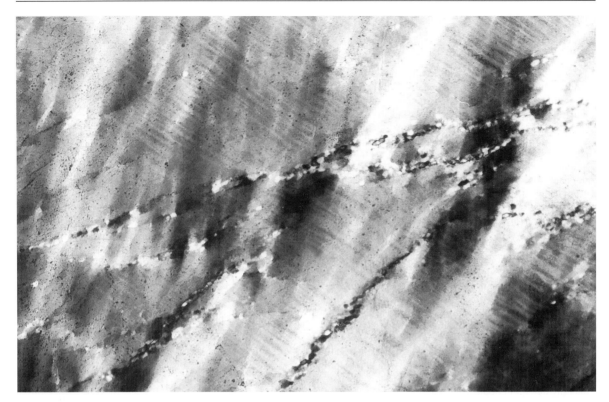

Fig. 3.19. Quartz grain with deformation lamellae *(top left to lower right)* and subgrain boundaries *(subvertical)* transected by bands of new grains *(lower left to top right)* formed by dynamic recrystallisation. Quartz vein in micaschist. Southern Alps, Italy. Width of view 1.8 mm. CPL

Fig. 3.20. Polycrystalline quartz with irregular grain boundaries formed in response to grain boundary migration recrystallisation. The white central grain is bulging into the dark grain at *lower right.* Quartzite, Yilgarn Craton, Australia. Width of view 1.8 mm. CPL

Fig. 3.21. Polycrystalline quartz aggregate, probably developed predominantly by subgrain rotation recrystallisation. Transitions exist between grains surrounded by high angle boundaries and subgrains. A relic of a deformed old quartz grain occurs at *upper left*. St Barthélemy, Pyrenees, France. Width of view 1.8 mm. CPL

Fig. 3.22. Relics of folded old quartz grains, nearly completely replaced by new grains during dynamic recrystallisation. The section is taken normal to the stretching lineation in a quartzite mylonite with a dominantly linear shape fabric. Aston Massif, Pyrenees, France. Width of view 1.4 mm. CPL

3.7.3 Competing Processes During Deformation

During deformation of a crystalline material, continuous competition exists between processes that cause distortion of the crystal lattice and processes such as recovery and recrystallisation that restore order. The state of affairs during any stage of the deformation and the final result that we observe in deformed rocks depend on the relative importance of these processes and, indirectly, on deformation parameters such as strain rate and temperature. In general, a high temperature and the presence of a fluid on grain boundaries promotes recovery and recrystallisation processes; high strain rate enhances crystal distortion. These facts have been known from the earliest age of metalworking; a sword or horse-shoe can be shaped from a piece of metal by hammering if it is sufficiently heated. In thin section, only structures related to the last stages of the competing processes are normally preserved, formed shortly before temperature and/or strain rate fell below a critical value and the structures were 'frozen in'.

There are two main types of deformation based on dislocation creep, depending on the accommodating process (Sellars 1978; Zeuch 1982; Tullis and Yund 1985); climb-accommodated dislocation creep (Yund and Tullis 1991) associated with SR recrystallisation (Guillopé and Poirier 1979); and recrystallisation-accommodated dislocation creep where GBM recrystallisation is the accommodating mechanism (Tullis and Yund 1985; Tullis et al. 1990). There are indications that, with increasing temperature, the accommodating mechanism in quartz is first GBM recrystallisation when dislocation climb and recovery is difficult, which switches to SR recrystallisation with the onset of recovery, and then to combined GBM and SR recrystallisation because of increasing ease of diffusion in the crystal lattice (Hirth and Tullis 1992).

3.8 Solid-State Diffusion Creep

If the temperature in a deforming rock is relatively high with respect to the melting temperature of con-

Fig. 3.23. Layer of fine-grained K-feldspar in quartz, both dynamically recrystallised. A perthitic fragment of a K-feldspar porphyroclast with flame-shaped albite lamellae is present in the recrystallised feldspar layer. Notice the difference in grain size of recrystallised quartz (coarse) and feldspar (fine). Granite mylonite. Qin Ling Mountains, China. Width of view 0.8 mm. CPL

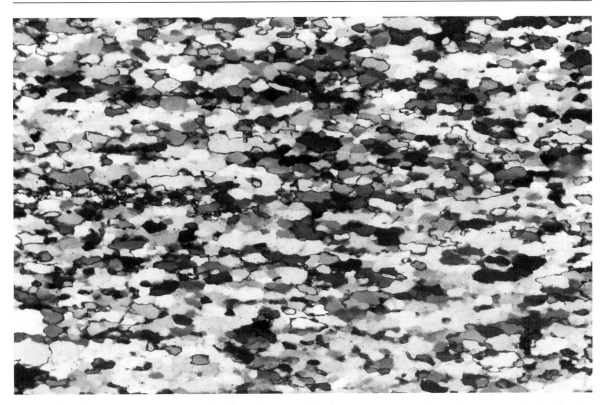

Fig. 3.24. Typical fabric of dynamically recrystallised quartz. Grains have a weak shape-preferred orientation which defines a continuous foliation (Chap. 4.7). Granite mylonite. Qin Ling mountains, China. Width of view 1.8 mm. CPL

stituent minerals, crystals can deform solely by migration of vacancy sites through the lattice. This process is known as *solid-state diffusion creep*. There are two basic types: *Coble creep* and *Nabarro-Herring creep*. The former operates by diffusion of vacancies in the crystal lattice along grain boundaries; the latter by diffusion of vacancies throughout the crystal lattice.

The term *crystalplastic deformation* is used loosely to describe deformation by dislocation creep or diffusion creep. It is a useful term in cases where the effects of the two mechanisms cannot be distinguished.

3.9 Grain Boundary Sliding and Superplasticity

Especially in fine-grained aggregates, crystals can slide past each other while the development of voids between the crystals is prevented by solid-state diffusion creep or solution and precipitation via a grain boundary fluid. This deformation process is known as *grain boundary sliding* (Boullier and Gueguen 1975; Gueguen and Boullier 1975). In metallurgy, some fine-grained alloys can be deformed up to very high strain in tension without boudinage, a process known as *superplastic deformation*. The term *superplasticity* has also been used in geology (Schmid 1982; Poirier 1985; Rutter et al. 1994) and refers to very fine-grained aggregates (1–10 μm) of equidimensional grains which deformed to very high strains without developing a strong shape fabric or lattice-preferred orientation. Grain boundary sliding is thought to play a major role in such deformation (Boullier and Gueguen 1975; Allison et al. 1979; Schmid 1982; van der Pluijm 1991; Rutter et al. 1994). Grain size seems to be the major parameter in determining whether an aggregate will deform by dislocation creep or by solid-state diffusion creep and grain boundary sliding (Schmid et al. 1977; Behrmann 1983); a small grain size favours grain boundary sliding since diffusion paths are then relatively short.

EVIDENCE FOR SOLID-STATE DIFFUSION CREEP AND GRAIN BOUNDARY SLIDING

Few microstructures have been proposed as evidence for diffusion creep. The process may give rise to strongly curved and lobate grain boundaries between two different minerals at high-grade metamorphic conditions (Fig. 3.25; Gower and Simpson 1992). Ozawa (1989) suggested that sector Al-Cr zoning observed in spinel grains in peridotite is formed by unequal diffusivity of these ions when spinel is deformed by solid-state diffusion creep in the mantle.

Solid-state diffusion creep combined with grain boundary sliding may prevent development or cause destruction of a lattice-preferred orientation. If a fine-grained mineral aggregate has undergone high strain but consist of equant grains and lacks a clear lattice-preferred orientation, this may be taken as indirect evidence for dominant grain boundary sliding as a deformation mechanism (Boullier and Gueguen 1975;

Allison et al. 1979; Behrmann 1983; Behrmann and Mainprice 1987). On the other hand, the presence of a preferred orientation cannot be used as proof against the action of grain boundary sliding (Rutter et al. 1994). Straight and parallel grain boundary segments, often in two directions throughout a sample, may be due to grain boundary sliding (Lister and Dornsiepen 1982; Drury and Humphreys 1988). Such boundaries are especially conspicuous in monomineralic aggregates of minerals such as quartz or calcite, for which this structure is unusual.

The presence of diffuse boundaries between strongly flattened fine-grained monomineralic aggregates of two different minerals may be a mixing effect due to grain-boundary sliding (Tullis et al. 1990). In the TEM, possible indications for grain-boundary sliding are a low dislocation density in grains; a lath shape of grains, and the presence of voids along grain boundaries (Behrmann and Mainprice 1987; Tullis et al. 1990).

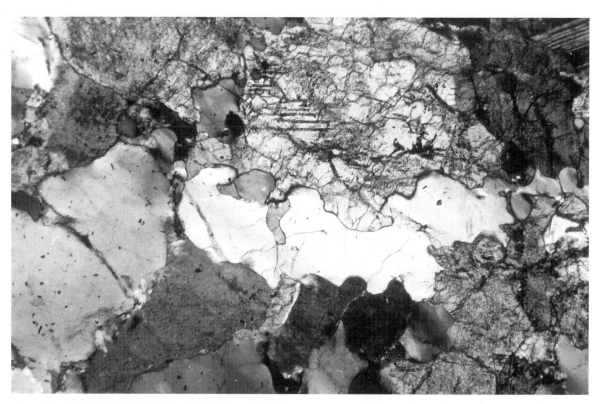

Fig. 3.25. Gneiss with lobate grain boundaries, especially between quartz and feldspar. The rock has been deformed at high-grade metamorphic conditions. St Barthélemy Massif, Pyrenees, France. Width of view 4 mm. CPL

3.10 Grain Boundary Area Reduction (GBAR)

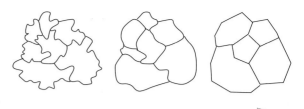

Grain boundary area reduction

Lattice defects are not the only structures that contribute towards the internal free energy of a volume of rock; grain boundaries are disordered structures with high internal free energy. A decrease in the total surface area of grain boundaries in a rock can reduce this internal free energy (Vernon 1976; Poirier 1985). Straight grain boundaries and large grains are therefore favoured and any polycrystalline material will strive towards a fabric with large, polygonal grains with straight boundaries to reduce the internal energy (Figs. 3.26, 9.10b,c). We call this process of grain boundary migration resulting in grain growth and straightening of grain boundaries *grain boundary area reduction* (abbreviated GBAR). The reduction in internal free energy gained by GBAR is generally much less than that gained by GBM or SR recrystallisation. Therefore, although GBAR occurs during deformation (e.g. Fig. 11.1) its effect is more obvious and may become dominant after deformation ceased, especially at high temperature (Chap. 3.11; Bons and Urai 1992).

Fig. 3.26. Illustration of the process of grain boundary area reduction (GBAR) through grain boundary adjustment and grain growth, resulting in a decrease in grain boundary energy. Irregular grain boundaries formed during deformation and dynamic recrystallisation are straightened to a polygonal shape, and some small grains are eliminated

The surface free energy of a grain boundary may depend on the orientation of the boundary with respect to the crystal lattice. If the dependence of grain boundary energy on the crystal lattice is weak for a certain mineral, GBAR in a monomineralic rock will lead to the approach of an 'equilibrium-fabric' of polygonal crystals with contacts tending to make tri-

Fig. 3.27. Polygonal fabric of scapolite grains formed by static recrystallisation. Mt Isa, Australia. Width of view 4 mm. CPL

ple junctions with *interfacial angles* of approximately 120° in three dimensions. Obviously, this angle can be smaller or larger in oblique cross sections (Fig. 10.2). Since similar structures form in foam, e.g. in a beer bottle, the fabric is often referred to as a *foam-structure* (Figs. 3.27, 11.2). Large grains with many sides tend to increase in size while small grains with few sides shrink and eventually disappear during GBAR.

Many aggregates where GBAR has been active show slightly curved grain boundaries; notably the small grains may have strongly outward curving boundaries (Fig. 3.27). This curvature may be due to migration of the grain boundary in the direction of the centre of curvature during GBAR (Vernon 1976; Shelley 1993). However, care must be taken when applying this principle to deformed rocks since in GBM recrystallisation, new grains have curved boundaries that migrate away from the centre of curvature (Figs. 3.17, 3.18).

If a correlation exists between grain boundary energy and the orientation of the crystal lattice, minerals are said to be anisotropic with respect to grain boundary energy (Vernon 1976). Minerals like quartz, feldspars, cordierite, garnet, carbonates, anhydrite and sulphides are weakly anisotropic; the effect is hardly visible in thin section but interfacial angles between grain boundaries in an equilibrium fabric commonly deviate from 120°. (Fig. 3.28a). Minerals like hornblende and pyroxene are moderately anisotropic and many grain boundaries are parallel to {110} planes (Fig. 3.28b). Micas, sillimanite and tourmaline are strongly anisotropic and show a strong dominance of certain crystallographic planes as grain boundaries (Figs. 3.28c, 4.27c); in micas, (001) is dominant.

Besides the anisotropy of individual minerals which influences interfacial angles in monomineralic aggregates, the nature of different minerals in contact is also of importance. In polymineralic aggregates, the boundaries between grains of the same mineral can have another (commonly higher) internal energy than those between grains of different minerals (Vernon 1976). As a result, there is a tendency for high energy boundaries to decrease, and for low angle boundaries to increase in length. Consequently, the interfacial angle between the boundaries separating unlike minerals (also known as the *dihedral angle*; Hunter 1987; Fig. 3.28d) deviates from 120°. An extreme example are the common orthogonal contacts between quartz and micas, where the dihedral angle is 180°. This gives a recrystallised mica aggregate or quartz-mica schist its typical aspect with euhedral or subhedral grains (Box p. 46–47; Figs. 3.28e, 3.29).

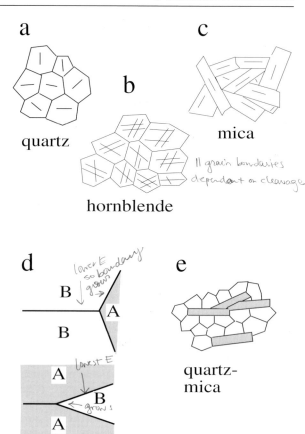

Fig. 3.28a–e. Effects of the anisotropy of minerals for grain boundary energy on grain boundary orientation. **a** If grain boundaries all have similar internal free energy, grains will be equidimensional and boundaries are not preferentially associated with specific crystallographic planes (indicated by *lines* in the crystal). **b** In the case of hornblende, some grain boundaries ({110} planes) have relatively lower internal free energy, and may be dominant in the aggregate. **c** In the case of micas, grain boundaries parallel to (001) are favoured over all others and euhedral grains are commonly abundant. **d** Illustration of the dihedral angle between minerals *A* and *B*, where the boundary between like minerals has a lower *(top)* or higher *(bottom)* energy than that between unlike minerals. **e** Typical shape of a quartz-mica aggregate with dominant 180° dihedral angles between quartz and mica

The anisotropy of minerals is also evident in the shape of included grains in rocks that underwent GBAR; grains of mica or sillimanite in quartz, for example, show usually a strong predominance of favoured crystallographic directions for their boundaries (Fig. 4.8). Notice, however, that this does not apply for inclusions in low to medium-grade rocks

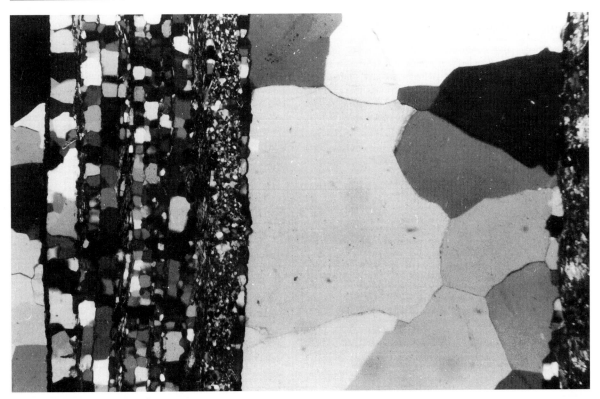

Fig. 3.29. Statically recrystallised quartz in a fabric with alternating quartz and feldspar layers. Feldspar is recrystallised and very fine-grained *(central band)*. Grain size of quartz depends on the width of the quartz layer; in thin layers, quartz grains are limited in their growth, leading to a clear dependence of statically recrystallised grain size on layer width. It is possible that quartz grain size was similar in all layers at the end of the deformation which formed the layering and before static recrystallisation started. Quartz vein. Yilgarn Craton, Australia. Width of view 4 mm. CPL

where inclusion boundaries have been relatively immobile after growth of the host grain (Chap. 7.3). The process of grain growth tends to lower the internal free energy of a grain aggregate even after a foam structure has been established. The grain size that is finally reached after GBAR depends on the possibility of grains to grow without obstruction by grains of other minerals; as a result, GBAR in layered rocks results in relatively coarse grains in wide monomineralic layers, and small grains in thin or polymineralic layers (Fig. 3.29). Especially the presence of small graphite grains in a rock may hamper the growth of other minerals. This is the reason why many graphite schists are fine-grained, even at high metamorphic grade. Similarly, in micaceous quartzites, pure quartzite layers are usually much coarser than quartz-mica layers (Fig. 3.29).

3.11 Static Recrystallisation

When the deformation of a volume of rock decelerates or stops, the polycrystalline material will not be in a state of minimum internal free energy, not even if recovery and recrystallisation during deformation were important. Crystals still contain dislocations, dislocation tangles and subgrain boundaries. Grain boundaries have an irregular, wavy shape, and some minerals may be unstable. If deformation was at relatively low temperature or if little free water was present in the rock, the deformed fabric may be preserved relatively unaltered during subsequent uplift to the surface. This situation allows the geologist to observe structures directly associated with the defor-

FABRIC NOMENCLATURE

An extensive and confusing terminology exists for the description of the geometry of grains and fabrics in metamorphic rocks (see also Box p. 1). Below, we give some of the most important terms, their meaning and their mutual relation (Moore 1970; Best 1982; Shelley 1993). The suffix 'blastic' refers to solid-state crystallisation during metamorphism.

Shape of individual grains
The following terms describe the shape of individual grains and can be used as prefix for 'grain' or 'crystal', e.g. euhedral crystal shape, anhedral grains (Fig. 3.30):

euhedral – with fully developed crystal faces. Less commonly, the term *idiomorphic* is used, mainly in igneous rocks. The term *automorphic* has similar meaning but is little used.
subhedral – with irregular crystal form but with some well developed crystal faces. Less commonly, the term *hypidiomorphic* is used, mainly in igneous rocks (Fig. 3.5). The term *hypautomorphic* has an equivalent meaning but is little used.
anhedral – without crystal faces. Less commonly, the terms *allotriomorphic, xenomorphic* and *xenoblastic* are used.
acicular – needle-shaped.

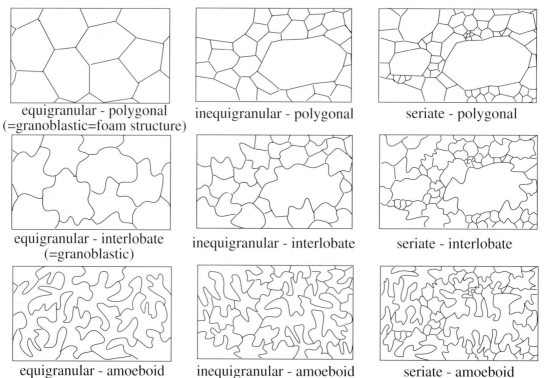

Shape of grains

euhedral

(idiomorphic)
(automorphic)

subhedral

(hypidiomorphic)
(hypautomorphic)

anhedral

(allotriomorphic)
(xenomorphic)

acicular

Shape of grain aggregates

equigranular - polygonal
(=granoblastic=foam structure)

inequigranular - polygonal

seriate - polygonal

equigranular - interlobate
(=granoblastic)

inequigranular - interlobate

seriate - interlobate

equigranular - amoeboid

inequigranular - amoeboid

seriate - amoeboid

Fig. 3.30. Schematic presentation of fabric nomenclature for the shape of grains and grain aggregates (After Moore 1970)

Three terms are commonly used for large grains with inclusions:

poikiloblastic – with numerous, randomly oriented inclusions of other minerals. The term *poikilitic* refers to a similar structure in igneous rocks. The term is mainly used for porphyroblasts.
skeletal – refers to a spongy shape of a grain that occurs in thin seams between grains of other minerals that are nearly in contact (Fig. 7.6).

Shape of grain aggregates

The following terms can be used as a prefix for fabric, e.g. polygonal fabric, decussate fabric (Fig. 3.30):

Grain boundary geometry
polygonal – with straight grain boundaries and consisting of anhedral or subhedral grains (e.g. Figs. 3.27, 11.2).
interlobate – with irregular, lobate grain boundaries (e.g. Figs. 3.21, 4.8).
amoeboid – with strongly curved and lobate, interlocking grain boundaries; like an amoeba.

Size distribution of grains
equigranular – all grains with roughly equal size.
inequigranular – non-gradational distribution of different grainsize; an example is a bimodal distribution, with large grains of approximately equal size in a fine-grained equigranular matrix.
seriate – a complete gradation of fine- to coarse-grained.

Special terms for the shape of grain aggregates

– *granoblastic* (less common crystalloblastic) – a mosaic of approximately equidimensional subhedral or anhedral grains. Inequant grains, if present, are randomly oriented (Fig. 3.23). The term *equigranular* has a similar meaning but is not restricted to metamorphic rocks. Many granoblastic fabrics exhibit a foam-structure (see main text; Fig. 3.27).
– *lepidoblastic* – a predominance of tabular mineral grains with strong planar preferred dimensional orientation (Fig. 4.7). This term is now generally substituted by a description of the foliation (Fig. 4.6; compare the first and second editions of Williams et al. 1954, 1982).
– *decussate* – an arrangement of randomly oriented elongate grains (such as mica) in a metamorphic rock.
– *granolepidoblastic* – a combination of granoblastic and lepidoblastic fabric in the same rock. The term has become obsolete.
– *nematoblastic* – a predominance of acicular or elongate grains displaying a linear preferred dimensional orientation. This term has become obsolete as well, substituted by a description of the mineral lineation.
– *porphyroblastic* – inequigranular fabric, with large grains that grew during metamorphism and which are embedded in a finer-grained matrix (Chap. 7; Fig. 7.5).
– *mylonitic* – see Chapter 5 for a detailed description of mylonitic fabrics.
– *flaser* – a type of mylonitic fabric in which elliptical porphyroclasts lie in a finer mylonitic matrix. Since most mylonitic rocks exhibit this kind of fabric, the term is not particularly informative and is therefore not recommended for metamorphic rocks. (In sedimentary rocks the term flaser structure refers to the presence of small lenses of pelite in sandstone, indicative of a particular sedimentary environment).

mation process. However, if temperature was relatively high when deformation stopped or if much water was present along grain boundaries, recovery, recrystallisation and GBAR can continue in absence of deformation until a minimum internal energy configuration is obtained. This combined process is known as *static recrystallisation* (Figs. 3.26, 9.10). Dynamic and static recrystallisation are also known as primary and secondary recrystallisation; use of the latter terms is not recommended, however.

In metallurgy, the term *annealing* is used to indicate processes of recovery and static recrystallisation induced by passive heating of a previously deformed material. The term is also sometimes used for the interpretation of microstructures in rocks, e.g. in xenoliths (Vernon 1976; Shelley 1993). Occasionally, the term is used (incorrectly) as a general synonym for static recrystallisation.

During static recrystallisation, unstable minerals are replaced by stable ones, dislocation tangles are removed, grain boundaries become straight and grains tend to grow in size due to GBAR. If dislocation density is high in an aggregate and if the temperature is high enough, some grains may grow to a large size and commonly irregular shape at the expense of others (Fig. 4.8).

EVIDENCE FOR STATIC RECRYSTALLISATION

Evidence for static recrystallisation and its principal mechanism, grain boundary area reduction (GBAR), is provided by the presence of crystals with straight or smoothly curved grain boundaries (Figs. 3.27, 9.10) which lack undulose extinction or subgrains in a rock that was strongly deformed as shown by the presence of folds in layering (Fig. 11.2), relic augen or the presence of a strong lattice-preferred orientation. Such grains are said to be *strain-free*. In a statically recrystallised fabric it is commonly possible to recognise relics of a largely destroyed older structure; relics of a foliation or porphyroclasts may be preserved. Static grain growth is indicated by small grains of a second mineral with a preferred orientation that are included in grains of the main mineral (Fig. 4.8), and by elongate strain-free crystals that define a foliation; these may have grown in a rock with an older foliation where they were hampered in their growth by grains of a second mineral (Figs. 3.29, 5.10, 5.11). Static recrystallisation may be followed once more by deformation inducing undulose extinction and dynamic recrystallisation, starting a new cycle.

3.12 Deformation of Some Rock-Forming Minerals

3.12.1 Introduction

This section gives examples of specific deformation structures and deformation mechanisms in some common rock-forming minerals. Criteria to recognise deformation mechanisms in thin section are mentioned. Aspects which deviate from the general trend as sketched above are stressed. Treatment is from low to high-grade metamorphic conditions unless stated otherwise. Most published work concentrates on crystalplastic deformation, especially on dislocation creep and this section is therefore somewhat biased in this direction.

3.12.2 Quartz

Although quartz is one of the most common minerals in the crust, its deformation behaviour is very incompletely understood. This is mainly due to the complex role that water plays in the deformation of quartz; pressure solution is very important, especially at low temperature and strain rate (see below). The presence of water in the crystal lattice may also have influence on the strength of quartz and on the dislocation slip systems that can be active. Important review papers on quartz deformation are Linker and Kirby (1981), Linker et al. (1984) and Hobbs (1985).

At very low-grade conditions (below 300 °C) brittle fracturing, pressure solution and solution transfer of material are dominant deformation mechanisms. Characteristic structures are fractures in grains, undulose extinction and evidence for pressure solution and redeposition of material, sometimes in veins. At low-grade conditions (300–400 °C) dislocation glide and creep become important, mainly on basal glide planes in the (c)<a> direction. Characteristic structures are 'sweeping' undulose extinction (Fig. 3.11) and deformation lamellae (Fig. 3.12).

At medium to high-grade conditions (400–700 °C) dislocation creep is dominant, and prism {m}<a> slip becomes important. Characteristic are relatively strongly flattened old crystals and abundant recovery and recrystallisation structures (Fig. 3.29). Pressure solution may still play a role under these conditions (den Brok 1992). There are some experimental indications that with increasing temperature, recrystallisation mechanisms change from dominant SR re-

crystallisation to combined SR and GBM recrystallisation (Hirth and Tullis 1992). Oblique foliations probably develop mainly in the combined SR and GBM recrystallisation regime. Above 700-800 °C, prism-slip ({m}<c>) becomes important (Mainprice et al. 1986) and rapid recrystallisation and recovery cause most grains to have a strain-free appearance. Under these metamorphic conditions some quartz crystals can consume neighbours in a process of *secondary grain growth* due to grain boundary area reduction (GBAR); this can lead to large, single crystals of irregular amoeboid shape (Fig. 4.8) and possibly to strain-free monomineralic quartz ribbons (Box. p. 70; Figs. 5.10, 5.11).

Temperature is an important, but not unique factor determining quartz deformation behaviour; this also depends strongly on strain rate, differential stress and the presence of water in the lattice and along grain boundaries. With increasing differential stress, more slip systems may become active since the critical resolved shear stress of other slip systems is activated. For example, at low temperature, with increasing differential stress the system (c)<a> is followed by {m}<a> and finally {r}<a>. At high temperature, the sequence is (m)<c>, {m}<a>, (c)<a> and {r}<a> (Hobbs 1985).

3.12.3 Calcite and Dolomite

If water is present, pressure solution is dominant in calcite at low-grade conditions and leads to stylolite development. Calcite is special in that deformation twinning becomes important from very low-grade conditions onwards (Schmid et al. 1981; Chap. 8.6.2 and 8.9). Twinning occurs along three {e}-planes inclined to the c-axis and is initiated at very low critical resolved shear stress (between 2-12 MPa, depending on temperature and mean stress; Turner et al. 1954; Wenk et al. 1986a; Burkhard 1993). However, the amount of strain that can be achieved by twinning is limited and must be accommodated at grain boundaries by pressure solution or grain boundary migration. Evidence for the activity of these accommodating mechanisms in thin section are partly dissolved twins at grain boundaries, or twins that end before the grain boundary is reached, left behind by the migrating boundary. Twins can be used as indicators of temperature, strain and possibly stress (Chap. 8.5.1 and 8.6.2). At low- to medium-grade metamorphic conditions, dislocation glide on r- and f-planes becomes important besides deformation twinning: {f}<r∩f> (six systems) at low temperature and {f}<a∩f> (three systems) at higher temperature (de Bresser and

* Twins in calcite used for T & Strain

Spiers 1993). In addition, c<a> slip may become important at high temperature (Schmid et al. 1987; de Bresser and Spiers 1993). GBM recrystallisation is active under low-grade conditions and increases in importance with increasing temperature. Grain boundary sliding and 'superplastic' behaviour may be important in calcite if the grain size is very small (Schmid 1982; Schmid et al. 1987).

Dolomite deforms by basal <a> slip at low to moderate temperatures and deformation twinning on f-planes at moderate to high temperatures. Twinning apparently does not develop below 300 °C, in contrast to calcite, which can even twin at room temperature. Notice that twinning occurs on different planes in calcite and dolomite. At low-grade conditions, dolomite is usually stronger than calcite, which causes commonly observed boudinage of dolomite layers in a calcite matrix.

3.12.4 Feldspars

Deformation behaviour of plagioclase and K-feldspar is rather similar and therefore the feldspars are treated together. Laboratory experiments and observation of naturally deformed feldspar have shown that feldspar deformation is strongly dependent on metamorphic conditions. The behaviour as observed by several authors (Tullis and Yund 1980, 1985, 1987; Hanmer 1982; Tullis 1983; Dell'Angelo and Tullis 1989; Tullis et al. 1990; Tullis and Yund 1991; Pryer 1993) is described below, according to increasing temperature and decreasing strain rate.

At very low metamorphic grade (below 300 °C) feldspar deforms mainly by brittle fracturing and cataclastic flow. Characteristic structures in the resulting cataclasite are angular grain fragments with a wide range of grain size. The grain fragments show strong intercrystalline deformation including grain scale faults and bent cleavage planes and twins. Patchy undulose extinction and subgrains with vague boundaries are normally present. TEM study of such structures has shown that they are not due to dislocation tangles or networks, but to very small-scale brittle fractures (Tullis and Yund 1987). In plagioclase, deformation twinning on albite and pericline law planes is important (Seifert 1964; Vernon 1965; Borg and Heard 1969, 1970; Lawrence 1970; Kronenberg and Shelton 1980; Passchier 1982a; Jensen and Starkey 1985).

At low-grade conditions (300–400 °C) feldspar still deforms mainly by internal microfracturing but is assisted by minor dislocation glide. Tapering defor-

mation twins, bent twins, undulose extinction, deformation bands and kink bands with sharp boundaries may be present (Pryer 1993). Clearly separable augen and matrix, or core-and-mantle structures are absent. *Flame-perthite* (Chap. 7.6.3), a perthite with tapering 'flame-shaped' albite lamellae may be present in K-feldspar, especially at grain boundaries and high stress sites (Figs. 3.23, 7.28; Spry 1969; Augustithis 1973; Debat et al. 1978; Passchier 1982a; Pryer 1993). Such perthite is thought to develop by exsolution of albite in K-feldspar that formed at high temperature during deformation at a lower temperature; exsolution proceeds preferentially at sites of intracrystalline deformation such as where two feldspar grains are touching (Passchier 1982a; Pryer 1993). 'Bookshelf' microfracturing in feldspar is common at low-grade conditions, splitting the grains up into elongate bookshaped fragments (Passchier 1982a; Pryer 1993; Chap. 5.6.11). Pryer (1993) claims that antithetic fracture sets are more common in the low temperature range, and synthetic fractures at higher temperature.

At low to medium-grade conditions (400–500 °C) dislocation climb becomes possible in feldspars and recrystallisation starts to be important, especially along the edge of feldspar grains. Recrystallisation is mainly by nucleation and growth of new grains (cf. Borges and White 1980; Gapais 1989; Gates and Glover 1989; Tullis and Yund 1991). This is visible in thin section by the development of mantles of fine-grained feldspar with a sharp boundary around cores of old grains, without transitional zones with subgrain structures; typical core-and-mantle structures develop and micro-shear zones of recrystallised grains may occur inside the feldspar cores (Passchier 1982a).

Fracturing in feldspar becomes less prominent under these conditions but microkinking is abundant, probably associated with cataclastic failure at sites of dislocation tangles (Tullis and Yund 1987). If large kink-bands occur, they have unsharp boundaries (Pryer 1993). Fine-grained recrystallised material may resemble feldspar cataclasite described above, but has a more uniform grainsize and polygonal grains. Grain boundary sliding has been proposed as a deformation mechanism in this fine-grained feldspar (Vernon and Flood 1987; Tullis et al. 1990), but this is difficult to assess by optical means, and even by TEM. Optically, the only useful criteria are lack of a lattice-preferred orientation and unusual homogeneous mixing of feldspar grains and other minerals in the fine-grained aggregates. According to Tullis et al. (1990), microscopic gouge zones can undergo recrystallisation and develop into small ductile shear zones, destroying most evidence for earlier brittle faulting.

Towards higher temperature, deformation twinning is less abundant. Myrmekite growth becomes important along the boundaries of K-feldspar porphyroclasts (Chap. 5.6.8, 7.8.3). Myrmekite occurs mainly along crystal faces parallel to the foliation (Simpson 1985; Simpson and Wintsch 1989). Flameperthite is abundant in K-feldspar (Pryer 1993).

[handwritten margin note: Myrmekite ⊥ Abundant ↑ perthite]

At medium to high-grade conditions (above 500 °C), dislocation climb and recovery are relatively easy in feldspar (Vidal et al. 1980; Olsen and Kohlstedt 1985; Pryer 1993), and real subgrain structures form. Both SR and GBM recrystallisation occur (Fig. 5.11). Core-and-mantle structures still occur, but the boundary between the core and the mantle is less pronounced than at lower temperature. Myrmekite along foliation planes is abundant. Feldspar grains are usually strain-free, but isolated micro-kink bands may be found. Flame-perthite is absent. Fracturing of grains is uncommon.

[handwritten margin note: Present / Absent]

Few dislocation slip systems seem to be active in feldspars, even at high temperature. In plagioclase, slip on (010)[001] seems to dominate at medium to high-grade metamorphic conditions while minor slip on (010)[100] is also reported (Montardi and Mainprice 1987; Ji and Mainprice 1988; Dornbush et al. 1994; Ullemeyer et al. 1994). The latter seems to be more important under very high temperature conditions (Kruhl 1987). Activity of (010)[100] has also been reported for K-feldspar by Gandais and Willaime (1984).

The limited number of active slip systems lead to the development of two types of mantled porphyroclasts (Chap. 5.6.5, 5.6.6) in plagioclase at high temperature: relatively little deformed 'globular' porphyroclasts, similar to those at low temperature, which have (010)[001] slip systems in an unfavourable orientation for slip, and ribbon plagioclase grains which were in a favourable orientation for slip on (010)[001] (Box p. 70). Deformation twins, undulose extinction and deformation bands are common in such ribbons.

3.12.5 Micas

Micas deform only by slip on (001)<110> or (001)[100], and therefore show abundant evidence for accommodation mechanisms such as pressure solution and fracturing (Mares and Kronenberg 1993), undulose extinction, kinking and folding (Wilson 1980; Lister and Snoke 1984; Bell et al. 1986). Folds and kinks are particularly common in mica; commonly, folding occurs on the outside and pressure solution or kinking in the core of a folded crystal. Fractures are commonly associated with deflection of basal

[handwritten margin note: Present]

planes and lead to barrel or fish-shaped boudinaged grains. Grain boundary migration recrystallisation becomes important at medium to high grade. In the brittle domain, biotite may show crude kinking or layer parallel slip to develop 'cleavage steps' or mica fish (Chap. 5.6.7, 5.7.3; Kanaori et al. 1991). Biotite behaves ductilely at temperatures above 250 °C (Stesky et al. 1974; Stesky 1978). Muscovite is generally more resistant to deformation than biotite and therefore commonly forms mica fish in mylonite (Fig. 5.27).

[handwritten note: mica fish = brittle mus]

3.12.6 Olivine

Different slip systems operate in olivine at different temperatures in the mantle (Nicolas and Christensen 1987; Mainprice and Nicolas 1989; Suhr 1993). At 'low' temperature (700–1000 °C), slip systems (010)[001] (Nicolas and Christensen 1987) or {110}[001] (Carter and Avé Lallement 1970) have been reported, and additional slip on several planes that intersect along the [100] direction. The latter is called pencil glide on (0kl)[100]. Old grains of olivine show strong undulose extinction and subgrain boundaries. Olivine recrystallises to fine-grained neoblasts that are concentrated in shear zones by flow partitioning (Suhr 1993). At medium temperature around 1000 °C, *pencil glide* on (0kl)[100] is dominant. At high temperature (T>1000 °C), only (010)[100] dominates and at very high temperature (T>1250 °C), (010)[100] is dominant and (001)[100] may be active (Nicolas and Christensen 1987; Mainprice and Nicolas 1989). A polygonal granoblastic fabric of coarse-grained, strain-free olivine develops. A strong lattice preferred orientation of olivine and trails or bands of other minerals in olivine may be the only indication that the rock was deformed. The relatively coarse grain size of olivine (0.4-1 mm; Suhr 1993) corresponds to low flow stresses in the mantle at these levels (Chap. 8.6.1).

[handwritten margin note: Present]

3.12.7 Orthopyroxene

In orthopyroxene, dislocation glide is dominantly on (100)[001] (Coe and Kirby 1975; McLaren and Etheridge 1976; Dornbush et al. 1994). Other slip systems that have been found are (100)[010] and (010)[001] (Nazé et al. 1987; Dornbush et al. 1994). Optically visible subgrain boundaries are usually parallel to (100), (010) and (001).

(100)[001] dislocations in orthopyroxene are usually split into partial dislocations, separated by a stacking fault along which the crystal lattice is transformed into that of a clinopyroxene (Coe and Kirby

1975; McLaren and Etheridge 1976); as a consequence, exsolution lamellae of clinopyroxene can easily develop parallel to (100) and are therefore common in deformed orthopyroxene (Suhr 1993).

Under upper mantle conditions (up to 1000 °C) orthopyroxene may form ribbon grains with aspect ratios up to 100:1 (Etheridge 1975; Nicolas and Poirier 1976; Mainprice and Nicolas 1989; Suhr 1993), or equi-dimensional porphyroclasts if grains had an orientation that was unsuitable for slip (Etchecopar and Vasseur 1987). The old grains may be surrounded by a mantle of fine recrystallised orthopyroxene. Ribbon grains probably form due to the dominant operation of the (100)[001] slip system (Dornbush et al. 1994).

3.12.8 Clinopyroxene

In clinopyroxene, the unit cell is half the length of that of orthopyroxene in the a-direction. As a consequence, Burgers vectors in that direction are shorter, and since the activation energy of a dislocation is proportional to the length of the Burgers vector, more slip systems are expected to be active in clinopyroxene than in orthopyroxene. Two deformation regimes can be distinguished; at high temperature (>500 °C) and/or low strain rate multiple slip occurs, mainly on $\{\bar{1}10\}1/2<110>$, $\{110\}[001]$ and $(100)[001]$, and rarely on $(010)[100]$ (van Roermund and Boland 1981; Phillipot and van Roermund 1992; van Roermund 1983). At low temperature and/or high strain rate, deformation occurs by (100) and (001) twinning in combination with (100)[001] slip, but in nature this is mainly restricted to meteorites due to the breakdown of clinopyroxene at low temperature. Optically visible subgrain boundaries are usually parallel to {110}, (100), (010) and (001).

Garnet, spinel, plagioclase or quartz can all form exsolution lamellae in ortho- and clinopyroxene. Exsolution in clinopyroxene can occur parallel to (100) and (001), but at temperatures above 700–750 °C only along (100).

3.12.9 Amphiboles

The deformation behaviour of amphiboles is as yet poorly understood. In amphiboles, the crystal unit cell in the direction of the b-axis has more than twice the length of that in pyroxenes. Theoretically, due to the increased Burgers vector length, amphiboles should therefore be stronger in ductile deformation than clinopyroxenes. The available data from experiments and natural amphiboles indicate that this is indeed the case.

At low temperature and/or high strain rate, amphiboles deform by twinning on $(10\bar{1})$ or (100) (Biermann 1981) and slip on (100)[001]. As in micas, slip on (100)[001] can lead to development of kinks. At high temperature and/or low strain rate, several slip systems have been documented, mainly (hk0)[001] but also $\{110\}1/2<\bar{1}10>$ and (010)[100] (Biermann and van Roermund 1983; Cumbest et al. 1989; Reynard et al. 1989; Skrotsky 1992). Subgrains are elongated parallel to the c-axis and subgrain boundaries consist of simple arrays of [001], [100] or <110> dislocations and are parallel to {110}, (100) or (010) (Biermann and van Roermund 1983; Reynard et al. 1989).

A characteristic structure in hornblende schists is that of 'garben' (German for stack), bundles of elongate hornblende crystals that are oriented in a spectacular fan-like arrangement in the foliation plane. Such 'garben' may develop by growth of subgrains in the direction of the c-axis in previously deformed hornblende crystals (Biermann 1979).

3.13 Deformation of Polymineralic Rocks

3.13.1 Introduction

Since most rocks are composed of more than one mineral, it is interesting to see how individual minerals behave in a polymineralic rock. Minerals do not always show the same dependence in behaviour on temperature and strain rate as in monomineralic aggregates, and may even behave in an entirely different way. The behaviour of polymineralic rocks is remarkably complex (Jordan 1987, 1988; Handy 1989, 1992; Bons 1993). The concept of a stress-supporting network is important; if 'hard' and 'soft' minerals coexist, the strength of an aggregate does not increase linearly with the amount of the hard mineral present. If few hard grains are present, the strength of the aggregate is similar to that of a monomineralic aggregate of the soft mineral; the hard minerals may rotate in the flow of the soft material, and may form core-and-mantle structures if they recrystallise on the outside. The strength of the aggregate increases suddenly when the grains of the hard mineral are so common and large that they touch and start to support the imposed differential stress. Obviously, the original shape of the grains is also important here. When the hard mineral is dominant, the strength of the aggre-

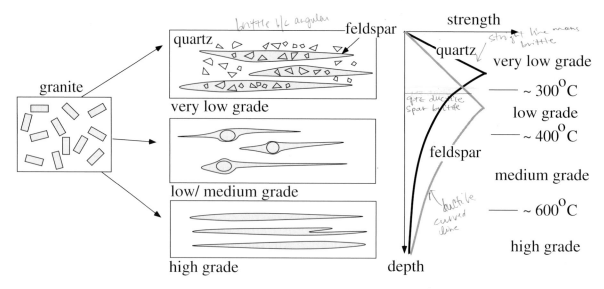

Handwritten annotations on figure: "brittle b/c angular", "straight line means brittle", "qtz ductile spar brittle", "ductile curved line"

Fig 3.31. Changes in the deformation behaviour of quartz-feldspar aggregates with depth. *At right,* a depth-strength graph with brittle *(straight line)* and ductile *(curved line)* segments for quartz and feldspar is shown. At very low grade, both quartz and feldspar are brittle, but feldspar is the weaker mineral. At low to medium-grade conditions, quartz deforms by dislocation creep and feldspar is the stronger mineral, developing core-and-mantle structure and mantled porphyroclasts (Figs. 5.6, 5.7, 5.15, 5.19–22). At high grade, feldspar and quartz deform by dislocation creep and have similar strength (Fig. 5.10)

gate will approach that of the pure hard mineral, but at high strain the pockets of the soft mineral may interconnect and form shear zones that weaken the aggregate. The contrast in rheology between two minerals may change and even reverse with changing external conditions. Below, we treat quartz-feldspar aggregates as an example of a polymineralic rock.

3.13.2 Quartz-Feldspar Aggregates

The study of deformed quartzo-feldspatic rocks such as granites shows an interesting dependence of structure on metamorphic grade (Vernon and Flood 1987; Tullis et al. 1990). At very low-grade conditions feldspar and quartz deform both by brittle fracturing (Fig. 3.31). Microstructural observations suggest that feldspar is actually weaker than quartz at these conditions (Chester and Logan 1987; Evans 1988). This is probably due to the fact that feldspar grains have cleavage planes that reduce their strength. As a result, aggregates of elongate cataclased feldspar and quartz develop (Fig. 3.31) where part of the feldspar (especially K-feldspar) is transformed to kaolinite and sericite. A cataclastic foliation of cataclased grain clusters, fractures and preferred orientation of sheet silicates commonly develops (Evans 1988).

Under low-grade conditions, feldspar is still brittle while quartz deforms ductilely by dislocation glide and creep (Fig. 3.31; Tullis and Yund 1977; Simpson 1985; Gapais 1989; Gates and Glover 1989; FitzGerald and Stünitz 1993; Stünitz and FitzGerald 1993). However, the strength contrast is now reversed, and quartz is the weaker mineral; feldspar deforms by development of core-and-mantle structures; cores show abundant evidence of brittle faulting and patchy undulose extinction. Mantled porphyroclasts can form, the wings of which define a compositional layering (Fig. 3.31). Quartz usually wraps passively around feldspar aggregates, and deforms much more homogeneously; cores of old quartz grains show abundant subgrains, that laterally pass into recrystallised (new) grains. At high strain, augen of feldspar develop, separated by a finely laminated aggregate of fine-grained quartz and feldspar.

At medium to high-grade conditions, both feldspar and quartz deform by dislocation creep assisted by diffusion and recrystallisation. Both minerals may form monomineralic and polymineralic ribbons that give the rock a banded appearance (Box p. 70; Fig. 3.31). Both have subgrains in old grain cores and a gradual transition from the core to a recrystallised mantle. Feldspar augen are rare. Feldspar and quartz show similar deformation intensity and seem to have a relatively small contrast in strength.

At high-grade conditions, grain boundaries between quartz and feldspars are commonly strongly curved, with lobate and cuspate and even amoeboid shapes (Fig. 3.25; Passchier 1982a; Gower and Simpson 1992). This geometry may be due to deformation at high-grade conditions, possibly with a large component of solid-state diffusive mass transfer such as Coble or Nabarro-Herring creep (Gower and Simpson 1992) or by solution precipitation creep (den Brok, pers. comm. 1994).

One of the characteristic differences in behaviour of feldspar and quartz at low temperature and high strain rate is the development of core-and-mantle structures in feldspar, and more homogeneous flattening and deformation in quartz. This has been explained by Tullis et al. (1990) as a result of different deformation mechanisms of feldspar and quartz at these conditions; in feldspar dislocation climb is difficult and deformation occurs by GBM recrystallisation-accommodated dislocation creep (Dell'Angelo and Tullis 1989). The newly produced grains of feldspar are free of dislocations and relatively soft, and grain boundary migration can easily replace them by new grains once they develop dislocation tangles. As a result, the mantle of recrystallised feldspar grains surrounding feldspar cores is much softer than the core, and deformation is concentrated in the mantle, which grows in volume as the core shrinks with progressive deformation (Dell'Angelo and Tullis 1989). Diffusion processes may also play a role in the recrystallised mantles. In quartz, dislocation creep is accommodated by dislocation climb and SR recrystallisation dominates. The new grains have the same dislocation density as old subgrains, and the new aggregate is as strong as the old grains; consequently, no core and mantle structure develops and quartz deforms relatively homogeneously.

3.13.3 Deformed Ignimbrites

Some deformed ignimbrites are an interesting exception to the rule that in quartz-feldspar aggregates deformed at low- to medium-grade conditions, quartz is the weaker mineral. In deformed ignimbrite, quartz phenocrysts remain as porphyroclasts (Figs. 3.3, 3.5, 3.6; Williams and Burr 1994). Probably, the fine-grained bimineralic matrix of an ignimbrite can deform by grain boundary sliding, or pressure solution and precipitation at such a low differential stress that limited intracrystalline deformation is induced in quartz. Deformed ignimbrites can be recognised by the euhedral quartz phenocrysts with typical wriggly embayments (Figs. 3.5, 3.6). Obviously, the behaviour of quartz and feldspar in an aggregate is dependent not only on external conditions, but also on the original geometry of the aggregate before deformation.

3.14 Flow Laws and Deformation Mechanism Maps

In order to establish under which conditions deformation mechanisms as described in this chapter are active, data from experimental deformation are used in combination with observations on rocks deformed at known metamorphic conditions. Experimental deformation of rocks at a range of pressure and temperature conditions can give us some idea of the activity of deformation, recovery and recrystallisation processes at specific conditions. One drawback of experimental work is, that geologically realistic strain rates in the order of 10^{-12} to 10^{-14} s^{-1} cannot be mimicked in experiments. Nearly all our data on deformation mechanisms are from experiments at much higher strain rate. However, for many deformation mechanisms, increase in temperature has an effect similar to a decrease in strain rate. Therefore, extrapolation of experimental results to geologically realistic strain rates is possible by 'projection' of data from experiments carried out at high temperature.

The rheological behaviour of minerals and rocks is usually expressed in *flow laws* (Poirier 1985). Some important and commonly quoted types of flow laws are given in the Box on page 54. In the equation for dislocation creep given here, strain rate is independent of grain size but has a strong non-linear (power law) dependence of strain rate on stress. In the equations for diffusion creep, strain rate has a linear dependence on stress but a non-linear dependence on grain size. Flow laws have been proposed on the basis of experiments and theoretical considerations.

The parameters in the equations have been determined experimentally for a range of conditions. In many cases, these data are incomplete or difficult to compare because of differences in confining pressure, sample preparation etc. However, if a suitable set of data on rheology of a particular mineral can be found, it is possible to integrate the data to determine which mechanisms are expected to operate under particular conditions; in general, the mechanism that operates at the lowest differential stress for a particular strain rate is thought to be dominant. Conditions at which specific deformation mechanism are dominant can be shown in a *deformation mechanism map*. Such a map shows fields in which certain deforma-

FLOW LAWS

The following flow laws are commonly quoted in the literature, and have been used to construct deformation mechanism maps in Fig. 3.32.

For one of the simplest models, bulk diffusion-controlled dislocation creep (also known as Weertman creep) the flow law is;

$$\dot{\varepsilon} = \frac{\mu b D_L}{kT} \cdot (\sigma/\mu)^3 \cdot e^{(-H_L/RT)}.$$

For Coble creep:

$$\dot{\varepsilon} = \frac{A_c \, \mu V D_G W}{RTd^3} \cdot (\sigma/\mu) \cdot e^{(-H_G/RT)},$$

and for Nabarro-Herring creep:

$$\dot{\varepsilon} = \frac{A_{NH} \, \mu V D_L}{RTd^2} \cdot (\sigma/\mu) \cdot e^{(-H_L/RT)}.$$

Notice that dislocation creep is non-Newtonian and that the diffusion creep flow types are Newtonian (Chap. 2.12). The symbols in the equation have the following significance (units in square brackets):

e	– exponential number (2.718281)
$\dot{\varepsilon}$	– shear strain rate $[s^{-1}]$
σ	– shear stress$[Nm^{-2}]$
T	– temperature [K]
b	– Burgers vector [m]
A_c	– numerical factor for Coble creep depending on grain shape and boundary conditions
A_{NH}	numerical factor for Nabarro–Herring creep depending on grain shape and boundary conditions
H	– molar activation enthalpy for self-diffusion [J mol^{-1}]
D	– diffusion constant for self diffusion [m²s^{-1}]
R	– gas constant [J mol^{-1}K^{-1}]
k	– Boltzmann constant [J K^{-1}]
μ	– shear modulus [Nm^{-2}]
d	– grain size [m]
W	– grain boundary thickness [m]
V	– molar volume of the solid [m³mol^{-1}]
σ/μ	– normalised shear stress [dimensionless number]

PARAMETERS FOR FIG. 3.32

For the deformation mechanism maps in Fig. 3.32 the following parameters have been used:

T_m	= 1550 K (melting temperature of quartz in the presence of water)
R	= 8.3143 J mol^{-1}K^{-1}
k	= 1.38062 x 10^{-23} J mol^{-1}K^{-1}
V	= 2.6 x 10^{-5} m³mol^{-1}
b	= 5 x 10^{-10} m
μ	= 42 x 10^9 Nm^{-2} (Sosman 1927)
A_c	= 141 (grain boundary sliding possible)
$A_{NH.}$	= 16 (grain boundary sliding impossible)
H_L	= 243 x 10^3 J mol^{-1} for grain boundary diffusion used in the flow laws for Weertman creep and Nabarro-

	Herring creep at 450–590 °C and a mean stress of 100 MPa (Farver and Yund 1991a)
D_L	= 2.9 x 10^{-5} m²s^{-1}
	Bulk oxygen self-diffusion in the presence of water for Weertman creep and Nabarro-Herring creep at 450–590 °C and mean stress = 100 MPa (Farver and Yund 1991a)
H_G	= 113 x 10^3 J mol^{-1} for grain boundary diffusion used in the flow law for Coble creep (Farver and Yund 1991b)
D_{GW}	= 3 x 10^{-17} m³s^{-1}
	Bulk oxygen self-diffusion in the presence of water for Coble creep at 450–800 °C and 100 MPa mean stress (Farver and Yund 1991b)

tion mechanisms are dominantly, although not exclusively, active. Also shown are projected curves for several strain rates, which give an indication of the relationship of stress and strain rate for a specific temperature. Cataclasis occurs only above a certain differential stress level, which is dependent on fluid pressure (Sibson 1977a) and temperature (Griggs et al. 1960). Since grain size plays a major role in determining which deformation mechanism will be active, several maps for different grain sizes are usually given.

Figure 3.32 shows an example of a deformation mechanism map for quartz, and the way in which it is constructed. Parameters that have been used are given in the inset. Using the equations given in the Box on page 54, graphs are first made which plot shear stress against temperature at given strain rates for each of the deformation mechanisms (Fig. 3.32a–c). In such graphs, *normalised units* are plotted. This is done to obtain numbers which are dimensionless since this allows easy comparison of different materials (Box. p. 16 right). For example, homologous temperature T_h ($T_h = T/T_m$ where T_m is the melting temperature of a mineral in K) is used on the horizontal scale instead of absolute temperature; $T_h = 0$ at 0 K and $T_h = 1$ at the melting temperature of the mineral. In this way, deformation behaviour of ice can be compared with that of steel if both are at the same T_h value. Similarly, normalised shear stress (σ/μ) is used instead of shear stress.

At any point in the graphs of Fig. 3.32a–c, a single strain rate is defined at a certain stress and temperature if other parameters are constant. When these diagrams are combined in pairs (Fig. 3.32d–e), each point will be attributed two strain rate values, one for each of the possible deformation mechanisms; the mechanism with the highest strain rate is thought to be dominant at that point. The boundaries between

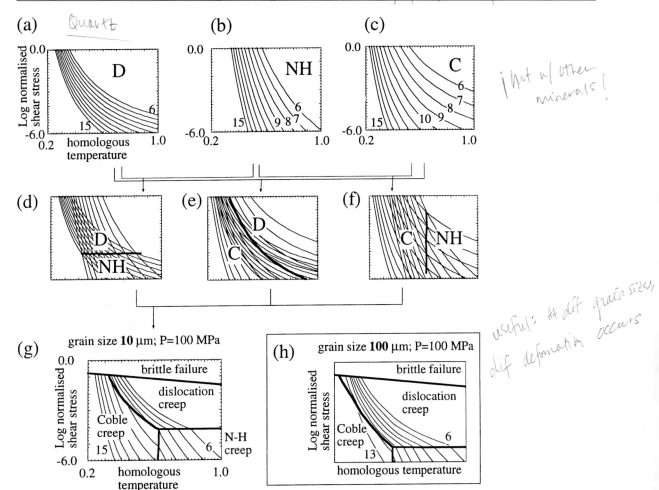

Quartz (a)

just w/ other minerals! (c)

useful: At dif grain size, dif deformation occurs (g,h)

Fig 3.32a–h. Method to construct a deformation mechanism map from experimental data. All graphs show contours of strain rate (10^{-6} to 10^{-15}, only exponents shown) in plots of normalised shear stress against homologous temperature (see text). *D* Dislocation creep; *C* Coble creep; *NH* Nabarro-Herring creep. **a–c** graphs for the three types of deformation mechanisms. If these graphs for single mechanisms are combined

(d–f) fields of dominant deformation mechanism can be defined. Combination of the graphs for two mechanisms gives a deformation mechanism map **(g)**. The constructed map is for a grain size of 10 μm of single crystals at 100 MPa confining pressure in dry environment. A similar map for 100 μm grain size **(h)** is shown for comparison

fields of dominant deformation mechanism can be found by simply joining the intersection points of the strain rate curves when two diagrams are overlapping. In a similar way, the combined data define fields for each deformation mechanism, the deformation mechanism map (Fig. 3.32g). Strain rate contours for each dominant mechanism alone are shown in the fields of Fig. 3.32g; these show sharp kinks on the bounding lines. Above a certain stress level, the material is thought to deform by brittle failure; the curve for brittle failure was taken from Griggs et al. (1960).

Figure 3.32g shows the deformation mechanism map for quartz with a grain size of 10 μm, and Fig.

3.32h with a grain size of 100 μm. The transition between Coble and Nabarro-Herring creep is mainly influenced by temperature; the transitions of Nabarro-Herring creep to dislocation creep, and dislocation creep to brittle failure are mainly an effect of shear stress. The transition from Coble creep to dislocation creep is influenced by both temperature and shear stress. Temperature and strain rate have conflicting influence, as mentioned above, and this allows extrapolation of experimental data to geological strain rates. Notice that with increasing grain size, the dislocation creep field increases in size and the diffusion creep fields shrink (Fig. 3.32g,h).

Deformation mechanism maps are most useful for the prediction and comparison of experimental results. For example, they are defined for only one mean stress value (100 MPa in the case of Fig. 3.32). This is useful for experimental purposes where mean stress is usually kept constant, while temperature and strain rate are varied. However, in nature, mean stress and temperature increase together with increasing depth and this effect is usually not shown in an ordinary deformation mechanism map. We should not imagine a situation where one deformation mechanism takes over abruptly from another at a set temperature, pressure or other variable. In this sense, the fields in a deformation mechanism map can be slightly misleading; they indicate *dominant* deformation mechanisms – other deformation mechanisms may also be active in these fields, and towards a boundary one mechanism will gradually take over from the other.

Like most geological diagrams, deformation mechanism maps suffer from the disadvantage that too many parameters must be shown in just two dimensions. The effect of grain size on rheology is also strong and is normally shown on separate maps (Fig. 3.32g,h). Another disadvantage of deformation mechanism maps is that they cannot show all deformation mechanisms to advantage. Pressure solution, a very important mechanism in quartz (and probably in feldspar and other minerals) is difficult to include because a deformation mechanism map is only valid for a specific mean stress. Since fluid pressure is important in pressure solution (but possibly also in dislocation creep; Tullis and Yund 1991), it is difficult to show exact boundaries for pressure solution in deformation mechanism maps. However, a field of pressure solution should plot on the low stress and temperature side, in the lower left-hand corner of Fig. 3.32g,h where it replaces the Coble creep field for quartz, calcite, feldspar and micas in most geological situations where water is present. Finally, flow laws and consequently deformation mechanism maps are valid for steady state flow; deformation of a recrystallising aggregate with porphyroclasts can therefore not be shown in deformation mechanism maps.

An alternative diagram to deformation mechanism maps is the *depth-strength diagram* commonly used to show a strength profile of the lithosphere (Figs. 3.31, 3.33) (Sibson 1983). Such diagrams are valid for a specific mineral, grain size, strain rate, geothermal gradient, and orientation of brittle faults. Differential stress or strength of the material is plotted against depth. There are two sets of intersecting curves. The straight curves show strength of a brittle fault; with increasing depth, the blocks on both sides

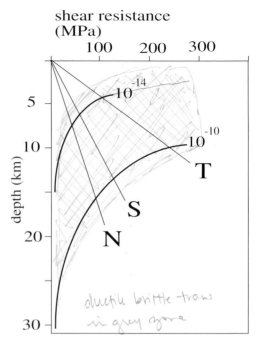

Fig 3.33. Depth-strength diagram for quartz at a geothermal gradient of 30 °C/km and hydrostatic fluid pressure in brittle faults (based on Sibson 1983). **Straight lines** are strength of brittle fracturing for thrust **(T)**, strike-slip **(S)** and normal faults **(N)**. **Curved lines** are for dislocation creep at strain rates of 10^{-14} and 10^{-10} s^{-1}

of a fault are pressed together and thereby increase the differential stress that is needed to make the fault move. The lower curves are for dislocation creep and represent a decrease in strength with increasing temperature at increasing depth. High in the crust, brittle faulting is therefore favoured and at deep levels dislocation creep. The crossover point is known as the *brittle-ductile transition*. Notice that this is not a simple surface in the crust; it lies at a different depth for different minerals (Fig. 3.31), bulk strain rate, fault orientation, geothermal gradient and grain size. In practice, a wide transitional zone where both mechanisms are active is usually present. The depth-strength diagram has other disadvantages; no deformation mechanisms other than just brittle faulting and dislocation creep have been considered. If a rock deforms by ductile flow and develops a crystallographic fabric, this can cause hardening and transition to brittle deformation without a change in external conditions. As shown above, in polymineralic rocks the situation is much more complex. Obviously, there is still some scope for development of diagrams to show distribution of deformation mechanism activity in geological applications.

4 Foliations, Lineations and Lattice Preferred Orientation

4.1 Introduction

Many microstructures in rocks are defined by a preferred orientation of minerals or fabric elements. We distinguish foliations, lineations and lattice-preferred orientation.

The word *foliation* (Fig. 4.1) is used here as a general term to describe any planar feature that occurs penetratively in a body of rock. It may refer to thin rhythmic bedding in a sedimentary rock, to compositional layering in igneous rocks or to cleavage, schistosity, or other planar structures in metamorphic rocks (Chap. 4.5). Joints are normally excluded for not being sufficiently penetrative. We prefer this broad use of a descriptive term over genetic terms since it is often difficult to decide what the origin of a planar structure in a deformed rock is. Foliations may be defined by a spatial variation in mineral composition or grain size (Fig. 4.1a), by a preferred orientation of elongate or platy grains or aggregates of grains (Fig. 4.1b–f), by planar discontinuities such as microfractures (Fig. 4.1g), or by any combination of these elements (Fig. 4.1h).

A *lineation* is defined as any linear feature that occurs penetratively in a body of rock (Fig. 4.2). The most important types are:
– intersection lineations, formed by intersecting foliations (Fig. 4.2a);
– crenulation lineations, defined by hinge lines of microfolds in a foliation plane (Fig. 4.2b);
– stretching lineations, defined by deformed, constricted grains of minerals such as quartz that more commonly form equidimensional grains (Fig. 4.2c) or by linear aggregates of equidimensional grains (Fig. 4.2d). Deformed objects such as pebbles in a conglomerate may also define a stretching lineation. The term linear shape fabric is also used for this structure (Chap. 4.7);

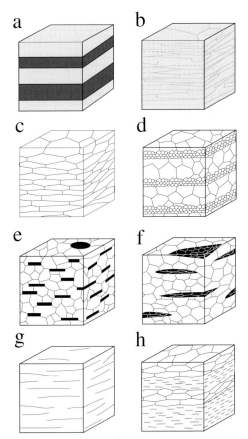

Fig. 4.1a–h. Diagrammatic presentation of various fabric elements that may define a foliation (after Fig. 5.1 in Hobbs et al. 1976). **a** Compositional layering. **b** Preferred orientation of platy minerals (e.g. mica). **c** Preferred orientation of grain boundaries and shape of deformed grains (e.g. quartz, carbonate). **d** Grain-size variation. **e** Preferred orientation of platy minerals in a matrix without preferred orientation (e.g. mica in micaceous quartzite or gneiss). **f** Preferred orientation of lenticular mineral aggregates. **g** Preferred orientation of fractures or microfaults (e.g. in low-grade quartzites). **h** Combination of fabric elements **a, b** and **c;** such combinations are common in metamorphic rocks

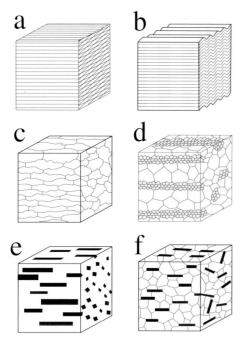

Fig. 4.2a–f. Diagrammatic representation of various types of fabric elements that may define a lineation. **a** Intersection lineation of two planar structures. **b** Crenulation lineation. **c** Stretching lineation defined by deformed (constricted) grains. **d** Stretching lineation defined by grain aggregates. **e** Mineral lineation defined by euhedral or subhedral grains with an elongate crystal shape (such as sillimanite or tourmaline). **f** Mineral lineation defined by euhedral or subhedral planar grains (such as micas) which share a common axis

– mineral lineations defined by the preferred orientation of euhedral or subhedral mineral grains with an elongate shape such as amphibole, tourmaline or sillimanite or by planar minerals such as micas that share a common axis (Chap. 8.2; Fig. 4.2e,f).

In three dimensions many foliations show an associated linear element, that is, the fabric elements defining the foliation may appear stronger in some sections normal to the foliation than in others. A complete transition from pure S tectonites (only a foliation) to LS tectonites (both a foliation and a lineation) to L tectonites (only a lineation) can be imagined. In practice, such transitions may actually exist within a single outcrop. Some lineations may develop from or into foliations with time. An example of the latter is the progressive development of slaty cleavage at a high angle to bedding (Box p. 79).

It is important in the description of a foliation to give the relation with a lineation, if present. The linear elements that are of the same age as foliations in a volume of rock are important in tectonic studies

because they may furnish information on the direction of tectonic transport (Fig. 5.9). Such lineations must definitely been taken into consideration when deciding how to cut a thin section from a rock sample (Chap. 10.5). Since lineations show essentially the same morphological features as foliations – in fact their distinction in thin section is impossible – they are not treated further in this book.

Many rocks have a *lattice-preferred orientation* (LPO), a non-random orientation of the crystallographic axes of constituent minerals. Some foliations or lineations are defined by an LPO. However, we use the term here in a more restricted sense for minerals with an equant shape like quartz and calcite, the LPO of which cannot be seen in the field or in thin section without the aid of special techniques. LPO is treated in Chapter 4.13–4.16.

4.2 Foliations

In many areas several successive foliations can be distinguished in the field by overprinting relations (Chap. 1.1). Their study in thin section, including the interpretation of the metamorphic and deformational conditions during their formation, is an important tool to unravel the tectonic and metamorphic evolution of an area. Foliations are also used as reference structures to establish the relative growth periods of metamorphic minerals, especially porphyroblasts (Chap. 7.4). Foliations and lineations are generally more penetratively developed in any volume of rock than folds and are therefore better reference structures for the definition of deformation phases (Chap. 1.1).

Primary foliations are structures related to the original rock-forming process. Bedding in a sedimentary rock and magmatic layering in igneous rocks are the most common examples. A *diagenetic foliation* may be formed by diagenetic compaction. *Secondary foliations* are generated later (in the case of sediments: after lithification) as a result of deformation and metamorphism. This group includes cleavage, schistosity, differentiated compositional layering, mylonitic foliation, etc.

Development of secondary foliations is usually seen as evidence that the rock deformed in a ductile way, but foliations may also develop in some cataclasite zones (Chap. 5.2.2). Secondary foliations which are not homogeneous may be difficult to distinguish from primary layering. The recognition of primary foliation is important, however, because in metasedi-

---

CRITERIA TO DISTINGUISH BETWEEN PRIMARY AND SECONDARY FOLIATIONS

The following arguments are useful to distinguish a primary foliation such as bedding from a spaced secondary foliation developed as a compositional layering.

Primary foliation	*Secondary foliation*
Sedimentary structures may be recognised	No sedimentary structures present
Thickness of layers may show any variation, especially across strike (Fig. 4.3)	Little variation in thickness, usually two alternating approximately constant thicknesses (Fig. 4.4)
Composition and grain size of layers may be variable (Fig. 4.3)	Composition of layers usually bimodal (Figs. 4.4, 4.12)
Layering usually planar	Layering commonly lensoid or anastomosing (Fig. 4.4)
Rarely a symmetry plane parallel to layering	Normally a symmetry plane parallel to layering (Fig. 4.4)
Foliation never parallel to the axial plane of folds (however do not mistake folds for refraction)	Foliation (sub)parallel to the axial plane of folds of an earlier foliation; commonly developed by differentiation of fold limbs (Figs. 4.11, 4.12)

---

ments it allows reconstruction of the structural evolution from sedimentation onwards [e.g. So (bedding), S_1, S_2, etc.]. If bedding is not recognised, only the last part of the evolution can be reconstructed (e.g. S_n, S_{n+1}, S_{n+2}, etc.).

4.3 Primary Foliation

In very low-grade metamorphic rocks which are not intensely deformed, the recognition of bedding may be a straightforward matter, since the main characteristics of a sedimentary sequence, including sedimentary structures, may be well preserved. In the case of more intense deformation and higher metamorphic grade, it is usually more difficult to distinguish between primary and secondary layering. In many metamorphic rocks such as gneisses a compositional layering may have a sedimentary, igneous or metamorphic/deformation origin, or may have a complex nature combining several of these origins (e.g. Passchier et al. 1990b).

Primary layering in sediments results generally from discontinuous processes, causing considerable variation in thickness and composition of individual beds or layers, with low symmetry about planes parallel to layers (Fig. 4.3). Secondary layering, however, forms by some kind of differentiation process in a stress field, usually producing a more monotonous bimodal structure with a symmetry plane parallel to the layering (Fig. 4.4). Some empirical criteria that may help to distinguish primary from secondary foliations are listed in the Box above. In fact, only the first and last of these criteria are conclusive: the presence of sedimentary structures is good evidence for bedding, and the relation of a compositional layering with the axial surface of folds clearly demonstrates the secondary nature of a layering (contemporaneous with the folding). The presence of two crosscutting layering structures in a metamorphic rock is also good evidence that one of them must be secondary (Figs. 4.4, 11.3).

Unfortunately, it is often impossible to recognise bedding, especially in rocks of medium to high metamorphic grade. Transposition processes (Box p. 88) may have obliterated angular relationships, or sedimentary structures may have disappeared by intense deformation and recrystallisation. In such cases, the oldest compositional layering has to be labelled S_n, keeping in mind that it may, at a certain scale, reflect remnants of bedding.

Structures in primary sedimentary layering can be used to establish younging direction in thin section. In many cases this can be done by recognition of asymmetric refraction of a secondary foliation through bedding. Care should be taken, however, since in some cases the growth of metamorphic minerals may invert graded bedding if large micas or other minerals grow in originally fine-grained pelitic layers.

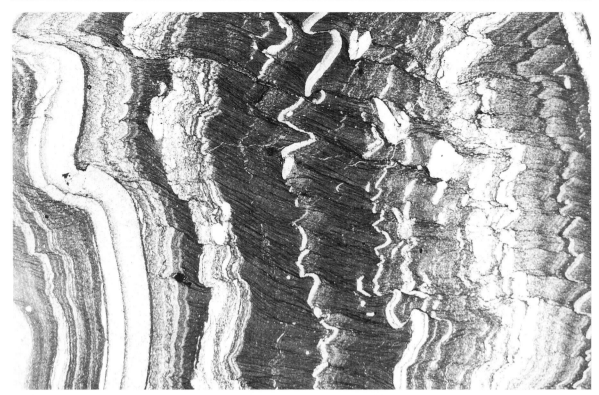

Fig. 4.3. Folded bedding S_0 (primary foliation - subvertical) with spaced cleavage S_2 (secondary foliation - close to horizontal), developed in dark layers. An older slaty cleavage (S_1) is present subparallel to S_0 but not visible at this magnification. Note variation in thickness and composition of bedding. (A detail of the central upper part is presented in Fig. 4.20). Pyrenees, Spain. Width of view 7 mm. PPL

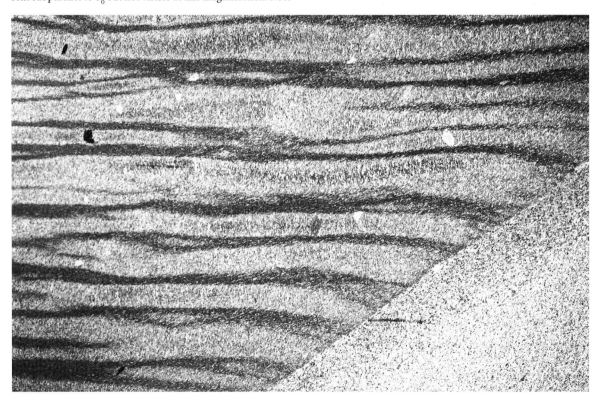

Fig. 4.4. Secondary foliation (S_2) *(horizontal)* developed by differentiation in limbs of crenulations. Remnant bedding (S_0) is visible in ***lower right corner.*** S_1 is parallel to S_0. The secondary compositional layering (S_2) has a monotonous bimodal character with a horizontal symmetry plane. Leiden Collection. Width of view 15 mm. Polarisers at 45°

4.4 Diagenetic Foliation

Diagenetic foliation, also referred to as bedding-parallel foliation, is commonly observed in very low-grade and low-grade pelitic sediments which have undergone little or no deformation (Borradaile et al. 1982). It is defined by parallel orientation of thin elongate mica grains with frayed edges (Fig. 4.5). These micas are usually subparallel to bedding. Diagenetic foliation is thought to be the result of diagenetic compaction of a sediment which contains detrital micas (Williams 1972a; Borradaile et al. 1982). The micas have rotated passively into an orientation parallel to bedding during compaction. Diagenetic foliation is an example of a foliation defined by the preferred orientation of micas that is not associated with folds. It is thought to precede and play an important role in development of secondary foliations in pelitic rocks (see below).

Maxwell (1962) and Roy (1978) have postulated that diagenetic or dewatering foliations may also be oblique to bedding and associated with synsedimentary folding, and may even be the initial stage of slaty cleavage. However, this idea is now largely abandoned since such foliations can usually be shown to have formed after the rock lithified. Oblique synsedimentary foliations do occur but seem to be extremely rare.

4.5 Secondary Foliations

Below, we present a morphological classification of secondary foliations and discuss the main processes involved in their development. Secondary foliations may show a large variation of morphological features. On the basis of these characteristics, a number of more or less descriptive names have been used such as slaty cleavage, crenulation cleavage, differentiated layering, fracture cleavage, schistosity etc. (see definitions in the glossary). Unfortunately, the use of these names is not uniform and some have been used with genetic implications. For example, the name *fracture cleavage* has been used for a discontinuous foliation with finely spaced compositional layering that possibly originated by preferential dissolution along fractures that are no longer visible; other interpreta-

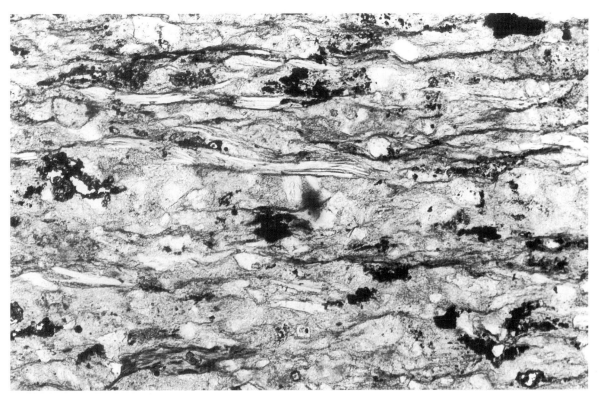

Fig. 4.5. Bedding-parallel diagenetic foliation defined by elongate detrital micas. Collio Formation. Southern Alps, Italy. Width of view 1.8 mm. PPL

Morphological classification of foliations
(using an optical microscope)

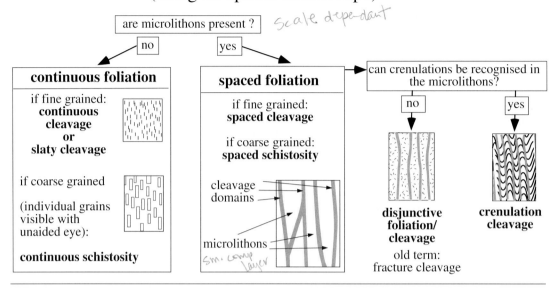

Useful criteria to describe spaced foliations :

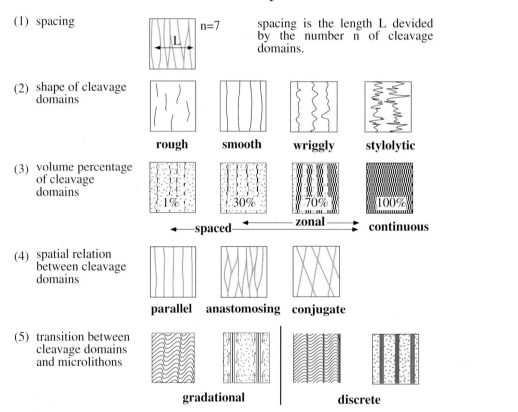

Fig. 4.6. Morphological classification of foliations using an optical microscope. (After Powell 1979 and Borradaile et al. 1982)

tions of such structures that do not involve fractures are possible and the use of such genetic names should therefore be avoided. For this reason, we aim to use purely descriptive terms.

The concepts of *cleavage* and *schistosity* are so widely used that we maintain them as general terms for foliations thought to be of secondary origin. Cleavage is generally used for fine-grained rocks up to the scale where individual cleavage forming minerals (e.g. micas) can be distinguished with the naked eye; schistosity for more coarse-grained secondary foliations. Cleavage and schistosity therefore cover the complete range of secondary foliations, especially in field descriptions. Notice, however, that this distinction by grain size is not expanded consistently to all parts of foliation terminology; terms like crenulation cleavage, shear band cleavage, cleavage domain and cleavage lamellae (Chap. 4.8; Fig. 4.6) are generally used regardless of grain size. Another term that is occasionally used is gneissosity, for a coarse-grained secondary foliation in gneiss; use of this term is not recommended because of possible confusion with compositional layering in gneiss.

4.6 Morphology of Foliations

Powell (1979) and Borradaile et al. (1982) have proposed a descriptive classification of foliations, independent of their primary or secondary origin, using only morphological features. This classification is based on the fabric elements that define the foliation such as elongate or platy grains, compositional layers or lenses, or planar discontinuities. The distribution of these fabric elements in the rock defines whether the foliation is *spaced* or *continuous*. In the first case, the fabric elements are not homogeneously distributed and the rock is divided into lenses or layers of different composition. Continuous foliation is used for rocks in which the fabric elements are homogeneously distributed, normally down to the scale of the individual minerals. Figure 4.6 summarises the classification used in this book. It is a simplified version of the classification proposed by Powell (1979) and Borradaile et al. (1982) with minor modification.

Fig. 4.7. Continuous schistosity defined by parallel crystals of biotite, muscovite and quartz. Mt Isa, Australia. Width of view 1.8 mm. PPL

4.7 Continuous Foliation

A continuous foliation consists of a non-layered homogeneous distribution of platy mineral grains with a preferred orientation. Most common are minerals such as mica or amphibole (Fig. 4.7), but quartz (Fig. 3.24) or other minerals (Fig. 3.27) may also define a continuous foliation. Fine-grained rocks such as slates, which show a continuous cleavage in thin section (Fig. 4.9), may reveal a spaced foliation if studied at stronger magnification, e.g. by scanning electron microscope (SEM – Chap. 9.5). Normally, the terminology used for a specific foliation is based on the geometry observed in thin section. If field or SEM observations are discussed, the scale of observation (field observation, thin section, SEM) should be mentioned in descriptions of foliation morphology. Continuous foliation may be further described through the fabric elements, e.g. grain shape and size. If the grains that define the foliation are visible by the unai-

ded eye, the foliation is called a *continuous schistosity* (Figs. 4.7, 4.8). If the grain size is finer, the structure is known as a continuous cleavage or *slaty cleavage* (Figs. 4.9, 9.3). Since the continuous nature of a foliation is scale-dependent, we include finely spaced cleavage with a spacing up to 50 μm in the definition of slaty cleavage in order to remain in line with the current use of this concept in the literature (cf. Fig. 9.3). Continuous foliations can be subdivided into mineral foliations, defined by the preferred orientation of platy but undeformed mineral grains such as micas or amphiboles (Fig. 4.7), and *planar shape fabrics* defined by flattened crystals such as quartz or calcite (Figs. 3.24, 3.27, 4.24). This distinction is similar to that between a mineral lineation and a stretching lineation: the former is defined by the preferred orientation of individual euhedral or subhedral mineral grains and the latter by stretched grains or aggregates of deformed grains. By analogy, such a stretching lineation is also known as a *linear shape fabric*.

Fig. 4.8. Continuous foliation (schistosity) in an upper-amphibolite facies micaceous quartzite, mainly defined by subparallel micas. Note the irregular shape of quartz crystals as a result of secondary grain growth (Chap. 3.12.2). Undulose extinction and subgrains are probably due to late deformation after grain growth. Ribeira Belt, Rio de Janeiro State, Brazil. Width of view 18 mm. CPL

new text Box 4.2 Shape Fabrics
p. 76 new text

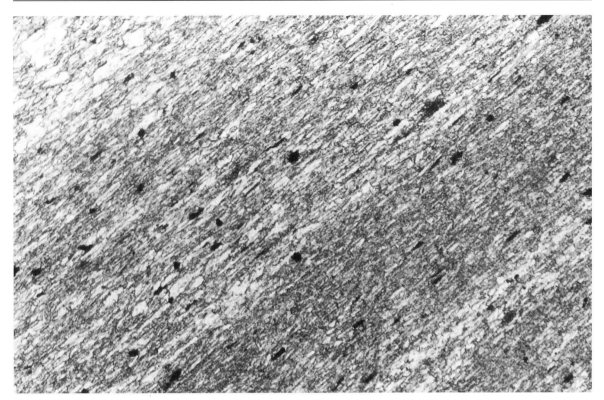

Fig. 4.9. Continuous cleavage on thin section scale (slaty cleavage) defined by fine-grained micaceous material. Fabrics like this may be spaced foliations that contain domains without fabric elements or with folded older fabric elements when studied by SEM (Fig. 9.3) or TEM. Castellbo, Pyrenees, Spain. Width of view 1.8 mm. PPL

4.8 Spaced Foliation

Rocks with spaced foliation consist of two types of domains, *cleavage domains* (also known as *cleavage lamellae*) and *microlithons* (e.g. Figs. 4.4, 11.3). As an alternative, the terms *M domain* (mica-rich) and *Q domain* (quartz-rich) have been used in micaschist or phyllite (Shelley 1993). Cleavage domains are planar and contain fabric elements subparallel to the trend of the domains. In metapelites, cleavage domains are usually rich in mica and in minerals such as ilmenite, graphite, rutile, apatite and zircon.

Microlithons lie between cleavage domains and contain fabric elements which have a weak or no preferred orientation, or which contain fabric elements oblique to the cleavage domains. Spaced foliations may be further subdivided according to the structure in the microlithons. If these contain microfolds of an earlier foliation (e.g. Figs. 4.4, 4.11, 11.3) the term *crenulation cleavage* is applied (Rickard 1961). If not, the structure is known as *disjunctive foliation* (or *dis-junctive cleavage* if fine-grained, e.g. Fig. 4.10). The more general terms *spaced cleavage* and *spaced schistosity* are also used to describe fine-grained and coarse-grained disjunctive foliation (Fig. 4.6). Some spaced foliations contain lens-shaped microlithons and may be called *domainal spaced foliation* (Fig. 4.13) or, if the spacing is sufficiently narrow, *domainal slaty cleavage*. Other morphological features of spaced foliations that may be considered in their description are (Fig. 4.6):

– The spacing of the cleavage domains.

– The shape of cleavage domains: rough (Gray 1978), smooth (e.g. Fig. 4.4), wriggly or stylolytic.

– The percentage of cleavage domains in the rock; if this is higher than 30%, the term zonal foliation may be applied (Fig. 4.12). At 100% the foliation becomes continuous.

– The spatial relation between cleavage domains: parallel, anastomosing or conjugate (two intersecting directions without signs of overprinting).

– The transition from cleavage domain to microlithon. This may be gradational (Figs. 4.11, 4.12) or discrete (e.g. Figs 4.13, 4.14, 4.19).

Fig. 4.10. Disjunctive cleavage in quartz-mica phyllite, defined by subhorizontal biotite-rich layers (cleavage domains) and quartz-mica layers (microlithons). Leiden Collection. Width of view 4 mm. PPL

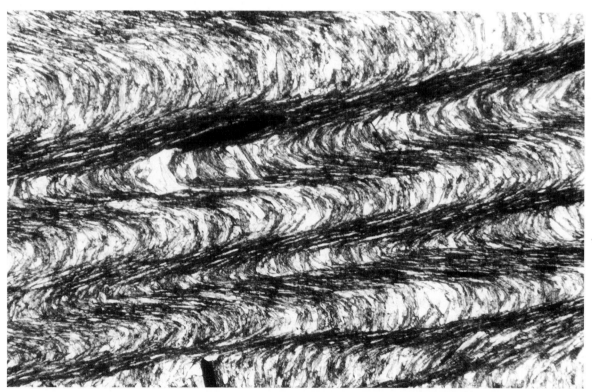

Fig. 4.11. Differentiated crenulation cleavage in phyllite with symmetric microfolds: the foliation is defined by cleavage domains (flanks of microfolds) and microlithons (fold hinge areas). Note the difference in composition of the two domains and the gradual transition between both. Cordillera Real, Equador. Width of view 4 mm. PPL

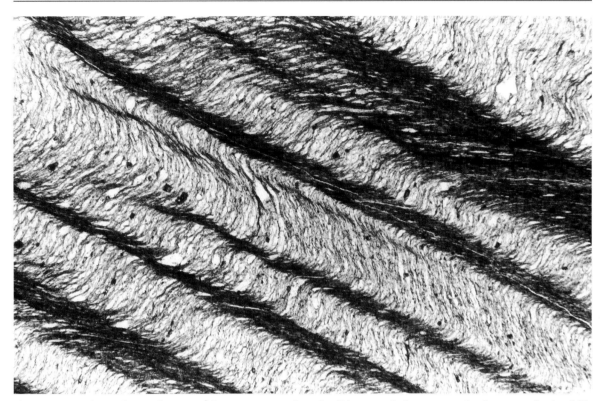

Fig. 4.12. Zonal crenulation cleavage with a percentage of cleavage domains variable from about 25% in the lower *left part* to almost 50% in the *upper right* part of the photograph; note the gradual transition between cleavage domains and microlithons, and the asymmetric character of microfolds resulting in relative mica enrichment predominantly in one of two alternating fold limbs (cf. Fig. 4.11, where both limbs are identical). Leiden Collection. Width of view 4 mm. PPL

Fig. 4.13. Domainal spaced cleavage with chlorite stacks (Chap. 7.4.2) in microlithons. Collio Formation. Southern Alps, Italy. Width of view 1.8 mm. PPL

Fig. 4.14. Discrete crenulation cleavage (S_2 *subhorizontal*) over-printing a slaty cleavage (S_1 *steep*) that is subparallel to bedding (S_0 *white layer at left*). The crenulation cleavage is selectively developed in more pelitic material and changes abruptly over a lithological boundary *(white layer).* Note the apparent offset of the white layer in the *lower left corner* that may reflect fault movement or removal of a flexure by pressure solution (cf. Fig. 4.20). Leiden Collection. Width of view 4 mm. PPL

– The shape of microfolds in crenulation cleavage. This may be symmetric (e.g. Fig. 4.11), asymmetric (e.g. Figs. 4.12, 11.3), tight, open, etc.

The morphology of crenulation cleavages may show a vast array of variation (Figs. 4.11, 4.12, 4.18–4.20, 4.35, 4.37); important factors that influence the final morphology, apart from the lithotype, are temperature and deformation intensity. Figures 4.17 and 4.18 show the inferred range of stages in crenulation cleavage development according to these two parameters (however, see also the Box on p. 76).

A special type of spaced foliation is *compositional layering*, where microlithons and cleavage domains are wide and continuous enough to justify the use of the term layering. Normally, this term is applied if the layering is visible to the unaided eye in a hand specimen.

Many transitional forms between foliation types as defined above occur in nature. In fact, the variation in morphology is almost infinite and we should realise that the proposed classification is meant as a way to facilitate communication between geologists and not as an objective in itself. For this reason, we have not tried to define strict boundaries between categories, and we advocate the use of a minimum of terminology. Where necessary, a good photograph or detailed drawing can supplement a description.

A foliation may change its morphology drastically within a single thin section (Fig. 4.14), or even disappear completely. This is generally related with the transition from one lithotype to another; foliation development is strongly dependent on lithotype. However, local strain distribution around fold hinges has its influence on foliation development too, and may produce a remarkable variation in foliation morphology along a single layer.

a

b

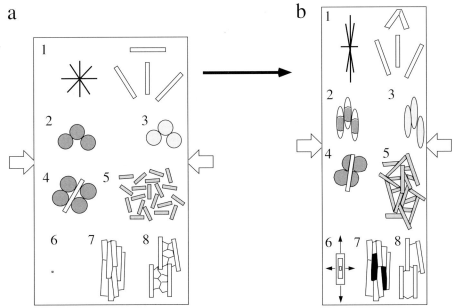

Fig. 4.15a,b. Schematic diagram of some important mechanisms contributing to development of secondary foliations in rocks. **a** Fabrics at the onset of deformation. **b** Fabric elements after deformation. *1* Elongate crystals *(open rectangles)* rotate in response to deformation in a way similar to theoretical passive markers *(solid lines)* but there are differences; minerals may fold when normal to the shortening direction and thus strengthen a preferred orientation, or rotate at slower rate than material lines when highly oblique to the shortening direction. *2* Mineral grains change shape by stress-induced solution transfer; *grey* is original material, *white* are overgrowths. *3* Mineral

grains change shape by crystalplastic deformation such as dislocation creep or solid state volume diffusion. *4* Polymineralic aggregates develop foliations by processes *1* + *2* when assisted by stress-induced solution transfer. *5* Grain growth of micas parallel to (001) during or after shortening leads to an increase of foliation intensity because grains oriented in the direction of the foliation can grow to greater length than those in oblique orientations. *6* Oriented nucleation and growth of a mineral in a stress field. *7* Mimetic growth of elongate grains due to restrictions in growth direction imposed by an existing foliation. *8* Restricted growth parallel to platy minerals

4.9 Mechanisms of Foliation Development

4.9.1 Introduction

Secondary foliations develop in response to permanent rock deformation. The main controlling factors on their development are rock composition, stress orientation and magnitude, metamorphic conditions including temperature, lithostatic and fluid pressure, and fluid composition. The relation between morphology and genetic processes is usually complex, and the description of foliation morphology should therefore be separated from the interpretation of processes involved. Our knowledge of these processes is still incomplete, although research over the last 20 years has increased our understanding considerably (see reviews by Siddans 1972; Wood 1974; Means 1977; Oertel 1983; Skrotzki 1994).

This section gives a list of the main processes that are currently thought to play a role during formation of secondary foliations (Figs. 4.15, 4.16). In a number of cases, like the examples cited below, it may be possible to indicate which processes have been important, but in general several of the processes probably operate together.

Figures 4.17 and 18 show a progressive sequence of development of crenulation cleavage with increasing pressure and temperature. This sequence can be understood as an example of progressive development of many spaced foliations (see also the Box on page 76).

4.9.2 Mechanical Rotation of Tabular or Elongate Grains

During homogeneous ductile deformation, a set of randomly oriented planes will tend to rotate in such a way that their mean orientation will trace the direc-

MYLONITIC FOLIATION AND MONOCRYSTAL-
LINE RIBBONS

A foliation in mylonite is usually referred to as *mylonitic foliation;* it is generally a spaced foliation composed of alternating layers and lenses with different mineral composition or grain size, in which more or less strongly deformed porphyroclasts are embedded; the mylonitic foliation wraps around these porphyroclasts (Chap. 5.3). Some lenses are single crystals with an unusual planar or linear shape that define or strengthen a foliation in the rock. Such lenses are known as monocrystalline *ribbons* (Chap. 5.3.5). Common examples are quartz ribbons, but ribbons of mica, feldspar and orthopyroxene are also known (Chap. 3.12). In low to medium-grade mylonites, quartz ribbons are strongly elongate and show strong undulose extinction, deformation lamellae, subgrain structures and dynamic recrystallisation, mainly along the rim of the ribbons. Commonly, such ribbons show extinction banding parallel to their long axis which may be due to folding of the crystal lattice (Boullier and Bouchez 1978; Passchier 1982a). Most ribbons probably form by extreme flattening or constriction of large single crystals.

In high-grade gneiss, quartz ribbons consist of single crystals with an elongate shape which lack intracrystalline deformation structures (Figs. 5.10, 5.11). Such monocrystalline quartz ribbons are also known as *platy quartz* (Behr 1965; Frejvald 1970; Boullier and Bouchez 1978) and commonly include equidimensional or elongate feldspar grains. The quartz may contain rutile needles that have a preferred orientation or show boudinage, indicating that these ribbons have been subject to strong deformation. Monocrystalline quartz ribbons in high-grade gneiss probably formed by strong deformation followed by recovery and significant grain boundary migration that removed most older grain boundaries and intracrystalline deformation structures (Chap. 3.12.2). In this case, static recrystallisation leads to elongate single crystals of quartz because other minerals hamper grain growth in directions normal to the ribbons.

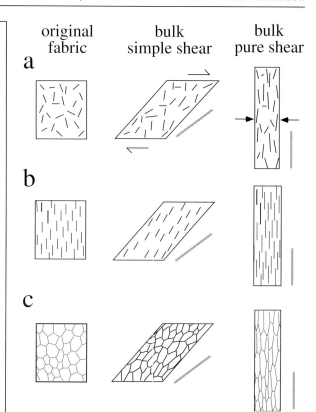

Fig. 4.16a–c. Development of some foliations by progressive simple shear and pure shear of: **a** a random initial orientation of isolated elongate or planar minerals; **b** an initial preferred orientation of isolated elongate or planar minerals; **c** originally equidimensional grains. In **c** a grain shape fabric is formed. *Grey bars* indicate the direction of the XY plane of finite strain for the deformation shown

tion of the XY plane of finite strain (Figs. 4.15,1, 4.16a; Jeffrey 1922; March 1932). A similar effect is thought to apply to tabular or elongate grains with a high aspect ratio such as micas or amphiboles in deforming rocks (Gay 1968; Oertel 1970; Tullis and Wood 1975; Tullis 1976; Wood et al. 1976; Willis 1977; Wood and Oertel 1980; Means et al. 1984; Lee et al. 1986; Ho et al. 1995; Fig. 4.15,1). If an earlier preferred orientation was present, the foliation will not trace the XY plane (Fig. 4.16b) in the case of bulk simple shear; deformed originally equidimensional grains will trace the XY plane in this case.

If deformation in a rock with random tabular or elongate grains, such as a mica-bearing granite, occurs along spaced shear zones, rotation of fabric elements in these shear zones can develop a spaced

foliation in a homogeneous parent rock (Wilson 1984); micas will tend to become parallel and relatively closely spaced in the shear zones, and less so in microlithons between shear zones (Wilson 1984).

4.9.3 Solution Transfer

Pressure solution and solution transfer (Chap. 3.3) may produce inequant grains that can help define a secondary foliation (Figs. 4.15,2, 4.21). They also produce dark seams of insoluble material along dissolution surfaces that may have a stylolytic or planar appearance (Engelder and Marshak 1985; Figs. 4.14, 4.19, 4.20). After the foliation has developed, the resulting anisotropy of diffusivity may enhance preferential grain growth in the direction of the foliation.

Solution transfer plays an important role in development of secondary foliation by microfolding (Trouw 1973; Cosgrove 1976; Gray 1979; Gray and Dur-

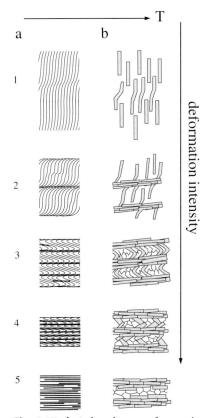

T

a   b

deformation intensity

1

2

3

4

5

Fig. 4.17a,b. Inferred range of stages in crenulation cleavage development with increasing deformation (vertical axis) and temperature (horizontal axis)(cf. Bell and Rubenach 1983). Figure 4.18 illustrates this same sequence with photographs. At low temperature (**a**, up to lower greenschist facies) the main mechanisms for crenulation cleavage formation are thought to be differentiation by solution transfer and rotation, whereas at higher temperatures (**b**) recrystallisation and grain growth (including new minerals) are probably dominant factors. At stage *1* gentle crenulations have formed in the original foliation S_1, but no S_2 cleavage is apparent yet. Some recrystallisation may occur in D_2 fold hinges. At stage *2* the crenulations are somewhat tighter and a discrete S_2 crenulation cleavage is visible. S_1 is still the dominant fabric. At stage *3* the new cleavage has developed to such an extent that S_1 and S_2 are of approximately equivalent importance in the rock. Recrystallised microfolds known as polygonal arcs may be visible at the higher temperature range, especially in **b3**. At stage *4* S_2 clearly predominates and S_1 is only recognisable in some relic fold hinges. In stage **b4** new grains grown along S_2 dominate the fabric. Finally, stage *5* shows the end product of the process where S_1 is completely transposed and not recognisable any more. Most rocks will follow some path *from the upper left to the lower right corner of* the diagram during development of a crenulation cleavage (cf. also Fig. 4.27). Other factors that influence the development of crenulation cleavage are the presence and activity of a fluid phase, the presence of soluble minerals and the growth of new minerals. The step to complete transposition at low temperature (**a4–a5**) seems to be difficult without recrystallisation and grain growth. This may be the reason that old foliations are commonly better preserved in low-grade rocks

ney 1979a; Beutner 1980; Wright and Platt 1982; Woodland 1985; Southwick 1987; Ho et al. 1995). The folding of an earlier foliation produces a difference in orientation of planar elements, such as mica-quartz contacts, with respect to the instantaneous shortening direction. This may enhance preferred dissolution in fold limbs, which produces a secondary foliation in the form of a differentiated crenulation cleavage (Figs. 4.11, 4.21) and eventually a compositional layering in which fold hinges may have been erased (Fig. 4.17). The efficiency of differentiation by solution transfer depends on the abundance of a fluid phase and is therefore most active under diagenetic and low-grade metamorphic conditions. The mechanism is also dependent on the presence of one or more soluble minerals. Gray and Durney (1979a) published the following mineral sequence according to decreasing mobility by solution transfer: calcite > quartz > feldspar > chlorite > biotite > muscovite > opaques. In quartz- or carbonate-bearing phyllites, solution transfer seems to operate quite well: certain minerals concentrate commonly in the fold hinges (quartz, calcite, feldspar, chlorite) and others (biotite, white mica, opaque minerals) in the limbs. This may be due to the high solubility of quartz and calcite, and the effect of enhanced permeability where micas are present (Gray and Durney 1979a,b; Engelder and Marshak 1985; Schweitzer and Simpson 1986). As a consequence, differentiation is not common in pure mica phyllites.

Examples are also known where ion exchange takes place between developing microlithons and cleavage domains. White mica and chlorite may be redistributed in this way, chlorite concentrating in the microlithons, and white mica in the cleavage domains (Waldron and Sandiford 1988; Price and Cosgrove 1990).

Stress-induced solution transfer may also aid development of foliations, either by increased rotation of elongate minerals due to selective solution and redeposition of material (Fig. 4.15,4) or by truncation and preferential dissolution of micas which lie with (001) planes in the shortening direction, coupled with preferential growth of micas with (001) planes in the extension direction (Fig. 4.15,5; Ishii 1988). The intrinsic growth rate of micas is anisotropic and fastest parallel to (001) planes (Etheridge et al. 1974; Rosenfeld 1985). Solution transfer including micas will therefore lead to a preferred orientation, even in the absence of rotation (Ishii 1988; see mimetic growth, Chap. 4.9.6).

Some spaced foliations which have mainly formed by solution transfer processes may occur as *cleavage bundles* (Fig. 4.22a; Southwick 1987) centred on

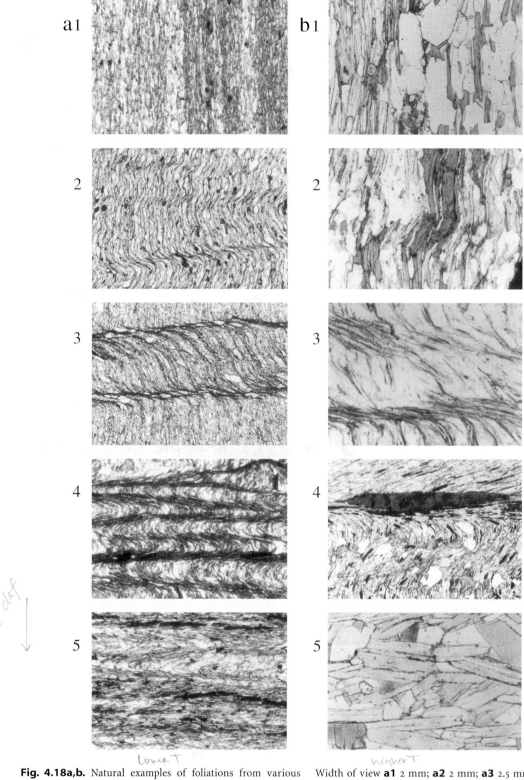

Fig. 4.18a,b. Natural examples of foliations from various areas which are thought to represent stages of the foliation development sequence shown in Fig. 4.17. Leiden Collection. Width of view **a1** 2 mm; **a2** 2 mm; **a3** 2.5 mm; **a4** 2 mm; **a5** 2 mm; **b1** 1 mm; **b2** 2 mm; **b3** 2 mm; **b4** 1 mm; **b5** 1 mm. PPL

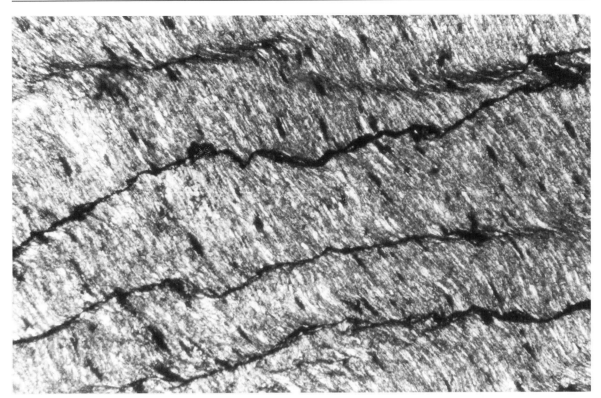

Fig. 4.19. Discrete crenulation cleavage (S_2 *subhorizontal*) overprinting a slaty cleavage (S_1 *trending from top left to bottom right*). The crenulation cleavage is defined by *horizontal* *dark seams* with wriggly to smooth appearance. The seams are interpreted as accumulations of insoluble material along dissolution surfaces. Concepción, Chile. Width of view 1.8 mm. PPL

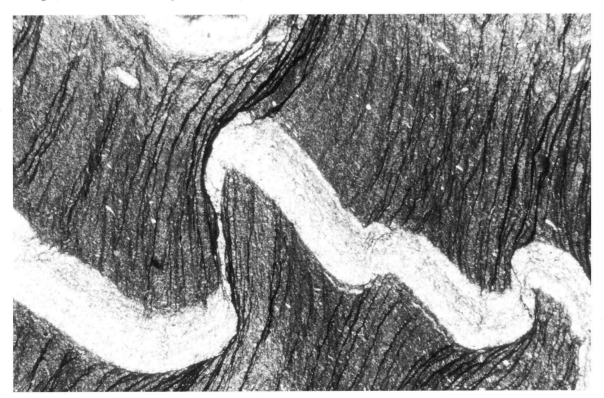

Fig. 4.20. Crenulation cleavage (S_2 *subvertical*) overprinting a slaty cleavage (S_1) that is parallel to bedding (S_0). Development of the crenulation cleavage was accompanied by solution effects. The extreme attenuation of the vertical fold limb in the quartz-rich *(light-coloured)* layer coincides with the presence of accentuated *dark seams* along the S_2 plane in adjacent micaceous layers. Both are interpreted as the result of preferred dissolution enhanced by the orientation of the fold limb, as explained in the text. This Figure is a detail of Fig. 4.3. Pyrenees, Spain. Width of view 5 mm. PPL

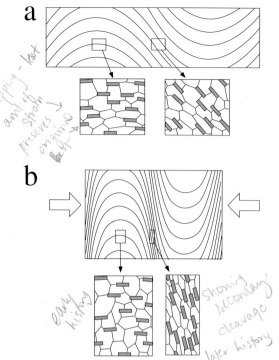

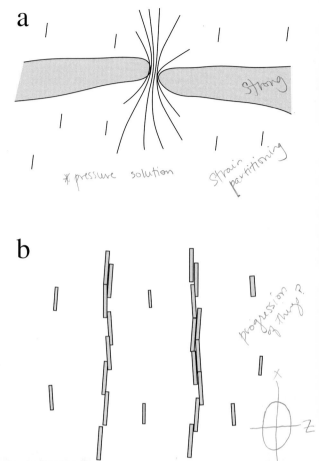

Fig. 4.21a,b. Progressive tightening of folds with formation of a differentiated crenulation cleavage (S$_2$) by preferential dissolution of quartz in fold limbs caused by the orientation of quartz-mica contacts with respect to the σ$_1$ direction; resolved normal stress over these contacts is higher in fold limbs than in hinges. **a** and **b** are two stages in progressive deformation (cf. Figs. 4.11, 4.12)

Fig. 4.22. a Cleavage bundle nucleated on a gap in a bedding plane, probably related to strain concentration. **b** Mica films developed in psammite as a result of solution transfer

thin parts of layers, fold closures or other objects that may have acted as stress concentrators, or as continuous 'mica films' in psammites (Fig. 4.22b; Gregg 1985). Such foliations probably nucleated near the stress concentration site, and grew out into the surrounding medium normal to the shortening direction (Fletscher and Pollard 1981; Gregg 1985; Tapp and Wickham 1987).

Solution transfer plays probably also a major role in the development of disjunctive cleavages that evolve by preferred dissolution along sets of parallel fractures; the fractures may act as channelways for the fluids, with enhanced dissolution along them, causing accumulation of residual material that results in the formation of cleavage domains.

4.9.4 Crystalplastic Deformation

Mineral grains that deform by crystalplastic processes such as dislocation creep or solid state diffusion (Chap. 3.4, 3.8) may obtain a flattened and/or elongate shape with maximum extension along the XY plane of finite strain (Fig. 4.23; Wilson 1984; but see Chap. 4.10). The result is a shape-preferred orientation, often accompanied by the development of undulose extinction (Fig. 4.24). In extreme cases, monocrystalline ribbons form, especially in minerals where only a single slip system operates. The deformation intensity of each individual grain depends on its lattice orientation, since the activity of slip systems is a function of their orientation with respect to the kinematic frame (see below) (Fig. 4.23). This can explain why some quartz grains in a deformed quartzite may be much less deformed than others; however, other reasons may be a considerable difference in original grain shape or late preferential grain growth of some crystals.

At high homologous temperatures (Chap. 3.14), diffusion of ions through a crystal lattice becomes

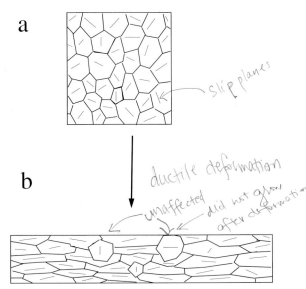

a

b

slip planes

ductile deformation

unaffected *did not grow after deformation*

Fig. 4.23a,b. Schematic diagram of development of a foliation by crystalplastic deformation illustrating the role of lattice orientation. *Tracing* in grains indicates active slip planes for dislocations in quartz. The grains with *horizontal* and *vertical slip planes* do not deform because of their special orientation

increasingly important (Nabarro-Herring creep). Grains can be flattened in this case without activity of slip systems or the presence of an intergranular fluid. This process may aid development of a grain shape-preferred orientation in high-grade rocks, but its importance is uncertain since the number of active slip systems also increases with temperature.

4.9.5 Dynamic Recrystallisation and Related Processes

Dynamic recrystallisation (Chap. 3.7) and oriented new growth of, e.g., mica are important mechanisms of foliation development (White and Johnston 1981; Ishii 1988; Kanagawa 1991). Dynamic recrystallisation is driven by the tendency to decrease free energy, such as stored strain energy in deformed grains and interfacial free energy. Kinking or tight folding of existing mica grains may accumulate sufficient strain energy to enhance grain boundary migration recrystallisation (Chap. 3.7.1). Little deformed fragments of old mica grains or strain-free nuclei can

Fig. 4.24. Low-grade metaconglomerate with highly elongated, mainly monocrystalline quartz pebbles. Undulose extinction of quartz indicates that crystalplastic deformation was important. Some pebbles are more deformed than others, pro-

bably due to favourable lattice preferred orientation for easy flattening (cf. Fig. 4.23b). Western Alps. Width of view 13 mm. Polarisers at 45°. (Sample courtesy Gordon Lister)

remnant
grains +
remores

Fig. 4.25. Elongate subgrains in a deformed quartz crystal. Note formation of new, elongate grains in ***lower right and*** ***upper left corners.*** St. Barthélemy, Pyrenees, France. Width of view 1.8 mm. CPL

FABRIC GRADIENTS

One of the problems in tectonics is that the evolution of structures cannot be directly observed in nature. As a result, there has been a tendency to look for intermediate stages or gradients in the geometry of structures, here referred to as *fabric gradients*. Fabric gradients are gradual changes in the fabric of a rock over a certain distance in the field or in thin section (e.g. Fig. 1.3). Examples are increasing tightness of folds; a decreasing grain size in a mylonite (Fig. 5.8); a decrease in angle between two foliations; an increase in amplitude of crenulations and gradual appearance of a second foliation (Fig. 4.18). If such fabric gradients are associated with changes in strain or metamorphic grade, it is tentative to interpret them as evolutionary stages in the development of the most evolved fabric. As far as can be determined with experiments, this assumption commonly holds. This is fortunate, since it allows us to reconstruct and study fabric evolution processes which would otherwise remain inaccessible. It is dangerous, however, to assume that such fabric gradients always and in all aspects represent a group of evolutionary stages. The simple fact that fabric gradients are found at the surface implies that intermediate stages of the fabric gradient cannot be regarded as intermediate stages on a PTt loop. For example, in a fabric gradient of increasingly complex foliations with euhedral micas, the grains may have been subhedral during the evolution of every part of the fabric gradient, but micas across the gradient may have obtained a euhedral shape by late static recrystallisation.

grow into the damaged crystal lattice with a preferred orientation that contributes to the secondary foliation (Fig. 4.17b). In the case of quartz and feldspars, recovery may lead to subdivision of equant grains into elongate subgrains (e.g. Fig. 4.25). If further deformation leads to subgrain rotation recrystallisation (Chap. 3.7.2), the subgrains may become new independent grains that, by their shape, define a foliation. Recrystallisation is associated with reequilibration of the chemical composition of minerals in the rock to metamorphic conditions during cleavage development (White and Knipe 1978; Gray 1981; Knipe 1981; White and Johnston 1981; Ishii 1988). In many cases the minerals in cleavage domains reflect metamorphic conditions during cleavage development, and those in the microlithons older, even diagenetic conditions (Knipe 1979, 1981; White and Johnston 1981; Lee et al. 1984, 1986).

4.9.6 Mimetic Growth

In some rocks, elongate crystals that help define a secondary foliation may actually have grown in the

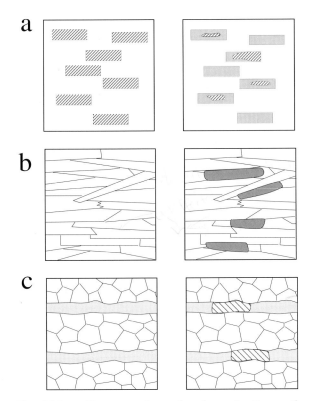

Fig. 4.26a–c. Three examples to show how mimetic growth may play a role in the formation of secondary foliation. **a** A foliation-defining mineral may be substituted, after deformation has ceased, by another mineral that inherits its shape and so continues to define the older foliation. **b** A new mineral may grow in a fabric with strong preferred orientation, mimicking this preferred orientation to a certain extent (e.g. biotite in a muscovite fabric). **c** Certain minerals may follow pre-existing compositional banding because of limited mobility of ions (Chap. 7.3; e.g. cordierite or staurolite may follow pelitic bands because of availability of Al^{3+} ions)

tion of interfacial grain energy can lead to strengthening of an existing preferred orientation (Fig. 4.15,5, 4.27; Etheridge et al. 1974; Ishii 1988). Crenulation cleavage may be progressively destroyed by this process transforming itself into an irregular schistosity (Fig. 4.27). Partly recrystallised relics of crenulation cleavage microfolds as in Fig. 4.27c are known as *polygonal arcs*.

An effect similar to mimetic growth is growth of normally equidimensional minerals such as quartz or calcite between micas or other elongate crystals with a preferred orientation (Fig. 4.15,8). Due to restriction in their growth direction imposed by the micas, such grains may obtain an elongate shape that strengthens the pre-existing foliation.

4.9.7 Oriented Growth Defined by a Stress Field

The possibility of oriented nucleation and growth of metamorphic minerals in a differential stress field (Fig. 4.15,6) was suggested by Kamb (1959) and is thermodynamically possible; it may produce a strong preferred orientation of both shape and crystal habit without necessarily being associated with high strain. However, rocks subject to high differential stress are usually deformed, and it is difficult to prove that a mineral-preferred orientation did not develop by one of the processes outlined above. Some well developed schistosities in medium to high-grade rocks with undeformed crystal habit and straight grain boundaries may be a result of this process, but static recrystallisation and mimetic growth of grains which obtained their preferred orientation by rotation may form a similar fabric (Fig. 4.27).

4.9.8 Microfolding

If an older planar fabric is present in the rock, the associated mechanical anisotropy may give rise to a harmonic, regularly spaced folding which produces some of the most intriguing structures in rocks, crenulation cleavage. The limbs of the folds may line up to form a crude foliation, but in many cases solution transfer or oriented crystallisation or recrystallisation of new grains (Gray and Durney 1979a,b) become important after the folds have reached a certain amplitude, and develop a spaced foliation along limbs of microfolds (Figs. 4.11, 4.12, 4.17, 4.18; White and Johnston 1981). Spaced foliations can, however, also form without folding of the older fabric (Fig. 4.19; Chap. 4.9.3; Durney 1972; Engelder and Marshak

direction of the foliation after the deformation phase responsible for that foliation ceased. This process is known as *mimetic growth*. The elongate crystals may have replaced existing minerals inheriting their shape (Fig. 4.26a); they may have nucleated and grown within a fabric with strong preferred orientation, following to some extent this orientation (Figs. 4.15,7, 4.26b); or they may have grown along layers rich in components necessary for their growth, in this way mimicking the layered structure in their shape fabric (Chap. 7.3; Fig. 4.26c). Some monocrystalline ribbons may develop in this way. Mimetic growth is probably an important process in the later stages of foliation development, especially at medium to high-grade metamorphic conditions. Since micas grow fastest in the (001) direction, grain growth catalysed by reduc-

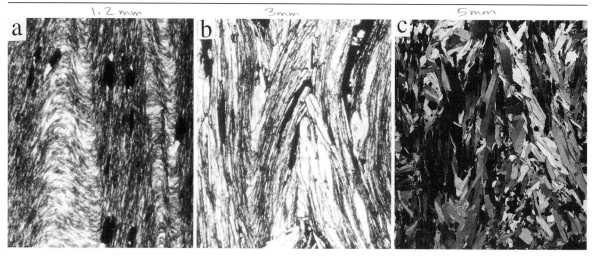

Fig. 4.27a–c. Progressive obliteration of crenulation cleavage structure by grain growth of micas. Many somewhat irregular schistosities may be the result of such a process (cf. Figs. 4.17, 4.18, 4.21). **a** Fine-grained phyllite with vertical crenulation cleavage (lower greenschist facies). Pyrenees, Spain. Width of view 1.2 mm. PPL. **b** Coarse phyllite with micas that grew at least partially after crenulation, lower amphibolite facies. Carrancas, Southern Minas Gerais, Brazil. Width of view 3 mm. PPL. **c** Schist with coarse micas showing a fabric in which 'ghost' folds or polygonal arcs are just recognisable (amphibolite facies). Marsfjällen, Sweden. Width of view 5 mm. CPL

1985). Besides harmonic microfolding of a foliation, disharmonic microfolding or kinking of individual micas can also increase mica-preferred orientation by rotation of mica segments away from the shortening direction (Fig. 4.15,1; Engelder and Marshak 1985).

4.10 Geological Context of Foliation Development

4.10.1 Foliations and Folds

Commonly, secondary foliations are referred to as *axial planar foliations* (e.g. Hobbs et al. 1976), i.e. they show a consistent geometrical relationship with the axial planes of folds (Figs. 4.3, 4.29, 4.30). This relation was recognised as early as Sedgwick (1835) and Darwin (1846), and is generally accepted to indicate that folds and foliation developed during the same deformation phase. Commonly, foliations are not perfectly parallel to axial planes of folds, but symmetrically arranged with respect to the axial plane (Fig. 4.30a). In some cases, a foliation may even be perpendicular to the axial plane (Fig. 4.30b). This effect is known as *foliation fanning*. A foliation may also *refract* where it passes from one lithology to another. Foliation fanning and refraction can be due to strain partitioning (Treagus 1983), or to passive rotation of relatively competent layers in the limbs of folds after initial bedding parallel shortening.

The intersection lineation of foliation and a folded surface is usually parallel to the fold axis if folds and foliation are of the same age. If the intersection lineation is oblique to the fold axis, the structures are known as a *foliation-transected folds* (Johnson 1991). Foliation transected folds may form if the vorticity vector of non-coaxial flow was oblique to the fold axis, or if folds and foliation are of different age. Some foliations, such as diagenetic foliation and foliations in shear zones, need not be associated with folds at all.

4.10.2 Foliations and the XY Plane of Tectonic Strain

The symmetric relationship between secondary foliations and the axial plane of folds has led early workers, from the middle of the last century onwards (e.g. Sorby 1853) to realise that such foliations may be par-

GEOMETRIC DEVELOPMENT OF FOLIATIONS

Irrespective of the processes involved in foliation development, the geometry of a developing fabric in rocks may change dramatically during its evolution. The simplest possible situation is deformation of a random fabric into a foliation or lineation, where fabric development simply reflects increasing strain. If an older fabric exists, its deformation may lead to inhomogeneities such as folding or boudinage, but may also lead to homogeneous deformation at some scales; such homogeneous deformation can show drastic changes in the geometry of the strain ellipsoid and the associated fabric. A well-documented example is the development of slaty cleavage at a high angle to diagenetic foliation and bedding (Reks and Gray 1982; Ramsay and Huber 1983). After deposition, a pelitic sediment will undergo diagenetic compaction that may lead to a significant volume loss, associated with expulsion of part of the pore fluid. This causes development of a diagenetic foliation parallel to bedding (Chap. 4.4; Fig. 4.28b). Subsequent superposition of a tectonic strain usually causes development of a new foliation oblique to the diagenetic foliation. At small tectonic strain, the tectonic and diagenetic strains may produce the same degree of anisotropy, and result in an effectively linear fabric. If such rocks are uplifted and eroded, the result has been called a *pencil cleavage* (Graham 1978; Reks and Gray 1982, 1983; Ramsay and Huber 1983; Fig. 4.28c). If tectonic strain increases beyond development of a linear fabric, a new foliation is formed, usually with relics of the diagenetic foliation in microlithons (Figs. 4.28d, 9.3). This sequence of fabrics seems to be common in development of a first slaty cleavage in pelitic sediments (Reks and Gray 1982; Ramsay and Huber 1983). It also illustrates the relevance of the distinction between diagenetic, tectonic and total strain (Box p. 80). It should be noted that linear fabrics similar to pencil cleavage can also form by constrictional strains under some circumstances, rather than by foliation overprint (Ramsay 1981).

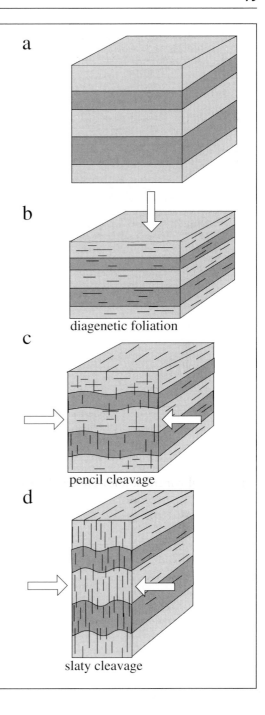

Fig. 4.28a–d. Development of slaty cleavage. **a, b** During diagenesis, the rock is vertically compacted and water is expelled, leading to considerable volume loss and a bedding parallel diagenetic foliation (Fig. 4.5). **c** With onset of tectonic shortening, a foliation starts to develop oblique to the diagenetic foliation. The interference of both gives rise to a linear fabric, pencil cleavage. **d** With increasing tectonic strain, the new foliation increases in importance and a slaty cleavage develops. In microlithons of the slaty cleavage, relics of the diagenetic foliation may be preserved (e.g. Figs. 4.13, 9.3)

allel to the XY plane of a finite strain ellipsoid. To be more specific, it is now generally believed that many secondary foliations approximately trace the XY plane of *tectonic* strain related to the deformation phase in which they developed (Box p. 80). However, exact parallelism is expected to be rare for reasons outlined below.

Many sediments and igneous rocks have been deformed before they start to develop secondary foliations; common examples are diagenetic foliations in sediments and flow banding in batholiths. Consequently, an overprinting secondary foliation, even if it is 'passive' and traces the XY plane of tectonic strain during progressive deformation, does not

Fig. 4.29. Secondary foliation *(subhorizontal)* defined by pre-ferred orientation of micas parallel to the axial plane of folds. Quartz mica schist. São Felix de Cavalcante, Goiás, Brazil. Width of view 17 mm. PPL

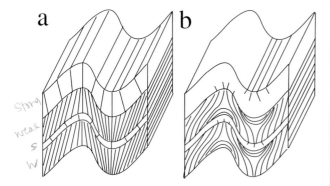

Fig. 4.30. a Refraction of foliation in competent layers. Apart from the refraction defined by a change in orientation, a change in morphology commonly occurs: in the psammitic layers the foliation is usually disjunctive whereas in the pelitic ones it may be continuous (after Fig. 5.3 in Hobbs et al. 1976). **b** Highly variable foliation orientation in a sequence of rocks with strong competency contrast. (After Roberts and Ström-gård 1972, and Fig. 5.16 in Hobbs et al. 1976)

STRAIN NOMENCLATURE

Strain may be subdivided into parts related to periods of the progressive strain history. The following terms are currently in use:

– *Diagenetic strain* – strain resulting from diagenetic processes such as compaction and dewatering.

– *Tectonic strain* – strain induced by tectonic deformation, usually after diagenesis.

– *Incremental strain* – (infinitesimally small) increment of strain.

– *Finite strain* – part of the tectonic strain, i.e. strain accumulated over a specific period of time. It may, for example, refer to the strain of the D_1 deformation episode in comparison to the combined strain acquired during D_2 and D_3, or even to the tectonic strain. The term 'finite' (accumulated over a measurable period of time) is also used as a contrast to 'incremental'.

– *Total strain* – normally this term refers to the total accumulated strain of a rock, including diagenetic- and tectonic strain.

A more detailed description of this terminology is given in Means (1979)

represent the total strain in the rock, which includes diagenetic compaction and other early deformation (Treagus 1985). Another problem is inhomogeneous deformation where foliation planes are 'active' as faults or shear zones.

'*Passive foliations*' act as material planes in a homogeneous flow. If they develop from a random fabric, continuous foliations can form in fine-grained rocks, or spaced foliations in coarse-grained material (Gray 1978). Another type are planar shape fabrics formed by flattening of grains or rock fragments (Chap. 4.7). Ideally, passive foliations will be parallel or subparallel to the XY plane of tectonic strain (Fig. 4.16a,c; Williams 1972a). However, if an older anisotropy existed, several paths can be followed. If an old foliation lies at a high angle to the shortening direction, it may rotate towards a new orientation without development of folds or new foliation planes (Fig. 4.16b). If the older anisotropy plane is oblique to the shortening direction, a new foliation may develop

oblique to the previous one, gradually replacing it (Fig. 4.31a); this is the case for many disjunctive foliations. Alternatively, the earlier anisotropy may cause microfolding or micro-shear zone development, and the new foliation follows the axial planes of folds, or the shear zones (Hobbs et al. 1982; Fig. 4.31b). Mawer and Williams (1991) describe a situation where fold hinges develop in a continuous foliation deformed in non-coaxial progressive deformation; new micas overgrow newly formed fold hinges, these become unrecognisable and a mixed foliation is formed with an orientation oblique to the XY plane of tectonic strain (Fig. 4.31b; Mawer and Williams 1991). Even ordinary slaty cleavage normally replaces a diagenetic foliation and is therefore not necessarily exactly parallel to the XY plane of tectonic strain (Figs. 4.28, 4.31a). In most of the cases mentioned above, the foliation is oblique to the XY plane of tectonic strain, except in the case of very high strain values.

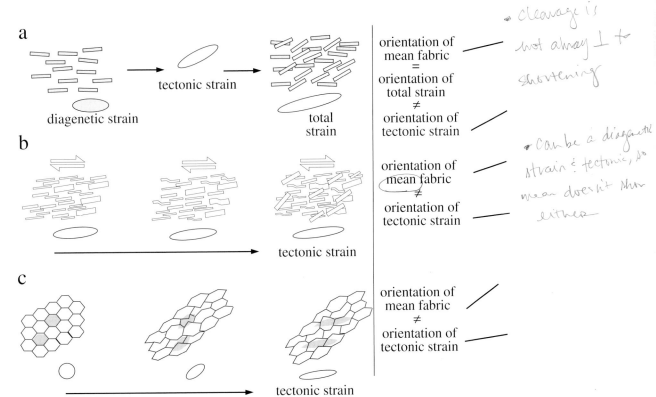

cleavage is not always ⊥ to shortening

Can be a diagenetic strain & tectonic, so mean doesn't show either

Fig. 4.31a–c. Three situations where a foliation is not parallel to the XY plane of tectonic strain. **a** A diagenetic foliation (*grey crystals*) is overprinted by oriented growth of new micas *(white)*. The resulting foliation has a mixed orientation and is oblique to tectonic strain axes. **b** A pre-existing foliation in non-coaxial flow may develop microfolds which become overgrown in the hinges by oriented new micas. The resulting mean fabric is oblique to tectonic strain axes. **c** An aggregate of dyna-

mically recrystallising grains obtains an oblique steady-state fabric representing only the last increments of strain. This fabric is oblique to the ellipsoid of tectonic strain (Chap. 5.6.3). *Grey* domains represent the material contained originally in two grains at *left:* these domains are stretched, while recrystallised grains retain the same orientation and slightly oblong shape

Some foliations are active as fold limbs or micro-shear zones. These *active foliations* will never be parallel to tectonic strain axes, unless they become passive by rotation. Examples are some compressional crenulation cleavages (Rajlich 1991), and shear band cleavages (Chap. 5.6.4). Care is needed even in assessment of apparently 'passive' foliations because foliation planes, once formed, are easily mobilised as planes of shear movement (Bell 1986). In many practical examples there is evidence of such 'reactivation', resulting in shear movement along foliation planes during deformation post-dating their formation.

Finally, there are *oblique foliations* also known as oblique fabric or steady state foliation (Chap. 5.6.3; Figs. 5.9, 5.27), which represent only part of the tectonic strain. These may be continuous, but are not normally parallel to the XY plane of tectonic strain (Fig. 4.31c; Ree 1991). They form in non-coaxial flow, where some process such as recrystallisation destroys part of the developing fabric. As a result, the foliation will only represent the last part of the deformation history (Fig. 4.31c). Planar shape fabrics are therefore only strictly parallel to tectonic strain axes if grain boundaries are immobile and act as passive markers (Fig. 4.16a).

4.10.3 Foliations, Strain and Volume Change

It is presently unclear to what extent solution transfer associated with foliation development leads to bulk volume change. Shortening values normal to the foliation up to 70% are mentioned in the literature, but most observations are in the range of 30 to 40% (Gray 1979; Southwick 1987). Bulk volume loss of up to 60% has been reported, especially for foliation

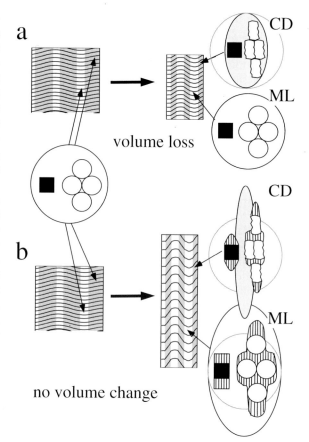

Fig. 4.32. Two end-member models of crenulation cleavage development in plane strain. The onset of crenulation cleavage development is shown in the squares at **left**. Schematic enlargements of an aggregate of four quartz grains *(white)*, a pyrite cube *(black)* and a passive **marker circle** are given. Deformed situations in cleavage domains *(CD grey)* and microlithons *(ML white)* are shown in **rectangles at right**. Local strain and volume loss in both situations are indicated schematically (not to scale) by the elliptical shape of the deformed marker circle and the outline of the original circle. **a** Significant volume loss in cleavage domains while microlithons are undeformed. Quartz grains are partly dissolved in cleavage domains but no fibres form near the quartz or pyrite grains. **b** Volume-constant deformation where volume loss in cleavage domains is compensated by volume increase of microlithons. Quartz grains are partly dissolved in cleavage domains but have fibrous overgrowths in cleavage domains and microlithons *(vertical striping)*; fibres also occur next to pyrite cubes. If no pyrite cubes or similar objects are present, and if overgrowths on quartz are not clear, situations **a** and **b** are difficult to distinguish

---

AREA AND VOLUME CHANGE

In geological practice, it is easy to confuse area change and volume change. Area change is a component of two-dimensional strain and is measured in a plane, e.g. from stretch values; it causes a change in the cross-sectional area of a structure (e.g. a fossil). Volume change is a component of three-dimensional strain. Area change is not a direct measure for volume change. For example, even if a thin section shows evidence for area increase, bulk volume loss may occur if shortening is significant in the direction normal to the thin section. Only if strain is two-dimensional, i.e. if stretch normal to the plane of observation equals 1 (plane strain), can area change be used as a measure of volume change (Fig. 4.32).

---

development at very low- and low-grade metamorphic conditions (Ramsay and Wood 1973; Wright and Platt 1982; Etheridge et al. 1983; Beutner and Charles 1985; Ellis 1986; Wright and Henderson 1992). On the other hand, on theoretical grounds, bulk volume loss on a large scale is expected to be of minor importance at deeper crustal levels since large volumes of fluid would necessarily have to flux through the rock to remove material in solution (Engelder 1984; Bhagat and Marshak 1990). The difficulty is that volume loss during foliation development can rarely be directly measured in deformed rocks (Chap. 8.2). The significance of volume change may be overestimated since evidence of shortening normal to a foliation (partly dissolved structures and fossils; Fig. 4.20) is usually clear, while evidence of extension parallel to the foliation (e.g. fibres around pyrite, boudinaged micas) is easily overlooked (Fig. 4.32).

In many cases, foliation development is probably associated with volume increase of microlithons and volume decrease of cleavage domains while bulk deformation may be approximately volume-constant (Fig. 4.32; Erslev and Mann 1984; Lee et al. 1986; Waldron and Sandiford 1988; Bhagat and Marshak 1990; Wintsch et al. 1991; Mancktelow 1994). Quartz, albite and, to a lesser extent, micas are exchanged in pelites while zircon, apatite and rutile are largely inert (Southwick 1987; Waldron and Sandiford 1988). In most rocks, solution transfer may therefore only occur on a small scale and spacing of foliation may actually depend on the distance over which solution transfer is capable of maintaining strain compatibility in a deforming rock (Waldron and Sandiford 1988).

4.10.4 Foliations, Lithotype and Metamorphic Conditions

Secondary foliations develop by processes mentioned in Chap. 4.9, but in different lithotypes and under different metamorphic conditions, these processes operate to different extents. A brief outline of present ideas is given below.

In pelites, mechanical rotation, pressure solution transfer, crystallisation, recrystallisation and oriented nucleation are all competing processes. In many cases, a diagenetic foliation may have been present before onset of foliation development. In some cases, at very low-grade metamorphic conditions, cleavage domains develop oblique to the diagenetic fabric by stress-induced solution transfer with no- or minimal folding, leading to spaced foliation (e.g. Fig. 4.13). In most cases, microfolds (mechanical rotation) develop in the diagenetic foliation and this initial stage is followed by solution transfer of material between hinges and limbs, usually quartz from limbs to hinges (Williams 1972a; Cosgrove 1976; Gray 1979; Waldron and Sandiford 1988), and/or syntectonic crystallisation or recrystallisation of micas in cleavage domains (Tullis

1976; White and Knipe 1978; Knipe 1981; White and Johnston 1981; Lee et al. 1986). These effects are thought to be mainly temperature-dependent, solution transfer occurring at lower grade than syntectonic crystallisation and recrystallisation (Kanagawa 1991). Consequently, solution transfer may be followed by syntectonic crystallisation (Weber 1981). With increasing temperature in the absence of deformation, a preferred orientation may even be strengthened further by mimetic mica growth (Siddans 1977; Weber 1981; Ishii 1988). In some slates, the stage of folding and rotation may be absent and the foliation develops by syntectonic crystal growth without mechanical rotation (Woodland 1982; Gregg 1985; Ishii 1988).

After a first foliation is developed, renewed shortening at a low angle to the existing foliation may cause development of a second foliation; again, the early foliation may be folded, or truncated by developing new cleavage domains, and either solution transfer or new growth of mica may dominate. This leads to disjunctive or crenulation cleavage. If differentiation is strong and accompanied by recrystallisation, evidence of early foliations may be obscured and a *compositional layering* develops. The term *differentiated layering* is also commonly used for such structures, but since it can be difficult to distinguish sedimentary layering from secondary layering, the non-genetic term compositional layering is preferred.

In psammites, continuous foliation can form in fine-grained rocks, or spaced foliations in coarse-grained material (Gray 1978). In the second case, *mica films* (Fig. 4.22b) may develop by solution transfer and mica growth (Gregg 1985).

In limestones, foliation development is strongly dependent on temperature and mica-content. Solution transfer and twinning are important at low temperature (Chap. 3.12.3) and can lead to a shape fabric defined by elongated carbonate grains, or a coarse spaced foliation (stylolites). A primary high mica content of limestone may cause development of slaty cleavage and cleavage bundles. Passive rotation of micas is mainly responsible for mica preferred orientation in limestone at low temperature (Alvarez et al. 1976; Mitra and Yonkee 1985; Kreutzberger and Peacor 1988). At higher temperature, crystalplastic flow and twinning are important, and a foliation is mostly formed by elongate grains. In all cases, foliations in limestones are less well developed than in pelites.

Metabasites deformed at low-grade conditions give rise to continuous or spaced foliations defined by preferred orientation of amphiboles, chlorite, epidote, micas and lenses of different composition. Mechanical rotation and oriented growth of new minerals is more important then solution transfer. At medium to high-grade conditions, oriented mineral growth and crystalplastic deformation are the main mechanisms of foliation development. Metabasites can be equally suitable to determine metamorphic grade as pelites, especially at low-grade metamorphic conditions.

4.11 Practical Use of Foliations

4.11.1 Introduction

Foliations can be used to obtain information on strain, metamorphic conditions and overprinting relations. In Chapter 4.10.2 it is shown how secondary 'passive foliations' can be used to find the approximate orientation of the XY-plane of tectonic strain related to the formation of that particular foliation (not the total strain), provided the problems mentioned in Chapter 4.10.3 are kept in mind. Especially continuous foliations may be used to a first approximation to identify the XY plane of strain. By analogy, a stretching lineation contained in a foliation normally traces approximately the X direction of strain. Foliations which are thought to have developed by mechanical rotation of fabric elements only, can in principle be used to estimate the magnitude of finite strain (Chap. 8.2).

If a foliation is defined by parallel minerals that show a "growth fabric" (e.g. Fig. 4.7) without signs of post-crystalline deformation, the foliation must have formed under metamorphic circumstances during which these minerals were stable. A foliation defined by euhedral amphiboles must have formed under circumstances where these amphiboles were stable. However, care must be taken to distinguish cases where a pre-existing foliation has undergone an increase in metamorphic conditions after deformation, producing new minerals that may have grown mimetically over the existing foliation (Fig. 4.26, 4.27). Relics of older mineral assemblages may help to recognise these situations.

In many areas where several overprinting foliations can be recognised, a "main foliation" may have formed under peak metamorphic circumstances, whereas later events are characterised by deformation of this main foliation to produce weaker and less penetrative foliations under lower metamorphic or drier circumstances. This may be related to the fact that during progressive metamorphism, water is generally released by mineral reactions favouring

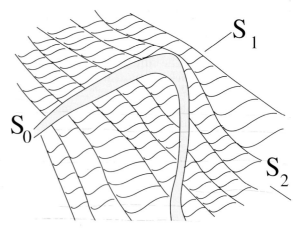

Fig. 4.33. D_1 fold, folding bedding (S_o) with development of S_1 foliation along the axial surface of the fold. Later D_2 deformation folded S_1 to produce an S_2 crenulation cleavage in pelitic layers that cut the D_1 fold through both limbs. Note the deviation of S_2 around the more resistant fold hinge

complete recrystallisation during deformation. After the peak of metamorphism, under retrograde circumstances when the rock has lost most of its water, recrystallisation is difficult and deformation results mainly in folding, distortion or mylonitisation of earlier fabrics.

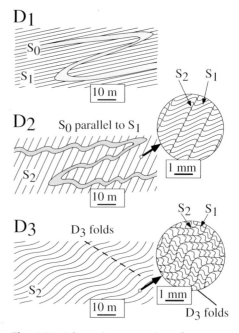

Fig. 4.34. Schematic presentation of a common sequence of foliation development in slate and schist belts. Enlargements of typical microstructures are shown at *right*. Further explanation in text

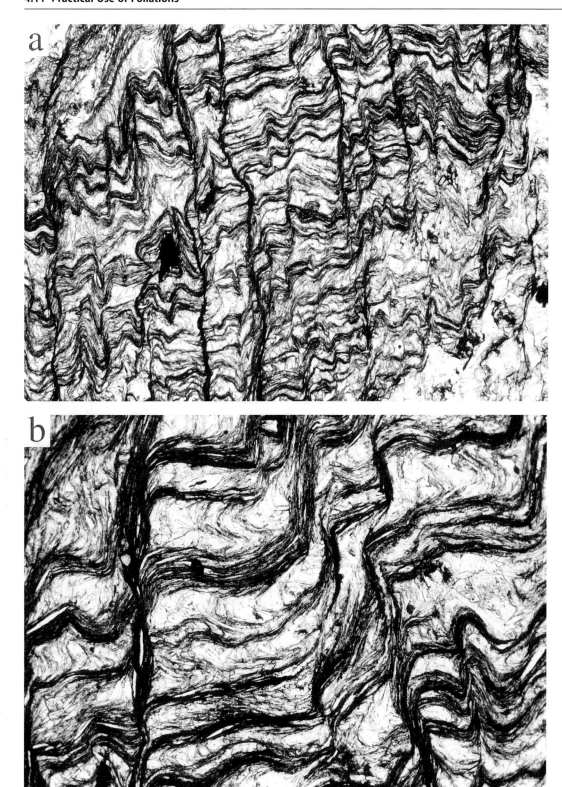

Fig. 4.35. a Crenulation cleavage S_3 *(vertical)* with micro-lithons in which the folded cleavage *(horizontal)* is an older crenulation cleavage (S_2). S_2 and S_3 correspond respectively to stages *4* and *3* in the scheme in Fig 4.17. Eastern Alps, Austria. Width of view 1.5 mm. PPL. **b** Detail of **a** showing folded S_1 in microlithons of S_2. Width of view 0.3 mm. PPL. (Photographs courtesy S. Wallis)

4.11.2 Overprinting Relations

Overprinting relations between foliations are probably the most useful tool to furnish a reference frame for the study of the tectonic evolution of a body of rock. They are particularly appropriate for study in thin section because of their penetrative nature and because of the usually small size of the fabric elements. The principle for establishing a sequence of foliation planes is quite simple: if microfolds are visible the folded surfaces are always older than the fabric elements developed along the axial surface, or cutting the folds. Any surface associated with the axial planes of folds is genetically related with those folds, but foliation planes that cut folds obliquely are younger than the folds (Fig. 4.33).

A general outline of a common sequence of events in slate and schist belts may serve to illustrate how the analysis of overprinting relations works (Fig. 4.34; cf. Hobbs et al. 1976, their Chap. 9; Williams 1985). During a first deformation phase (D_1), a penetrative slaty cleavage is developed at varying angles with bedding, according to the position in large D_1 folds that are commonly asymmetric. In the long limbs the angle between S_1 and S_0 may become so small that it is not visible any more in the field or even in thin sections (Fig. 4.34). The slaty cleavage (S_1) may be spaced or continuous, but is generally not a crenulation cleavage as analysed under normal microscopic amplification. However, if analysed by SEM, it may show crenulation cleavage features, folding a bedding-parallel foliation of diagenetic origin.

A second phase of deformation (D_2) commonly produces a crenulation cleavage, folding S_1 (Fig. 4.34). Various stages or morphologies may be present depending on the intensity of deformation (cf. Bell and Rubenach 1983) and according to grain growth in response to metamorphic circumstances (Figs. 4.17, 4.18).

A third phase of deformation may be recognised by folding of the S_2 crenulation cleavage (Figs. 4.34, 4.35). This may in some cases result in interesting structures, since according to their orientation certain limbs may be refolded and others straightened out (Figs. 4.36, 4.37). Later phases of deformation may be recognised in a similar way by overprinting (folding) of earlier foliations.

The main problem of this analysis is to establish how to correlate foliations from one thin section to another, from one outcrop to another, or even from one analysed area to another. This is a matter that is hard to solve with general rules, but the following suggestions may be of help (see also Williams 1985).

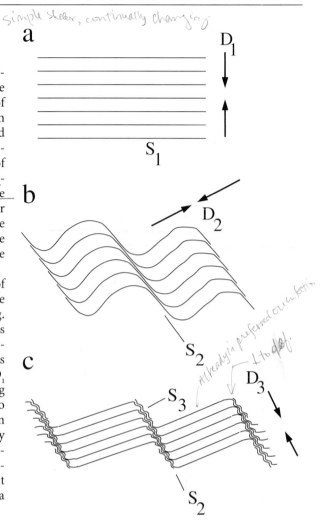

Fig. 4.36a–c. Sequence of events leading to selective refolding of a second foliation *(S_2)* by D_3 while the older foliation (S_1) seems unaffected. **a** S_1 is formed by vertical compression. **b** Lateral compression by D_2 caused a steep S_2 differentiated crenulation cleavage. **c** Oblique D_3 compression is applied, resulting in selective refolding of differentiated limbs of D_2 folds because of their orientation. The other limbs are progressively unfolded until S_1 becomes approximately parallel to the axial plane of D_3 folds

Deformation may be quite heterogeneously distributed through a rock body, especially the deformation that post-dates peak metamorphic conditions. It is, for instance, common to find D_3 or D_4 deformation features concentrated in narrow zones, leaving other areas without visible effects. Shear zones are, of course, the most spectacular example of this local concentration of deformation. On the other hand, foliations induced during peak metamorphic conditions are normally widespread and remarkably conti-

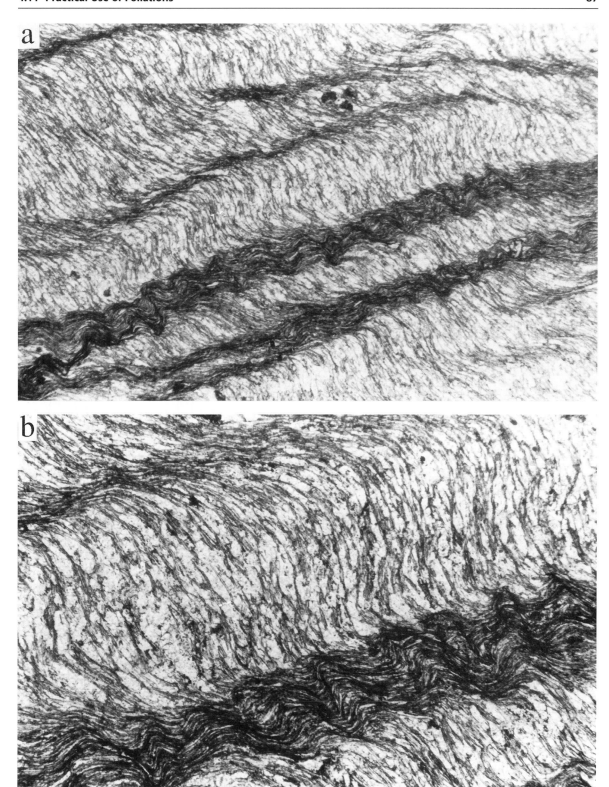

Fig. 4.37. a Differentiated crenulation cleavage (S$_2$ *lower left to upper right*) deforming a finely spaced disjunctive cleavage (S$_1$ *upper left to lower right*). S$_2$ is folded during D$_3$. This is an example of a structure thought to have developed according to the scheme explained in Fig. 4.36. Açunguí, São Paulo State, Brazil. Width of view 4 mm. PPL. **b** is a detail of **a**. Width of view 1.8 mm. PPL

TRANSPOSITION

In many metamorphic terrains it is difficult or impossible to use bedding as a reference plane in outcrop. The distribution of lithotypes on the map may allow establishment of approximate contacts between stratigraphic units, but these may not coincide with lithologic contacts in outcrop. The latter contacts are usually parallel to "the main foliation" and may be difficult to follow along strike. In such areas, *transposition* of one or more foliations (including bedding) has occurred. Transposition is usually defined as the progressive erasure of a reference surface (S_0, S_1, S_n, etc.) due to tight folding accompanied by some differentiation process. However, it can also be used in a more general sense for erasure of older structure by strong younger deformation. Turner and Weiss (1963; see also Davis 1984) have given some good examples of bedding transposition on the outcrop scale. The concept is clearly scale-dependent; a number of en-echelon disrupted bedding lenses may be mistaken for real bedding if seen in an outcrop smaller than these lenses. In a large outcrop where a number of lenses are visible, the oblique position of the enveloping surface of bedding may still be recognisable.

Transposition may also occur on the scale of a thin section. The sequence of crenulation cleavage development (Figs. 4.17, 4.18) is a good example of transposition of S_1 by S_2. Figure 4.38 shows a natural example of a D_2 fold where S_2 is clearly distinct from S_0/S_1 in the fold hinges, whereas in the limbs transposition has occurred and all three planes, S_0, S_1 and S_2, have become parallel. The parallelism of S_0 and S_1 probably indicates that a similar process occurred during D_1.

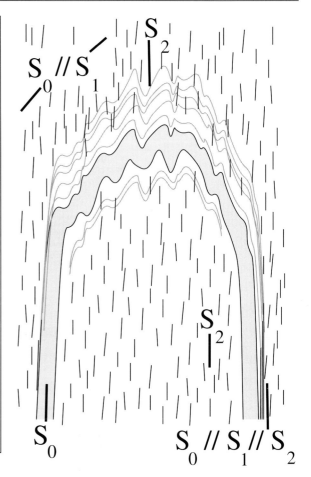

Fig. 4.38. Isoclinal D_2 fold showing the parallel orientation of S_0, S_1 and S_2 in fold limbs and S_2 oblique to S_0/S_1 in the hinges

nuous over large areas. These may, however, vary abruptly because of lithological variation (e.g. strong foliations may disappear abruptly at the contact of a calc-silicate rock because of the lack of platy minerals to define a foliation). It is important in the correlation of foliations to pay attention to their relation with metamorphism, since metamorphic conditions usually do not change much from one outcrop to the next, unless post-metamorphic faulting is involved.

Especially in the field, intrusive veins or dykes can be important to distinguish phases of deformation and their associated foliations of different age. These bodies may have intruded over a relatively short period of time and may be recognised over a large area by their similar composition and orientation. Structures cut by the veins are older, whereas younger structures affect the veins by folding, shearing or other deformation.

4.12 Lattice-Preferred Orientation (LPO)

In many deformed rocks, the lattice orientation of crystals is not randomly distributed, but arranged in a systematic way. Such rocks have a *lattice-preferred orientation* (LPO) for a specific mineral. In the case of crystals with a planar or elongate shape in a particular crystallographic direction such as micas and amphiboles, an LPO is easy to recognise as a foliation or lineation. However, for minerals such as quartz and calcite this is more difficult. In the case of quartz, the presence of an LPO can be checked by inserting a gypsum plate under crossed polarisers; when the microscope table is turned, a dominant blue or yellow colour for a quartz aggregate in different orientations is an indication for an LPO. In other minerals with higher birefringence, special techniques are required to determine if an LPO is present. LPO patterns and LPO development in quartz is treated in some detail as an example.

4.13 Origin of Lattice-Preferred Orientation

LPO can be formed by the processes mentioned in Chapter 4.9, but for minerals with equant grain shape, dislocation creep seems to be the most important mechanism (Chap. 3.4). Dislocation creep changes the shape of a crystal and the interaction with neighbouring crystals may result in its rotation with respect to the instantaneous stretching axes (ISA) of bulk flow (Fig. 4.39). Deformation twinning has a similar rotation effect. The effect can be visualised by a pile of books sliding on a shelf; the books change orientation with respect to the shelf and their normal rotates towards the direction of gravity. If deformation starts in a crystalline aggregate with random initial orientation, e.g. in a sandstone, the result after some deformation will be a preferred orientation. As an example, Fig. 4.39b–c shows how an LPO pattern may develop in a deforming crystal aggregate with a single slip system in coaxial flattening progressive deformation. When several slip systems are active, the rotational behaviour of grains and the resulting LPO patterns will be more complex.

The type of slip systems or deformation twinning that will be active in a crystal depends on their critical resolved shear stress (CRSS) and therefore indirectly on metamorphic and deformation conditions (Chap. 3.4). Usually, more than one slip system can operate in a mineral and the CRSS of each slip system changes with temperature and chemical activity of certain components, and may even 'overtake' that of other slip systems. At low differential stress, only one slip system may be active, but at higher differential stress, several slip systems can operate simultaneously. In fact, for maintenance of cohesion between grains, five independent slip systems should be operating (Lister 1977). In silicates, however, which usually have low crystal symmetry, fewer slip systems are active and space problems are accommodated at low temperature by lattice bending, kinking, fracturing and, at high temperature, by dynamic recrystallisation or grain boundary sliding.

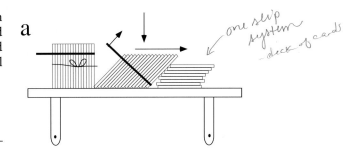

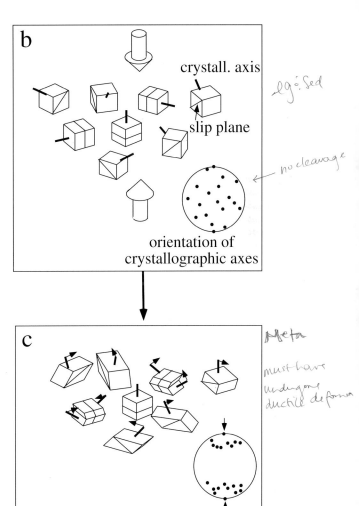

Fig. 4.39. a Reorientation of a pile of books by slip: an axis normal to the books *(bold line)* rotates towards the direction of gravity. Development of LPO in crystals due to dislocation glide on slip planes operates in a similar way. **b** Flattening of an aggregate of crystals with a single slip system normal to a crystallographic axis *(bold line)*. **c** All crystal axes rotate towards the compression direction except those parallel or normal to this direction. Those parallel to the compression direction may deform by kinking or twinning with rotation of the segments

The type of LPO pattern that is formed in a rock depends on many factors, the most important of which are (Schmid 1994):

1. The slip systems that are operating and the amount of activity on each slip system.

2. The ratio of stretching rates along the ISA of the flow, i.e. plane strain, flattening or constrictional flow. These rates determine in which direction crystals rotate and thereby the shape of the fabric (Fig. 4.41).

3. The finite strain. Usually, if the flow pattern does not change during deformation, the LPO pattern increases in strength and sharpness with increasing strain but undergoes only slight changes in geometry (Chap. 4.15.2).

4. The kinematic vorticity number. In initially isotropic materials, non-coaxial progressive deformation leads to LPO patterns with monoclinic symmetry, and coaxial progressive deformation to patterns with higher symmetry.

5. The activity of dynamic recrystallisation. Recrystallisation may influence an LPO pattern in several ways but the effect is difficult to predict; it may weaken an existing pattern by generation of new, randomly oriented grains; or it may strengthen a pattern or part of a pattern by removing (consuming) certain grains with a relatively high dislocation density. Grains that are unfavourably oriented for slip may be removed by this process if they developed a high dislocation density because of constriction by neighbours (Jessell 1987; Ree 1990). However, the reverse is also possible; such grains may have low dislocation density, since all deformation is taken up in softer neighbours, and therefore consume grains favourably oriented for slip (Gleason et al. 1993). Evidence for both processes has been found in experiments.

6. Growth of grains from solution. The growth rate in many minerals is dependent on crystallographic direction, and growth of minerals from solution can therefore produce a preferred orientation (Shelley 1979, 1989, 1994)

Theoretically, it should be possible to use LPO patterns as a source of information on the six parameters mentioned above. However, our understanding of the development of LPO is unfortunately still sketchy. Most successful has been the application of LPO patterns with monoclinic symmetry to determine sense of shear (Chap. 4.15.3).

The study of the development of LPO proceeds through several channels. Observation of natural LPO patterns and comparison with known temperature, strain geometry and vorticity of the progressive deformation can give an indication of the influence of these parameters on LPO development. However, in natural LPO, the deformation history is usually unknown and may have been more complex than is assumed; early parts of the development are most likely erased. Slip systems may be identified by observation of lattice defects in naturally deformed crystals by TEM (Blacic and Christie 1984; Hobbs 1985). However, lattice defects in natural deformed rocks may be formed late, after the LPO was developed (White 1979a; Ord and Christie 1984). Theoretical and numerical modelling of fabric development using a pre-set choice of slip systems have been very successful in modelling LPO patterns (Etchecopar 1977; Lister 1977; Lister and Price 1978; Lister et al. 1978; Lister and Paterson 1979; Lister and Hobbs 1980; Etchecopar and Vasseur 1987; Jessell 1988b), but theoretical studies suffer from assumptions that may be wrong and simplifications necessary to operate computer models. Furthermore, only monomineralic aggregates have been simulated, while most of the interesting fabrics in rocks occur in polymineralic aggregates. The most successful, but possibly also most laborious approach to study LPO development, is experimental deformation of rocks at high pressure and temperature and subsequent analysis of the LPO patterns in deformed samples, in combination with TEM analysis of lattice defects (Green et al. 1970; Tullis et al. 1973; Dell'Angelo and Tullis 1989).

4.14 Presentation of LPO Data

The orientation of a crystal in a reference frame is only completely defined if the orientation of three crystal axes is known; this means that three numbers are needed to represent the orientation of a single crystal in a reference frame. A complete LPO pattern can therefore only be presented as points in a three-dimensional diagram. Such a diagram is known as an orientation distribution function diagram or ODF (Fig. 4.40a). In practice, it may be difficult for the inexperienced to read such diagrams. Geologists usually rely on polar diagrams such as stereograms to plot the orientation of crystals (Fig. 4.40a); however, these are only useful if just one crystallographic direction, such as the c-axis of quartz, is plotted. In this way, only part of the LPO pattern of a crystalline aggregate is presented. Other methods of presentation are cross sections through an ODF, and inverse pole diagrams where the crystal axes are taken as a reference frame and the orientation of the lineation in the rock with respect to this frame is plotted for

Fig. 4.40. a Orientation of a quartz crystal in a reference frame defined by a foliation *(S_r)*, lineation *(L_r)* and foliation pole. The full crystal orientation is given by Eulerian angles φ, ψ and θ. Orientation of the c-axis is given by angles α and β. Three diagrams that are commonly used to present LPO patterns are shown. In an ODF diagram the full orientation of the crystal is represented. In a pole diagram the orientation of individual axes of the crystal can be plotted; in this case, only the c-axis. In an inverse-pole diagram the orientation of L_r is plotted with respect to crystallographic axes. **b** Examples of pole diagrams with contours of pole density showing two types of crossed girdles (Lister 1977) of quartz c-axes. The shape of the girdles is highlighted by use of a fabric skeleton which traces the crests of the contour diagram

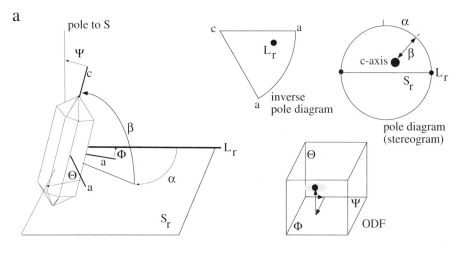

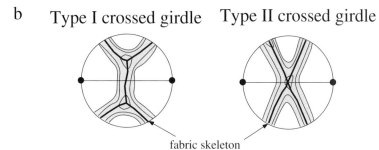

each grain (Fig. 4.40a). ODF can also be useful if the preferred orientation of a certain crystal direction which is of interest cannot be measured directly; from an ODF it is always possible to calculate such orientations.

Since ODF are difficult to read, stereograms are most commonly used, either directly plotted from measured data or derived from the ODF through calculation (Schmid and Casey 1986). LPO patterns in stereograms can appear as point maxima or as small- or great circle girdles. In complex LPO patterns, the girdles are connected with each other to form crossed girdles of either Type I or Type II (Lister 1977; Fig. 4.40b). Cleft girdles (actually small circles) are formed in flattening strain. If a preferred orientation is present, but the pattern is vague, *pole-free areas* can be distinguished. In order to enhance visibility of girdles and maxima, LPO patterns are usually contoured. Contours can be used to derive a *fabric skeleton;* a pattern of lines connecting the crests of the contour diagram (Fig. 4.40b).

LPO patterns are interpreted in terms of their internal and external asymmetry. Internal asymmetry is defined by the shape of the pattern itself; exter-

nal asymmetry is determined with respect to a reference frame (Chaps. 2.4, 5.6.1); lacking other possibilities, fabric elements such as foliations and lineations in a rock are normally used as a reference frame, notably those that are thought to have formed at the same time as the LPO. For briefness, such reference foliations and lineations are given in this chapter as S_r and L_r.

In stereograms, standard presentation of LPO patterns is with the Y-direction of finite strain vertical and the X and Z directions along the EW and NS axes (Fig. 4.42). This implies that a corresponding foliation and lineation are presented in the diagram as an E-W-trending vertical plane (S_r) and horizontal line respectively, the latter indicated by dots on the circle (L_r; Fig. 4.40b). L_r is usually a stretching or mineral lineation. This orientation shows the symmetry of most LPO patterns advantageously.

It is commonly useful to show which grains in an aggregate have a particular orientation. The distribution of grains with particular orientations can be given in a map of the sample under consideration, known as an *AVA diagram* (German: 'Achsenvertei-lungsanalyse' – analysis of orientation of axes; Sander

1950; Heilbronner and Pauli 1993). In practice, AVA diagrams are made for the LPO pattern of a single crystal axis, such as c-axes. An AVA diagram can be presented by plunge direction of c-axes for each grain, presented as lines (Fig. 4.23) or, more advanced, by colours representing different orientations. AVA can be of great help for the interpretation of LPO patterns and of the way in which they develop (Chap. 9.8.5).

4.15 LPO Patterns of Quartz

4.15.1 Introduction

Figure 4.41 shows the influence of flow type and finite strain on the geometry of c-axis LPO patterns of quartz that accumulated by coaxial progressive deformation at low- to medium-grade metamorphic conditions (Tullis 1977; Lister and Hobbs 1980; Schmid and Casey 1986; Law 1990). Small circle girdles are most common but in plane strain, small circle girdles

are connected by a central girdle to produce Type I crossed girdles (Fig. 4.40b). Other c-axis LPO patterns that develop in coaxial progressive deformation are Type II crossed girdles, which seem to form in constriction (Fig. 4.40b; Bouchez 1978), and point maxima around the Y-axis of strain. Both patterns seem to form at higher temperature than the patterns shown in Fig 4.41 (Schmid and Casey 1986). Increasing temperature also seems to cause an increase in the opening angle of the small circle girdles.

In the case of non-coaxial progressive plane strain deformation, other c-axis patterns develop (Fig. 4.42) (Behrmann and Platt 1982; Bouchez et al. 1983; Platt and Behrmann 1986). Most common are slightly asymmetric Type I crossed girdles, and single girdles inclined to S_r and L_r (Burg and Laurent 1978; Lister and Hobbs 1980; Schmid and Casey 1986). At medium to high-grade conditions, single maxima around the Y-axis are common, while at high grade (>650 °C), point maxima in a direction close to the stretching lineation L_r occur (Mainprice et al. 1986). c-axis patterns as shown in Figs. 4.41 and 4.42 represent only a small part of the full LPO of quartz and the orientation of other directions, such as <a>-axes, should also be known to allow interpretation of LPO deve-

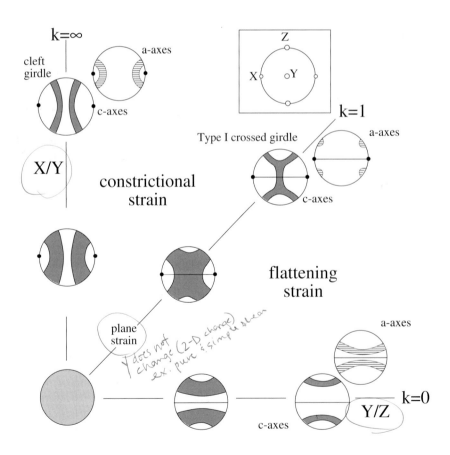

Fig. 4.41. Flinn diagram showing the relation of geometry of LPO patterns of quartz c-axes *(grey contours)* and a-axes *(striped ornament)* with strain in the case of coaxial progressive deformation. An inset shows the orientation of principal strain axes in the pole diagrams. *Horizontal solid lines* in pole diagrams indicate reference foliation. *Dots* indicate reference lineation. (After Lister and Hobbs 1980)

Fig. 4.42. Pole diagrams showing four types of contoured LPO patterns of quartz c-axes *(grey)* and a-axes *(striped)* such as develop with increasing metamorphic grade in non-coaxial progressive deformation. The variation is due to a change in the dominant slip systems. Explanation in text

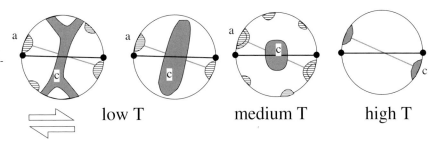

lopment; in Figs. 4.41 and 4.42, patterns for <a>-axes are therefore shown beside c-axes. Nevertheless, c-axis patterns are most commonly represented in the literature since they can easily be measured on a U-stage; for other crystallographic directions more advanced equipment such as a goniometer (Chap. 9.8.6) is needed.

The patterns in Fig. 4.41 can be explained as an effect of the activity of slip planes in quartz; at conditions below 650 °C, slip in <a> directions on basal, prism and rhomb planes is dominant in quartz. As a result, <a>-axes tend to cluster close to planes and directions of maximum incremental shear strain (at 45° to ISA; Fig. 4.43a). In flattening, <a>-axes cluster in small circles around the shortening direction, similar to the situation in Fig. 4.39c. In constriction, a small circle girdle of <a>-axes around the extension direction forms and in plane strain there are two directions in the XY plane. Slip on basal planes contributes mainly to c-axes in the periphery of the diagram, slip on prism planes to those in the centre, and slip on rhomb planes between both (Fig. 4.43a). Type II crossed-girdle c-axis patterns probably develop in constriction when rhomb slip is dominant over prism slip (Bouchez 1978; Schmid and Casey 1986).

In non-coaxial progressive deformation, domains of material line rotation are not of equal size as in coaxial progressive deformation (Chap. 2.7). As a result, one of the <a>-axes maxima is favoured and the c-axis patterns may be similar to those in Fig. 4.41 but one part will be better developed than the other. Consequently, the pattern of <a>- and c-axes obtains a monoclinic symmetry. For example, at high strain accumulated by simple shear at low to medium-grade metamorphic conditions, the Type I crossed girdle and double <a>-axes maxima are replaced by a single <a>-axes maximum parallel to the movement direction (the fabric attractor) and a single girdle of c-axes normal to the flow plane (Figs. 4.42, 4.43b; Chap. 2.9). The c-axes from the periphery to the centre of the girdle stem from c-axes of grains deformed by basal, rhomb and prism slip respectively (Fig. 4.43). At low

temperature, basal <a> slip is most important and the girdles may have a strong cluster of c-axes in the periphery. With increasing temperature, prism <a> slip becomes more important (Wilson 1975; Bouchez 1977; Lister and Dornsiepen 1982; Law 1990) and the girdle tends to a maximum around the Y-axis (Fig. 4.42, 4.43b). At very high temperature and hydrous conditions, prism <c> slip operates (Lister and Dornsiepen 1982; Blumenfeld et al. 1985; Mainprice et al. 1986), and causes a c-axis maximum subparallel to the attractor (Fig. 4.42, 4.43), and <a> axes normal to it.

4.15.2 The Effects of Strain and Recrystallisation

Increasing strain at constant flow parameters and temperature will theoretically lead to strengthening of an LPO pattern (Fig. 4.41; Lister and Hobbs 1980), but fabric geometry may also change with increasing strain. The opening angle of small circle girdles of c-axes in Type I crossed girdles of a flattening progressive deformation regime (Fig. 4.41) may decrease with increasing strain if dynamic recrystallisation is subdued; low temperature and high strain rate also produce relatively small opening angles (Tullis et al. 1973; Marjoribanks 1976; Jessell 1988b). This is an effect of the competition of grain rotation in response to dislocation glide and dynamic recrystallisation. Small circle girdles of c-axes are mostly due to grains with basal slip planes at 45° to the shortening ISA; these grains have high resolved shear stress on the slip system and are in optimal orientation for 'easy slip'. However, the slip planes in such grains rotate away from this orientation towards the fabric attractor with increasing strain, causing a decrease in the opening angle of the small circle girdle (Fig. 4.39). High temperature and low strain rate promote grain boundary migration that may consume grains which have rotated towards the shortening direction and this may hamper the decrease in the opening angle with increasing strain.

a   coaxial

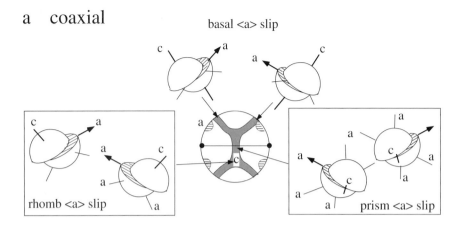

b   non-coaxial

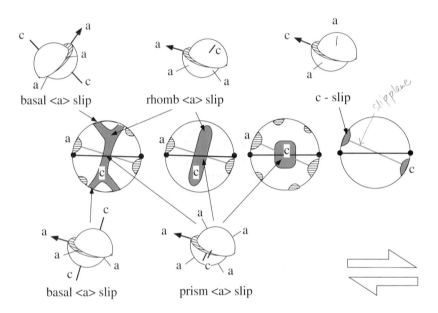

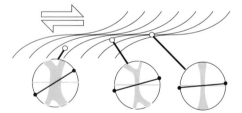

Fig. 4.43. a Illustration of the contribution of equidimensional quartz crystals with aligned <a> – axes and basal, rhomb or prism slip planes to a Type I crossed girdle pattern formed in coaxial progressive deformation. Ornamentation of contoured patterns of c- and a-axes in polar diagrams as in Fig. 4.42. **b** The same for several patterns that develop in non-coaxial progressive deformation. At *right* a pattern that developed by slip in direction of the c-axis

There are also indications that single c-axis girdles with external asymmetry can form in simple shear through an intermediate stage with symmetric crossed girdles (Fig. 4.44; Garcia Celma 1982,1983; Schmid and Casey 1986). This effect may be due to an increasing effect of dynamic recrystallisation on development of LPO patterns with increasing strain; the change in fabric can be due to selective removal of grains in unfavourable orientations for slip by recrystallisation (Schmid and Casey 1986; Jessell 1988a,b). A change in LPO pattern geometry similar to that shown in Fig 4.44 may occur in transitions between pure shear and simple shear progressive deformation (Schmid and Casey 1986).

Fig. 4.44. Pole diagrams with contoured LPO patterns of quartz c-axes for three samples from a ductile shear zone, from the edge to the centre. *Black solid line* and *dots* represent reference foliation and lineation. The *horizontal grey line* marks the fabric attractor plane. The pattern changes from a Type I crossed girdle to a single girdle and becomes sharper with increasing strain to the centre of the zone but does not rotate with respect to the fabric attractor

The reader should be aware of possible pitfalls in the assessment of shear sense using quartz LPO. First, the shear sense observed may not be associated with the other fabric elements visible in the rock. For example, where thin quartz seams occur between other mineral grains, the flow kinematics may have been completely different from the bulk flow. Another possible error occurs at high strain if fabrics are vague or incomplete, e.g. due to recrystallisation or the presence of grains of a second mineral. In this case, the orientation of the LPO pattern with respect to a reference foliation S_r that is approximately parallel to the fabric attractor will give the wrong shear sense if it is interpreted as an external asymmetry (Fig. 4.45). It is therefore wise not to rely exclusively on quartz c-axis fabrics to determine shear sense.

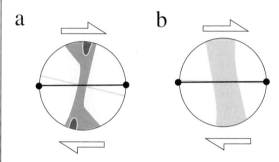

Fig. 4.45. a Contoured LPO pattern of quartz c-axes with a clear internal asymmetry and external asymmetry with respect to S_r indicating dextral shear sense. **b** A similar but more vague pattern in which the internal asymmetry is lost, resulting from high finite strain with dextral sense of shear; S_r and L_r are approximately parallel to the fabric attractor. The pattern in **b** could be mistaken for external asymmetry of a single girdle oblique to S_r at low strain, and erroneously interpreted to represent a sinistral shear sense. ***Black solid line*** and ***dots*** represent S_r and L_r. The inclined ***grey line*** marks the fabric attractor plane

4.15.3 Shear Sense Determination Using Quartz Fabrics

Patterns of c- and <a>-axes of quartz obtain an asymmetry (actually a monoclinic symmetry) when they accumulate by non-coaxial progressive deformation, and this asymmetry can be used to deduce sense of shear. There are two elements; some patterns, such as the skewed Type I c-axis crossed girdles, have an internal asymmetry, independent of other fabric elements (Fig. 4.42). More important, however, is an external asymmetry of the patterns with respect to S_r and L_r in the rock (Fig. 4.42). <a>-Axes cluster near

the fabric attractor, and c-axes in a girdle normal to the attractor. At very high temperature, c-axes cluster near the fabric attractor (Fig. 4.42); S_r and L_r in the same rock rotate towards the fabric attractor but will lie in the extension quadrant of the flow; consequently, there will be an angle between S_r or L_r and elements of the LPO fabric which can be used to determine sense of shear (Fig. 4.42).

4.16 LPO Patterns of Other Minerals

As in quartz, LPO in other minerals strongly depends on active slip systems and on the geometry and symmetry of the flow pattern, resulting in a similarity of LPO geometry and strain geometry. As for quartz, slip systems and fabric elements tend to rotate towards the fabric attractor, resulting in a common subparallel orientation of components of the LPO, and S_r and L_r in the rock.

Calcite c-axis LPO patterns show a similar influence of flow symmetry on pattern geometry. At low temperature (<300 °C) coaxial progressive flattening produces a maximum around the Z-axis of strain. In constriction a girdle through Y and Z develops and in coaxial plane strain a maximum around Z and a minor girdle through Y (Wenk et al. 1986a; Shelley 1993). In simple shear flow, a c-axis girdle develops as for quartz, but *dipping in the opposite direction* (in the direction of the shortening ISA). This is due to the fact that in calcite at low temperature, e-twinning is largely responsible for development of the LPO fabric (Schmid 1982; Behrmann 1983; Schmid et al. 1987; Wenk et al. 1987; Rutter et al. 1994).

Experimental and computer models indicate that at high temperature in plane strain, split maxima may develop around the shortening axis (Wagner et al. 1982; Wenk et al. 1986a, 1987; Schmid et al. 1987; Takeshita et al. 1987; de Bresser 1991). A possible natural example of such a high temperature LPO pattern in calcite was reported by de Bresser (1989).

In *plagioclase,* (010) trends to parallelism with S_r and [001] with L_r at medium to high-grade metamorphic conditions (Olsen and Kohlstedt 1985; Montardi and Mainprice 1987; Ji and Mainprice 1988; Shaosheng and Mainprice 1988; Mainprice and Nicolas 1989; Dornbush et al. 1994). At very high grade, however, [100] tends to parallelism with L_r (Kruhl 1987; Dornbush et al. 1994). In shear zones, the pole to (010) tends to show an external asymmetry with respect to a planar and linear shape fabric, which can be used to determine shear sense as in the case of quartz c-axes.

Olivine has a complex behaviour that is strongly dependent on temperature (Mainprice and Nicolas 1989). At relatively 'low' temperatures (700–1000 °C) corresponding to lower crustal or upper mantle levels where olivine is at the limit of crystalplastic behaviour, diffuse girdles of principal axes may occur. At medium temperature ($\approx$1000 °C), a girdle of [okl] normal to L_r and a point maximum of [100] parallel to L_r may form. At high temperature (>1100 °C) a point maximum of [010] normal to S_r and [100] parallel to L_r develops; and at hypersolidus conditions (>1250 °C) a point maximum of [100] parallel to L_r and partial girdles of [010] and [001] are formed. Fabrics with external asymmetry do occur and can be used to determine shear sense (Avé Lallemant and Carter 1970; Mercier 1985).

In *clinopyroxene* three main types of LPO have been described; (a) [100] normal to S_r and [001] parallel to L_r or S_r (Mainprice and Nicolas 1989; Phillipot and van Roermund 1992); (b) [010] normal to S_r and [001] parallel to L_r or S_r (Mainprice and Nicolas 1989); (c) [010] normal to L_r and [001] parallel to L_r (Helmstead et al. 1972; van Roermund 1983, 1992). (a) is mainly found in peridotite massifs with pyroxenite layers and may either be formed at low temperature and high strain rate or, if this is unlikely, by post-tectonic crystal growth (van Roermund 1992). (b) and (c) form by crystalplastic deformation as a conse-quence of multiple slip in medium to high temperature eclogites by activity of dislocations with predominantly [001] and <110>Burgers vectors (van Roermund 1983, 1992; Buatier et al. 1991). Their difference seems to reflect different strain types, constriction for type (b) and flattening for type (c) (Helmstead et al. 1972; van Roermund 1992). Asymmetric fabrics have not been reported for clinopyroxene in the literature.

In *orthopyroxene* deformed at high-grade metamorphic conditions, LPO of [100] has been reported at a high angle to S_r and of [001] gently inclined with respect to L_r (Dornbush et al. 1994). This preferred orientation is associated with the dominance of (100)[001] as a slip system. The LPO reported by Dornbush et al. (1994) is slightly asymmetric and can be used to determine sense of shear.

Little is known about LPO in *amphiboles,* but the available data indicate a strong similarity with clinopyroxene. [001] is commonly parallel to L_r (Gapais and Brun 1981; Rousell 1981; Shelley 1994) and either (100) (Mainprice and Nicolas 1989) or (110) (Gapais and Brun 1981) parallel to S_r. Preferred orientations at medium to high grade may be due to crystalplastic deformation, but LPO in amphiboles at low-grade conditions may be due to rigid body rotation or oriented growth (Ildefonse et al. 1990; Shelley 1993, 1994). Hornblende fabrics reflect the strain symmetry (Gapais and Brun 1981).

5 Shear Zones

5.1 Introduction

In general, deformation in rocks is not homogeneously distributed. One of the most common patterns of heterogeneous deformation is the concentration of deformation in planar zones that accommodate movement of relatively rigid wall-rock blocks. Deformation in such high-strain zones usually contains a rotation component, reflecting lateral displacement of wall rock segments with re-

spect to each other; this type of high-strain zone is known as a *shear zone*. Deformation in a shear zone causes development of characteristic fabrics and mineral assemblages that reflect P-T conditions, flow type, movement sense and deformation history in the shear zone. As such, shear zones are an important source of geological information.

Shear zones can be subdivided into brittle zones or faults, and ductile zones. Ductile shear zones are usually active at higher metamorphic conditions than brittle shear zones (Figs. 3.33, 5.1). Major shear zones which transect the crust or upper mantle have both

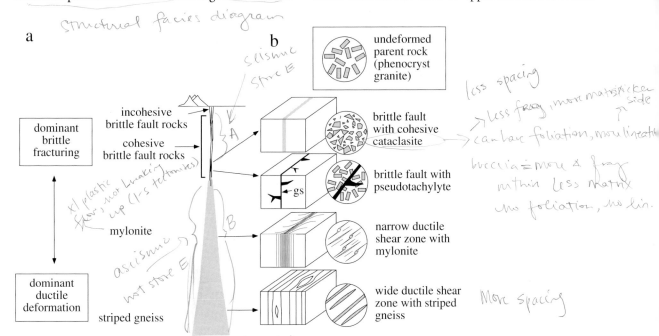

a

structural facies diagram

seismic
slow E

incohesive
brittle fault rocks

cohesive
brittle fault rocks

mylonite

aseismic
hot store E

striped gneiss

← wider as deeper →

dominant
brittle
fracturing

dominant
ductile
deformation

b

undeformed
parent rock
(phenocryst
granite)

brittle fault
with cohesive
cataclasite

brittle fault with
pseudotachylyte

narrow ductile
shear zone with
mylonite

wide ductile shear
zone with striped
gneiss

less spacing
less frag, more matrix thicker
side
can have foliation, more lineate
breccia = more + frag
within less matrix
no foliation, no lin.

More spacing

Fig. 5.1. a,b. Distribution of the main types of fault rocks with depth in the crust. **a** Schematic cross section through a transcurrent shear zone. The zone may widen, and changes in geometry and dominant type of fault rock occur with increasing depth and metamorphic grade. **b** Schematic representation of four typical fault rocks (out of scale) and the local geometry of the shear zone in a 1m-wide block, such as would develop from a phenocryst granite; *gs* generation surface. Inclined (normal or reverse) shear zones show a similar distribution of fault rocks and shear zone geometry with depth. No vertical scale is given since the depth of the transition between dominant ductile deformation and brittle fracturing depends on rock composition, geothermal gradient, bulk strain rate and other factors (Chap. 3.14)

brittle and ductile segments (Chap. 3.14). The depth of the transition between dominantly brittle and ductile behaviour depends on many factors such as bulk strain rate, geothermal gradient, grain size, lithotype, fluid pressure, orientation of the stress field and pre-existing fabrics (Chap. 3.14). Ductile shear zones may develop in marbles at metamorphic conditions where quartzites would deform by brittle fracturing, and different minerals in a small volume of rock can show contemporaneous brittle and ductile deformation (Fig. 3.31).

Major shear zones can be active for considerable periods of time, and material in the shear zone may be transported upwards or downwards in the crust. Consequently, rocks in major shear zones commonly show evidence of several overprinting stages of activity at different metamorphic conditions. Minor shear zones may also show several overprinting stages since shear zones, once formed, are easily reactivated. A special terminology is used for rocks that have been deformed in shear zones, partly independent of their lithology (Sibson 1977b). They are usually referred to as *fault rocks,* even if deformed in ductile shear zones. The most common types are *brittle fault rocks, mylonites* and *striped gneiss.*

5.2 Brittle Fault Rocks

5.2.1 Incohesive Fault Rocks

Brittle fault rocks can be subdivided into incohesive and cohesive types. Incohesive brittle fault rocks are usually found in faults which have been active at shallow crustal levels. They occur in fault zones of variable thickness and can be subdivided into *incohesive breccia, incohesive cataclasite* and *fault gouge.* Incohesive breccia consists for more than 30%vol of angular fragments of the wall rock or of fractured veins, separated by a fine-grained matrix. In cataclasite, less than 30%vol fragments are present in the fine-grained matrix. In fault gouge, few large fragments occur isolated in the matrix. This matrix may be foliated, and fragments commonly have a lensoid shape. The wall rock and included fragments in incohesive cataclasite and fault gouge commonly show polished surfaces (slickensides) with striations or fibres (slickenfibres – Chap. 6.2.1) that can be used to determine movement direction and shear sense (Chap. 5.7.2) along the fault zone.

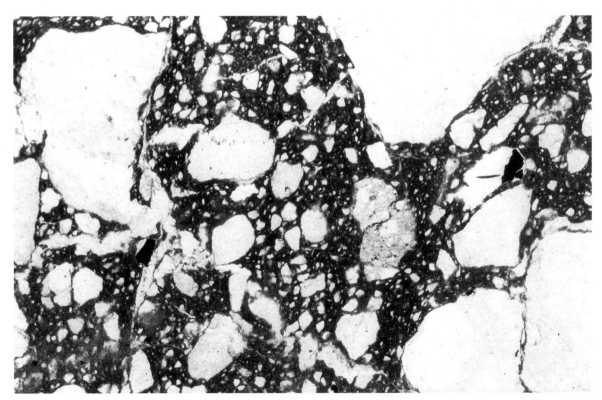

Fig. 5.2. Cohesive fault breccia in quartzite. Angular fragments of variable size are present. Orobic Alps, Italy. Width of view 8 mm. PPL

5.2.2 Cohesive Fault Rocks

Cohesive fault rocks can be subdivided into *cohesive breccia* (Fig. 5.2), *cohesive cataclasite* and *pseudotachylyte*. The distinction between breccia and cataclasite is as discussed for incohesive fault rocks. The cohesive nature of the rock is due to precipitation crystallisation of minerals such as quartz, calcite, epidote or chlorite from a fluid.

Cohesive breccia and cataclasite are less easily identifiable in outcrop than incohesive fault rocks; for example, incohesive cataclasite in quartzite is obvious because of weathering contrasts, but cohesive cataclasite may differ from undeformed host rock only by a darker colour. Cohesive breccia and cataclasite can be formed in any rock type. Usually, fragments of all sizes occur hampering a clear distinction between matrix material and inclusions (Figs. 3.1, 5.2). The contact between the fault rock and the intact wall rock is usually a gradual transition of decreasing brittle deformation intensity. Cohesive cataclasite and breccia commonly show evidence for abundant pressure solution and precipitation effects. Rock fragments are transected by healed cracks aligned with fluid inclusions. Veins of quartz, calcite, epidote or chlorite, and in ultramafic rocks, serpentine, are common. These veins form during and after brittle deformation, since they have commonly been fractured. Although most cataclasites have random fabrics, *foliated cataclasite* does occur, especially where the host rock is rich in micas (Chester et al. 1985; Evans 1988; Kano and Sato 1988). Such rocks may contain a compositional layering (Kanaori et al. 1991) and a preferred orientation of mica fragments or new-grown micas (Evans 1988). The foliation can also be a result of parallel alignment of minor shear fractures (Chester et al. 1985). Shear band cleavage structures (Chap. 5.6.4) are common in such foliated cataclasites. Deformation mechanisms in cataclasite are mainly cataclastic flow in and between grains, grain boundary sliding and pressure solution. Cohesive breccia and cataclasite are thought to develop at greater crustal depth than incohesive ones. Unless stated otherwise, cataclasite and breccia are understood to mean the cohesive form in the following sections.

5.2.3 Pseudotachylyte

Pseudotachylyte is a cohesive glassy or very fine-grained fault-rock with a very distinct fabric. Its curious name derives from its resemblance to tachylyte, a mafic volcanic glass, while the material is obviously

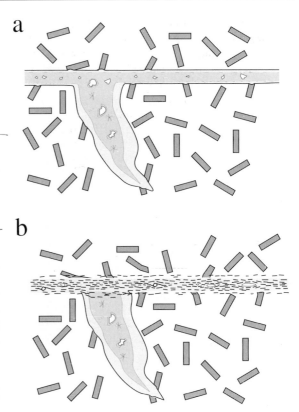

Fig. 5.3. a Schematic drawing of a typical pseudotachylyte with generation surface, injection vein, internal compositional banding and typical inclusions. The boundary with the wall rock is sharp. Mica grains in the wall rock show corrosion along the contact with pseudotachylyte. **b** Pseudotachylyte in which the generation surface has been reactivated as a mylonite zone. The mylonite can be recognised as a former pseudotachylyte by its fine-grained homogeneous nature and the presence of injection vein relics

not of volcanic origin. Pseudotachylyte has a number of characteristic geometric features which usually allow its distinction from other brittle fault rock types. It is composed of a dark matrix material with minor inclusions of mineral or wall rock fragments (Figs. 5.3–5.5). It usually occurs in a characteristic geometrical setting of a planar *generation surface*, up to a few mm thick and irregular *injection veins* which branch from the generation surface into the wall rock (Figs. 5.1, 5.3, 5.4). Generation surfaces are usually planar fractures up to a few centimetres wide that occur as straight bands in outcrop. Occasionally, they occur as pairs of parallel surfaces, connected by injection veins. Generation surfaces can be difficult to spot in the field, especially if they lie parallel to older layering or foliation; injection veins are more conspicuous and allow recognition of pseudotachylyte in outcrop.

Fig. 5.4. Pseudotachylyte in a foliated amphibolite. The foliation is cut by the pseudotachylyte. A generation surface transects the rock *from top right to lower left.* An injection vein occurs at *left.* Isolated fragments lie in a dark pseudotachylyte matrix. Boundaries between pseudotachylyte and wall rock are sharp. Paine, South Chile. Width of view 14 mm. PPL

Pseudotachylyte veins have distinct, sharp and (for generation surfaces) straight boundaries with the wall rock. They never show transitional zones of decreasing brittle deformation intensity towards the wall rock as in the case of cataclasite or breccia. The wall rock can be cataclased or faulted, but these structures are usually transected by the (younger) pseudotachylyte. Pseudotachylyte is thought to form by local melting of the rock along a brittle fault plane due to heat generated by rapid frictional sliding (10^{-2} to 1 m s^{-1}; Philpotts 1964; Sibson 1975, 1977a,b; Grocott 1981; Maddock 1986; Maddock et al. 1987; Spray 1987, 1992; Lin 1994). As such, pseudotachylyte generation is thought to be associated with seismic activity on faults. Melting at temperatures exceeding 1000 °C is thought to occur on the generation surface. Some of the melt may intrude minor faults which branch from the generation surface into the wall rock, and form injection veins (Figs. 5.1, 5.3a, 5.4). The small volume of melt formed in this way cools rapidly to the temperature of the host rock. As a result, the melt quenches to a glass or very fine-grained, aphanitic material which occurs along fault planes and adjacent branching injection veins (Figs. 5.3a, 5.4). Pseudotachylyte is normally not associated with growth of quartz- or calcite veins and generally occurs in massive, dry, low-porosity rocks such as granite, gneiss, gabbro and amphibolite. This is because the fluid present in porous rocks lowers the effective normal stress over a fault plane upon heating; consequently, not enough frictional heat can be produced to cause local melting. Therefore, pseudotachylyte is not normally found in porous sedimentary rocks (for a possible exception see Killick 1990). It is not found in marble because of the dissociation of carbonates at high temperature and the resulting decrease in normal stress over a fault, and the ductile flow in carbonates which inhibits build-up of high differential stress. It may seem curious that pseudotachylyte is a product of high temperature (melt generation) related to low temperature brittle fault zones, while such local melting is rare in higher-grade ductile shear zones. In brittle fault zones, however, elastic strain energy may be stored for a long period of time and is released in a matter of seconds in a small volume of rock along faults; in ductile shear zones, heat is dissi-

Fig. 5.5. Contact of a pseudotachylyte vein *(top)* and the wall rock *(bottom)*. The boundary is sharp where quartz and feldspar grains *(white)* are in contact with the matrix, but an embayment exists where a biotite grain *(centre)* is in contact. This structure is attributed to preferential corrosion of the biotite crystal by pseudotachylyte melt along an originally straight fracture surface. The biotite grain is strongly kinked, probably due to brittle deformation preceding pseudotachylyte generation. Vestfold Hills, Antarctica. Width of view 5 mm. PPL

pated continuously over a larger volume of rock and is therefore usually insufficient to cause a significant rise in temperature.

The matrix of pseudotachylyte is commonly dark brown, green or red and relatively homogeneous, but may contain a compositional layering of irregular thickness which follows the contours of the vein (Fig. 5.3a). This layering is commonly of a different colour along the vein wall and in the interior, and is interpreted to result from selective melting of the wall rock. The layering may be folded and folds are interpreted to have formed by fluid flow in the melt. Even sheath folds (Chap. 5.3.2) parallel to the displacement direction of the wall rock have been observed in the layering (Berlenbach and Roering 1992). Amygdales derived from gas bubbles are sometimes present in the matrix.

The mineral composition of inclusions in pseudotachylyte is commonly disproportional to the mineral composition of the wall rock; quartz and to a lesser extent feldspar are common as inclusions, while Fe-Mg rich Al-silicates are under-represented

(Figs. 5.3a, 5.4, 5.5; Maddock 1986; Maddock et al. 1987; Lin 1994). Micas are rarely present as inclusions. Quartz fragments have angular outlines with numerous internal fractures and fluid inclusion planes while fragments of feldspar, hornblende or pyroxene tend to be rounded. Where the contact of pseudotachylyte and wall rock is a straight fracture, as along generation surfaces, embayments of pseudotachylyte exist where micas or amphiboles were in contact with the pseudotachylyte matrix. The matrix of a pseudotachylyte differs from that of cataclasite or breccia in that the smallest size fragments are lacking and isolated fragments are contained in a relatively homogeneous matrix (cf. Figs. 5.2, 5.3a, 5.4, 5.5). All these features are attributed to preferential dissolution of Fe-Mg Al silicates and feldspar in the pseudotachylyte melt (Lin 1994). Another typical microstructure of pseudotachylyte is the presence of aggregates of small sulphide particles in larger quartz fragments.

Devitrification features or structures formed by growth from a melt are common in the matrix of pseudotachylytes (Maddock 1986; Maddock et al.

MISIDENTIFICATION OF PSEUDOTACHYLYTE

Some dark cataclasites and layers or veins filled with dark minerals such as chlorite or tourmaline resemble pseudotachylyte in the field and even in thin section. Pseudotachylyte differs from these rocks by (1) the sharp boundaries with the wall rock; (2) the occurrence of injection veins; (3) evidence for melting such as a relative scarceness of micas, pyroxene and hornblende as inclusions in the matrix and the corrosion of such minerals along vein contacts; (4) presence of spherulites and devitrification structures and (5) the absence of contemporaneous quartz or calcite veins. Most pseudotachylyte has a chemical composition almost identical to the host rock, while other veins or cataclasite zones will usually show a different composition.

5.3 Mylonite

5.3.1 Introduction

A *mylonite* is a foliated and usually lineated rock that shows evidence for strong ductile deformation and normally contains fabric elements with a monoclinic shape symmetry (Figs. 5.1, 5.6–5.8; Bell and Etheridge 1973; Hobbs et al. 1976; White et al. 1980; Tullis et al. 1982; Hanmer and Passchier 1991). Mylonite is a strictly structural term that refers only to the fabric of the rock and does not give information on the mineral composition. Mylonite should therefore not be used as a rock name in a stratigraphic sequence.

Mylonite occurs in high-strain zones known as *mylonite zones,* interpreted as exhumed, 'fossil' ductile shear zones. The contact of a mylonite zone and unaffected wall rock tends to be a gradual fabric transition. Grain size in the mylonite is usually smaller than that in the wall rock. (Fig. 5.8). Mylonite zones can occur in any rock type and have been described

1987; Lin 1994). They are similar to those observed in obsidian and include *spherulites* of feldspar or biotite, coronas of radially arranged idiomorphic small crystals of biotite or feldspar around inclusions, and small dendritic crystals of feldspar and rarely pyroxene (Clarke 1990).

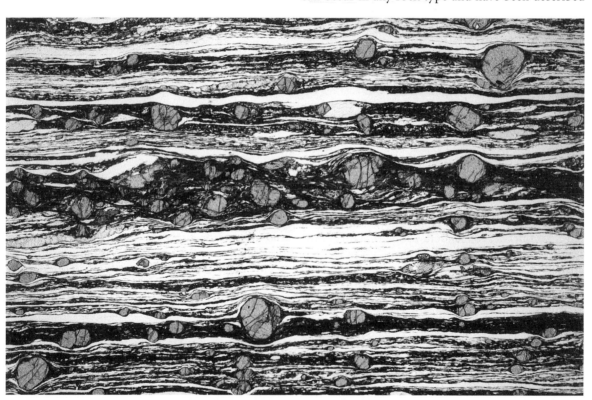

Fig. 5.6. Mylonite derived from pelitic gneiss with quartz, feldspar, garnet and micas, in a section parallel to the stretching lineation and normal to the foliation. Alternating layers rich in quartz *(clear)* and feldspar *(grey),* with porphyroclasts of garnet define the mylonitic foliation. Sense of shear indicators are poorly developed in this section but subtle stair-stepping (Chap. 5.6.5, 5.6.7) of wings on porphyroclasts and small C'-type shear bands (Chap. 5.6.4) indicate a dextral shear sense. Marsfjällen, Sweden. Width of view 13 mm. PPL

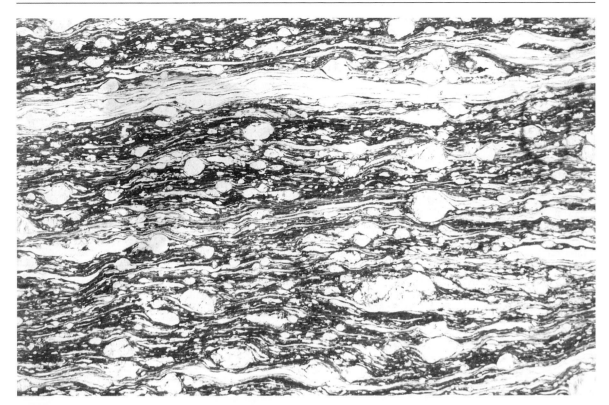

Fig. 5.7. Quartz-feldspar mylonite. Section parallel to the stretching lineation and normal to the foliation. Lenses of recrystallised quartz and feldspar define the mylonitic foliation. The foliation wraps around feldspar porphyroclasts. Minor shear bands (Sect. 5.6.4) define the sense of shear as sinistral. St. Barthélemy, Pyrenees, France. Width of view 10 mm. PPL

from a sub-millimetric scale to zones several km wide (Bak et al. 1975; Hanmer 1988). The intensity of deformation may vary from one mylonite zone to another but is always high. The word 'mylonite' derives from the Greek 'μυλων' (a mill) since the original opinion on these rocks was that they formed by brittle 'milling' of the rock (Lapworth 1885). However, present use of the word mylonite refers to rocks dominantly deformed by ductile flow, while brittle deformation may play a minor role in isolated included lenses or grains (Bell and Etheridge 1973; Tullis et al. 1982); in other words, the stress-supporting network is affected by crystalplastic deformation (Chap. 3.8).

5.3.2 Characteristic Fabric Elements

Mylonites can be recognised in the field by their small grain size and strongly developed, unusually regular and planar foliations (Figs. 5.6–5.8) and straight lineations. Lenses and layers of fine-grained material that are common in mylonites are thought to derive

from a more coarse-grained parent rock by intracrystalline deformation and recrystallisation. Such deformed lenses usually have a 'surf-board' shape defining both a planar and linear fabric element. This shape may be explained by common development of mylonites in a plane strain regime.

Many mylonites contain *porphyroclasts* (Figs. 5.5, 5.6; Box p. 104), remnants of resistant mineral grains of a size larger than grains in the matrix. The foliation in the matrix wraps around porphyroclasts (Figs. 5.6, 5.7, 5.9, 11.1, 11.8, 11.9). Porphyroclasts develop because of a difference in rheology between constituent minerals; relatively 'hard' minerals will form porphyroclasts, while relatively soft ones form part of the matrix. However, porphyroclasts do not always form in the same minerals, since rheologic properties of minerals depend on metamorphic conditions and initial grainsize (Chap. 3.12).

The planar fabric element of mylonites is known as a *planar shape fabric* or more specifically as a *mylonitic foliation* (Box p. 70); the linear fabric element is known as a *linear shape fabric* or *stretching*

PORPHYROCLASTS AND PORPHYROBLASTS

Porphyroclasts and porphyroblasts are relatively large, single crystals in a fine-grained matrix. The word porphyroclast is also used for a rounded polycrystalline rock fragment in a more fine-grained matrix. Porphyroclasts (from 'clasis' – breaking) are inferred to have formed by diminution of the grain size in the matrix. They are therefore typical for mylonites and cataclasites; they are relic structures of a more coarse-grained original fabric. The word *clast* is often used as a short equivalent commonly with the constituent mineral as a prefix (feldspar clast). Common minerals that form porphyroclasts are feldspar, garnet, muscovite, hornblende and pyroxenes. Quartz forms porphyroclasts only in very special cases (Chap. 3.13.3; Figs. 3.5, 3.6). Porphyroclasts should not be confused with detrital clasts in sediments. Porphyroblasts (from 'blasis' – growth) are inferred to have formed by growth of crystals of specific mineral species, while crystals in the matrix did not grow to the same extend (cf. Chap. 7). The word *blast* is commonly used as a short equivalent. They are common in non-mylonitic phyllites and schists. In some cases, original porphyroblasts in a schist or gneiss may become porphyroclasts when the schist or gneiss is mylonitised (Fig. 11.15).

lineation (Fig. 5.9). Low-strain lenses around which the shape fabric anastomoses occur in most mylonites (Fig. 5.9), from lozenge-shaped single feldspar crystals (Figs. 5.7, 5.11) to km-scale lenses.

Well developed stretching lineations are mainly found in polymineralic rocks where grain size reduction has taken place; in fine-grained monomineralic rocks or at high-grade conditions, dynamic recrystallisation may inhibit development of a linear shape fabric. In high-grade rocks, mineral lineations are therefore common.

Mylonites commonly contain two or even three foliations, inclined to each other at small angles, that are thought to have developed contemporaneously (Fig. 5.9). These are further explained in Chapter 5.6. Quartz, calcite and feldspar commonly also show evidence of lattice preferred orientation (Chap. 4.16). Foliations in mylonite are locally subject to tight or isoclinal folding (Figs. 1.2, 5.9, 11.6, 11.8). In most cases, the axial planar foliation in these folds cannot be distinguished from the main foliation in the mylonite; this indicates that such folds should not be

Fig. 5.8. Zone of ultramylonite with straight internal layering *(left)* in a coarse-grained host rock composed of quartz, feldspar and biotite. Section parallel to the stretching lineation and normal to the foliation. A minor mylonite zone transects the *centre* of the photograph. Along this zone deflection of the foliation in the wall rock indicates dextral sense of shear. Pernambuco, Brazil. Width of view 8 mm. CPL

regarded as the effect of a separate phase of deformation affecting an older mylonitic fabric, but as an effect of a local distortion in the flow field during mylonite genesis (Chap. 2.5; Cobbold and Quinquis 1980). Some of these folds are *sheath folds,* that is, they have a tubular shape parallel to the mylonite lineation (Fig. 5.9; Cobbold and Quinquis 1980; Lacassin and Mattauer 1985). Others are non-tubular but cylindrical with a straight fold axis parallel to the lineation; these are known as *oblique folds* (Fig. 5.9; Passchier 1986a). Oblique folds commonly decrease in amplitude and fade out laterally (Fig. 5.9).

An important characteristic of many mylonites is a clear difference in geometry of structures in thin sections cut normal and parallel to the mylonitic lineation (Fig. 5.9). In sections normal to the lineation, the rock may seem relatively undeformed or structures have orthorhombic symmetry (Fig. 3.22); in sections parallel to the lineation, the deformation fabric is usually much stronger, and structures with monoclinic symmetry are visible which may be used as shear sense indicators (Chap. 5.5-5.7). Characteristic is the curved shape and decreasing intensity of mylonitic foliations away from the core of the shear

most 'o' rx is:
ductile def.

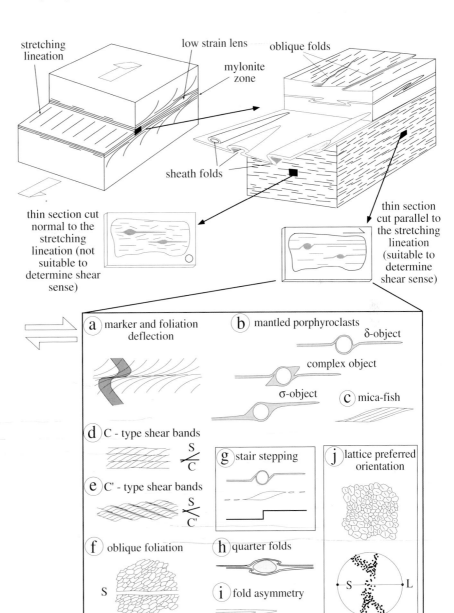

Fig. 5.9. Schematic diagram showing the geometry of a mylonite zone and the nomenclature used. For thin sections parallel to the stretching lineation, the most common types of shear sense indicators are shown. Further explanation in text. This Figure is schematic and does not show all possible geometries. Other Figures in this chapter show more detail

zone (Fig. 5.9, at left). The overall monoclinic symmetry of mylonite zones and of fabric elements in them reflect the monoclinic symmetry of non-coaxial flow in a shear zone.

It is sometimes difficult to decide if a certain strongly deformed rock in an isolated outcrop should be called a mylonite. In such cases it is important to use good illustrations in publications.

5.3.3 Mylonite Classification

Mylonites are classified according to the metamorphic grade at which deformation took place (e.g. high-grade mylonite) or according to the lithotype or mineralogy in which they are developed (e.g. quartzite-mylonite, granodiorite-mylonite, quartz-feldspar mylonite). If mylonite develops in a monomineralic rock it is referred to as calcite-mylonite, quartz-mylonite etc. Another commonly used classification of mylonites is based on the percentage of matrix as compared to porphyroclasts (e.g. Spry 1969; Sibson 1977b). Rocks with 10–50% matrix are classified as *protomylonites* (Fig. 5.8, right hand side); with 50–90% matrix as mylonites (or mesomylonites; e.g. Figs. 5.6, 5.7) and rocks with over 90% matrix as *ultramylonites* (Fig. 5.8 at left; Fig. 11.6). The problem with this classification is that an arbitrary limit has to be defined between matrix grain size and porphyroclast grain size. Another problem is that mylonites developed at high metamorphic grade or in fine-grained or monomineralic parent rocks do not normally develop porphyroclasts; for this reason, ultramylonite does not necessarily represent a higher strain than mylonite or protomylonite. Other commonly used terminology is *blastomylonite* for a mylonite with significant static recrystallisation and *phyllonite* for a fine-grained mica-rich mylonite (resembling a phyllite). Some authors use the term phyllonite as a synonym for ultramylonite.

5.3.4 Dynamics of Mylonite Development

The relatively high finite strain values reached in mylonites imply that strain rate in the mylonite zone must have exceeded that in the wall rock for some time, and that the material in the zone must have been 'softer' than the wall rock. Nevertheless, many mylonites have the same chemical and mineral composition as the wall rock. Apparently, changes occur in the rheology of material in a ductile shear zone after its nucleation. This effect is known as *softening*

or *strain-softening* (Chap. 2.12). The most important mechanisms that contribute to softening are (White et al. 1980; Tullis et al. 1990):

1. A decrease in grain size, which enhances activity of grain size-dependent deformation mechanisms such as diffusion creep and grain boundary sliding (Chap. 3.9; Fig. 3.32; White et al. 1980; Schmid et al. 1977). This decrease in grain size is caused by the fact that the size of new grains formed by dynamic recrystallisation is a function of differential stress (Chap. 8.6.1).

2. Grain boundary migration-recrystallisation which replaces hardened crystals by new, easily deformable crystals without dislocation tangles (Fig. 3.17a). Notice that subgrain rotation recrystallisation (Fig. 3.17b) will not lead directly to softening since new grains have the same dislocation density as the old ones (Tullis et al. 1990).

3. Growth of new minerals which are more easily deformable than minerals of the host rock (reaction softening; Mitra 1978; White et al. 1980). The replacement of feldspars by aggregates of white mica and quartz is an example.

4. Development of a lattice-preferred orientation of mineral grains which places them in a position for easy dislocation glide (geometric softening).

5. Enhanced pressure solution due to decrease in grain size and opening of voids and cracks (Rutter 1976; Stel 1981).

6. 'Hydrolythic' weakening of minerals due to diffusion of water into the lattice.

5.3.5 Mylonite and Metamorphic Conditions

The fabric of mylonites is strongly dependent on the lithotype and original structure of the rock in which it develops. Nevertheless, a general fabric gradient exists for all rock types with increasing metamorphic grade, depending on the rheology and melt temperature of constituent minerals (e.g. structures in granite mylonite formed at 400 °C may resemble those in peridotite mylonite formed at 800 °C). As an example, consider the effect of metamorphic grade on mylonitisation of a bimineralic rock with a mineral A that is 'hard' and a mineral B that is 'soft' at low-grade conditions due to a different number of active slip systems and differences in critical resolved shear stress (Chap. 2.3.4; compare feldspar-quartz in Chap. 3.13.2).

At very low grade, A and B deform by brittle fracturing and a brittle fault rock forms.

At low-grade conditions, A deforms in a brittle manner and B by dislocation creep. Differential stresses are high (Figs. 3.31, 5.1) and mylonites are therefore fine-grained with fragmented, angular porphyroclasts of A between ductilely deformed grains of B that wrap around the porphyroclasts. Foliations and lineations may be well developed. Mylonite zones tend to be narrow with sharp boundaries.

At medium grade, A and B both deform by crystalplastic processes, but A is still stronger than B. As a result, spectacular mylonites form with a mylonitic foliation containing fragments of partly recrystallised porphyroclasts of A. Most of the shear sense indicators mentioned in Chap. 5.6 can be recognised in mylonites formed under such conditions. Foliations and lineations are well developed. At high grade, the difference in rheology between A and B decreases, diffusion becomes more important and differential stresses are low. The result is a layered rock with few porphyroclasts and a relatively coarse grain size. Except from the layering, foliations and lineations are weakly developed. The rock may appear to be almost undeformed, but isoclinal folds in layering may show the intensity of strain. Such high-grade mylonites are also known as *striped gneiss* (Fig. 5.10). They may be recognised by elongate

recrystallised ribbons of B (Box. p. 70) and by few large porphyroclasts of A (e.g. Fig. 5.11), which are usually symmetric. In granitoid rocks, monocrystalline quartz ribbons and polycrystalline feldspar ribbons are common in such striped gneisses (Fig. 5.11).

The fabric gradient sketched above is generally valid for polymineralic rocks but metamorphic conditions of transitions depend on mineral composition of the parent rock. However, fabric is only a rough indicator and cannot be used alone to determine metamorphic grade in mylonites; this should be done using minerals which have grown or recrystallised during the deformation. Since mylonite zones may have a long history of reactivation, relics of older fabrics may be present in low strain lenses. It is tempting to use these low strain lenses to determine the metamorphic conditions of mylonite genesis because of the large, weakly deformed crystals they contain, but the results may commonly indicate metamorphic conditions prior to mylonitisation. Another factor that has to be taken into account is static recrystallisation, which may re-equilibrate minerals in mylonites after deformation.

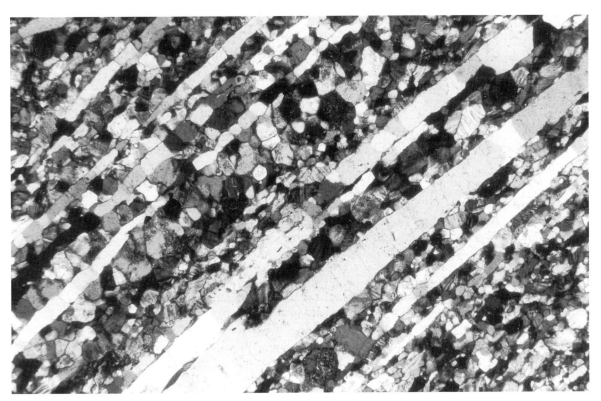

Fig. 5.10. Striped gneiss, composed of alternating layers of recrystallised feldspar and quartz ribbons. Some of the quartz ribbons contain strongly elongated single crystals, probably formed by grain boundary migration within the ribbon. Section parallel to the stretching lineation and normal to the foliation. Tres Rios, Rio de Janeiro State, Brazil. Width of view 2.3 mm. CPL

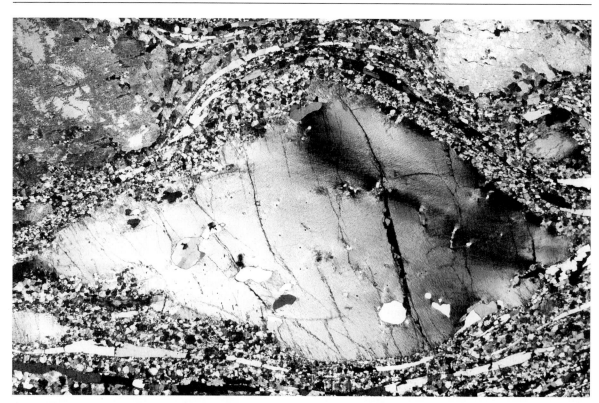

Fig. 5.11. K-feldspar porphyroclast with undulose extinction. A mantle of recrystallised feldspar with isolated polycrystalline quartz ribbons surrounds the porphyroclast. Notice the strongly elongated single crystals of quartz in the ribbons. Section parallel to the stretching lineation and normal to the foliation. Tres Rios, Rio de Janeiro State, Brazil. Width of view 10 mm. CPL

5.4 Complex Fault Rocks

Since many shear zones have a long period of activity or can be reactivated, several fault rock types can overprint in a single shear zone. Most common are brittle fault rocks which transect mylonite, since mylonite forms at depth and has to pass the field of brittle fracturing before it reaches the surface (Grocott 1977; Strehlau 1986; Scholz 1988; Passchier et al. 1990a). Such overprinting by brittle structures is usually easy to recognise. However, it may be difficult to tell apart a low-grade mylonite where some minerals were deformed by brittle fracturing from a mylonite overprinted by cataclasite formation. These situations can be distinguished because cataclasite will transect all minerals in the mylonite, usually along narrow zones.

A less common type of interference is ductile deformation of brittle fault rocks. Ductilely deformed cataclasite or breccia can be difficult to recognise if the ductile overprint is strong. Some pseudotachylyte veins have undergone ductile deformation after their solidification; these are more easy to recognise, even after strong ductile overprint. In fact, pseudotachylyte veins seem to act as the preferred nucleation sites of mylonite zones in many locations (Fig. 5.3b; Allen 1979; Sibson 1980; Passchier 1982b, 1984; Passchier et al. 1990a). The recognition of ductilely deformed pseudotachylyte is important, since the presence of a brittle deformation phase is an indication for either deformation at shallow crustal depth, or unusually high strain rates (Passchier et al. 1990a).

Evidence for weak ductile deformation of pseudotachylyte is the presence of flattened inclusions and a mica-preferred orientation in the matrix (Passchier 1982b, 1984). Strongly deformed pseudotachylyte veins are difficult to distinguish from thin ultramylonite zones which lack a brittle predecessor. Indications may be an unusual ultra fine-grained (<5 μm) homogeneous matrix of biotite, quartz and feldspar with isolated porphyroclasts of quartz, but fewer or no clasts of other minerals, the presence of sulphide aggregates in quartz inclusions, and sharp boundaries of ultramylonite with the wall rock (Passchier 1982a, 1984). Ductile deformation of pseudotachylyte is usually restricted to the generation surfaces, and injection veins may be less deformed and still recognisable; if a suspicion exists that a mylonite may have a pseudotachylyte predecessor, the presence of injection veins should be investigated in the field or in hand specimen. Any narrow, dark mylonite zone in metamorphic rocks should be checked for relics of pseudotachylyte structures.

Ductile deformation of pseudotachylyte may be caused by a separate tectonic event after increase in metamorphic conditions to the depth where the rock deforms ductilely (Passchier et al. 1990a), or by ductile deformation at the level where the pseudotachylyte formed; the latter could happen in the transition zone between dominant ductile deformation and brittle fracturing (Fig. 5.1; Sibson 1980; Passchier 1982b, 1984). A pseudotachylyte vein may rapidly crystallise into a fine-grained aggregate under such conditions. At the high differential stress level sustained at these conditions, a fine-grained aggregate such as a crystallised pseudotachylyte may deform ductilely by diffusion-assisted grain boundary sliding while the coarse-grained wall rock is rigid (Chap. 3.14; Sibson 1980; Passchier 1982b, 1984).

It has to be kept in mind that mylonites, like other metamorphic rocks, record mainly peak and retrograde metamorphic conditions. Brittle faulting or early mylonitisation that predates these conditions may be completely obliterated by recrystallisation. Important early thrust structures in many metamorphic terrains do not contain any brittle fault rocks due to this process.

5.5 Sense of Shear

5.5.1 Introduction

The direction of movement on a shear zone is usually assumed to lie subparallel to striations, slickenfibres or stretching and mineral lineations. Once this direction is established, it is necessary to determine the sense of displacement (sinistral or dextral, normal or reverse) or *sense of shear*. Traditionally, this was mainly done using markers in the wall rock such as displaced layering and dykes or deflection of layering or foliation into a shear zone (Chap. 5.5.2, 5.5.3). Additionally, the geometry of structures in the zone can be

used to determine sense of shear. This means that it is possible to determine shear sense for a shear zone in thin section, even without seeing the zone in the field. Microstructures that can be used to determine shear sense in mylonite are described in Chap. 5.6. Some microstructures can also be used to determine shear sense for brittle fault rocks in thin section. These are discussed in Chap. 5.7.

5.5.2 Displacement and Deflection of Markers

The simplest and best known sense of shear indicator is the displacement of markers such as dykes, veins, xenoliths and bedding over a shear zone. Commonly, there is also a deflection of markers near the zone, due to a strain gradient. Interpretation of both structures is straightforward in the case of a linear marker, or if the movement direction is normal to a planar marker (Fig. 5.9a). Notice, however, that in other cases the apparent offset on an outcrop surface or in a thin section may give the wrong sense of shear (Fig. 5.12; Wheeler 1987b).

5.5.3 Foliation Curvature

Foliated ductile shear zones may show a gradient in foliation development from an undeformed wall rock towards the core of the zone; the foliation has a

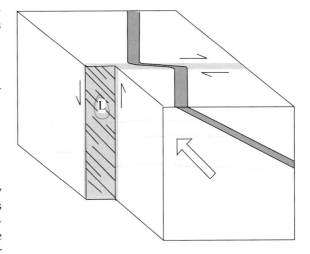

Fig. 5.12. Schematic presentation of a shear zone illustrating how deflection of a marker can give the wrong sense of shear if not used in a section parallel to the movement direction (here marked by a lineation *L*); the frontal block moves up and to the left, but the deflected layer indicates an apparent sinistral displacement on a horizontal surface

CAUTION!

characteristic curved shape that can be used to determine sense of shear (Fig. 5.9a). This structure develops if the foliation is 'passive' (Chap. 4.10.2) and reflects the orientation of the finite strain axes (Chap. 4.10.2); the curvature reflects a gradient in finite strain from its peak in the core of a shear zone outwards (Chap. 8.2). It develops because foliations rotate from a position between the instantaneous extension axis and the fabric attractor towards the latter with increasing strain in non-coaxial progressive deformation (Ramsay and Graham 1970; Ramsay 1980a).

Foliation curvature is a reliable shear sense indicator if the movement direction, indicated by a lineation, is normal to the axis of curvature of the foliation. However, care should be taken not to confuse it with deflection of an older foliation, where the movement direction may be oblique to the axis of curvature of the foliation, in which case some sections through the structure may give the wrong shear sense (Chap. 5.5.2).

5.6 Microscopic Shear Sense Indicators in Mylonite

5.6.1 Introduction

One of the most characteristic properties of mylonites and some other rocks from ductile shear zones is that fabric elements and structures show monoclinic shape symmetry (Fig. 5.9). This effect is a result of the non-coaxial progressive deformation in shear zones due to relative displacement of the wall rocks. Lineations, finite strain axes and most foliations rotate towards the fabric attractor, which is oblique to the extensional ISA (Chap. 2.9) and their sense of rotation usually equals the sense of shear. Since different fabric elements track the fabric attractor to different degrees, complex structures with a distinct monoclinic shape symmetry (in the literature usually referred to as an *asymmetry*) develop in mylonites. This asymmetry can be used to deduce sense of shear. We distinguish *internal and external asymmetry* for either single objects and fabric elements, or combinations of fabric elements with a characteristic monoclinic shape symmetry. A similar terminology is used for LPO patterns (Chap. 4.14). With internal asymmetry we mean that the object itself has an asymmetry

without the need to involve other fabric elements or a reference frame; with external asymmetry we mean that the orientation of the object with respect to other fabric elements determines its asymmetry. This section describes the most common monoclinic microstructures, and explains how sense of shear can be derived from them.

In order to determine shear sense in a mylonite zone, thin sections should be properly oriented. Sections normal to the symmetry axis of shear sense markers give best results. This symmetry axis will be near the vorticity axis for flow in the shear zone. In most mylonite zones, this axis lies subparallel to the intermediate strain axis. This means, that a hand specimen should be sectioned parallel to the stretching or mineral lineation and normal to the compositional layering or main foliation (Fig. 5.9). Problems may arise when several lineations and foliations are present: this is usually due to overprinting of several deformation phases. In this case, it will be necessary to reconstruct the deformation sequence first, then to decide which phase is of interest: usually, sense of shear can only be determined for the last phase. Obviously, only oriented samples should be used to determine shear sense.

In crustal mylonite zones which developed under low- to medium-grade metamorphic conditions, a large number of sense-of-shear markers are available, and most are empirically established. (Reviews are given by Bouchez et al. 1983; Simpson and Schmid 1983; Passchier 1986a; Hanmer and Passchier 1991). The most important ones visible in thin section are shown schematically in Fig. 5.9 and are discussed below; *All observations are for sections parallel to the stretching lineation and normal to the foliation. In all other sections the structures either show a less pronounced monoclinic symmetry, or orthorhombic and higher symmetry.*

5.6.2 Foliation Orientation

Many shear zones do not show foliation curvature (Chap. 5.5.3) as in Fig. 5.9a, but have sharp boundaries with the wall rock. The orientation of 'passive' foliations such as mylonitic foliation in such shear zones, however, is commonly slightly oblique to the shear zone boundary. (Fig. 5.9a; Ramsay and Graham 1970; Simpson and Schmid 1983). This external asymmetry is due to rotation of the foliation towards the fabric attractor in non-coaxial flow, and has the same external asymmetry as the foliation gradient discussed in Chapter 5.5.2.

5.6.3 Oblique Foliations

In mylonites, several foliations with different orientation may be present. If they develop during mylonite genesis, they are good shear sense indicators. An example is one foliation oblique to another. Aggregates of small grains in mylonites (usually formed by dynamic recrystallisation) can be characterised by a slightly elongate shape of most of the grains (Means 1981; Lister and Snoke 1984). The elongate grains commonly define a shape fabric oblique to compositional layering or mica preferred orientation in a mylonite (Fig. 5.9f). The relation between shear sense and geometry of such an *oblique foliation* is as shown schematically in Figs. 4.31c and 5.9f. Examples are shown in Figs. 5.19, 5.21, 5.27). Oblique foliations have been reported for quartz (Law et al. 1984; Lister and Snoke 1984; Dell'Angelo and Tullis 1989), carbonates (de Bresser 1989), olivine (van der Wal et al. 1992) and rock analogues such as ice (Burg et al. 1986) and octachloropropane (Jessell 1986; Ree 1991). They are assumed to develop by an interplay of passive flattening and rotation of grains in non-coaxial flow, and grain boundary migration which destroys the developing shape fabric (Fig. 4.31c; Means 1981; Ree 1991). In this way, the foliation will remain fixed in orientation with respect to the kinematic frame of progressive deformation, usually at an angle of 20–40° to the fabric attractor (Dell'Angelo and Tullis 1989; Ree 1991;

Fig. 4.31c). The actual angle probably depends on the efficiency of fabric-developing and fabric destroying processes (Hanmer 1984a). For olivine, an alternative mechanism of kinking and grain boundary migration has been proposed (van der Wal et al. 1992).

Oblique foliations occur mostly in monomineralic layers of quartz and calcite in layered low- to medium-grade mylonites (Fig. 5.27); examples of polymineralic oblique foliations are less common, and occur mainly in medium- to high-grade mylonites (Hanmer and Passchier 1991); an example is the mica-preferred orientation (S_m; Fig. 5.21) oblique to the mylonitic compositional layering observed in some micaceous mylonites (Passchier 1982a). In ultramylonites such an oblique foliation is common and visible under crossed polarisers as a preferential extinction of the matrix at an angle of less than 5° to the layering. Such oblique foliations result from the fact that some fabric elements (elongated new quartz grains, micas) rotated through a smaller angle than the mylonitic foliation during non-coaxial progressive deformation.

5.6.4 Shear Band Cleavages

A mica-preferred orientation or compositional layering may be transected at a small angle by sets of subparallel minor shear zones (Figs. 5.9d–e, 5.13–5.16). Such minor shear zones are known as *shear*

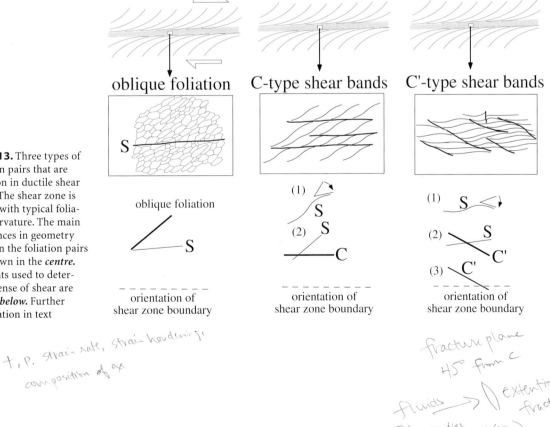

Fig. 5.13. Three types of foliation pairs that are common in ductile shear zones. The shear zone is shown with typical foliation curvature. The main differences in geometry between the foliation pairs are shown in the **centre.** Elements used to determine sense of shear are shown **below.** Further explanation in text

oblique foliation

C-type shear bands

C'-type shear bands

oblique foliation

orientation of shear zone boundary

orientation of shear zone boundary

orientation of shear zone boundary

DIFFERENCE BETWEEN COMPRESSIONAL (NORMAL) CRENULATION CLEAVAGE AND SHEAR BAND CLEAVAGE

Shear band cleavage (Fig. 5.13) and compressional crenulation cleavage (Figs. 4.11, 4.14, 4.17) have a similar geometry and could be confused by a casual observer. Nevertheless, they have a different morphology and kinematic significance. We outline some morphological and kinematic differences below.

Compressional crenulation cleavage (ccc)	Shear band cleavage (sbc)
Morphology	
Angles between older foliation and ccc generally between 45° and 90°	Angle between older foliation and sbc less than 45°
Folds in older foliation have a large amplitude with respect to ccc spacing	Folds in older foliation have a small amplitude with respect to sbc spacing
ccc Planes irregular but penetrative	sbc Planes smooth and short, commonly anastomosing
Host rock is usually a folded phyllite	Host rock is usually a mylonite or phyllonite
Kinematics	
ccc Develop at a high angle (close to 90°) to the bulk shortening direction and represent a foliation approaching the fabric attractor	sbc Develops oblique to the bulk shortening direction and represents a zone of enhanced non-coaxial flow
Usually a shortening component normal to ccc	Usually an extension component normal to sbc

bands and the complete structure is a *shear band cleavage* (White 1979b; Gapais and White 1982). Shear band cleavage may superficially resemble crenulation cleavage but develops by extension of the older foliation rather than shortening. Some authors (e.g. Platt and Vissers 1980) therefore use the terms 'compressional' crenulation cleavage (as treated in Chap. 4), and *extensional crenulation cleavage* for shear band cleavage. Geometric differences between these two groups of structures are given in the Box above.

Two types of shear band cleavage are distinguished: *C-type* and *C'-type* (Figs. 5.9d-e, 5.13). In the literature, this distinction is not always made. Our C- and C'-type shear band cleavage correspond to C- and C'-bands of Berthé et al. (1979a,b). C'-type equals extensional crenulation cleavage of Platt and Vissers (1980); we favour the term C'-type because it is older and non-genetic.

C'-type shear band cleavage is oblique to shear zone boundaries and to the older foliation in micaceous mylonites (Figs. 5.14, 5.15; White 1979b; Platt and Vissers 1980). The angle between the shear bands and the shear zone margin is 15–35° (Dennis and Secor 1987; Passchier 1991b; Blenkinsop and Treloar 1995). C'-type shear band cleavage develops mainly in strongly foliated mylonites such as phyllonites and

mylonitic micaschists; usually, shear bands fail to continue into more weakly foliated layers (e.g. quartz layers) in such rocks (Fig. 5.14). The shear bands are usually anastomosing, short and wavy (Figs. 5.13, 5.14). An older mylonitic foliation is cut by the shear bands and is deflected in the bands in the same way as foliation curvature in a large-scale shear zone (Chap. 5.5.3). The older foliation may contain isoclinal folds or other shear sense indicators. Normally, the intersection of the older foliation and the shear bands is normal to stretching or mineral lineations on both these surfaces. This is taken to indicate that both the older foliation and the shear band cleavage formed during the same event of mylonitic deformation. However, the C'-type shear band cleavage may have a deviant mineral composition, usually indicative of retrograde metamorphic conditions (McCaig 1987; Norrell et al. 1989). Commonly, only one set of C'-type shear bands is developed in fabrics but occasionally a second, less developed set may be present almost orthogonal to the main set (Fig. 5.13; Harris and Cobbold 1985; Behrmann 1987). Also, a younger set of shear bands may overprint an older set that has a more gentle inclination to the shear zone boundary (Platt and Vissers 1980; Passchier 1991b).

Development of C'-type shear band cleavage is

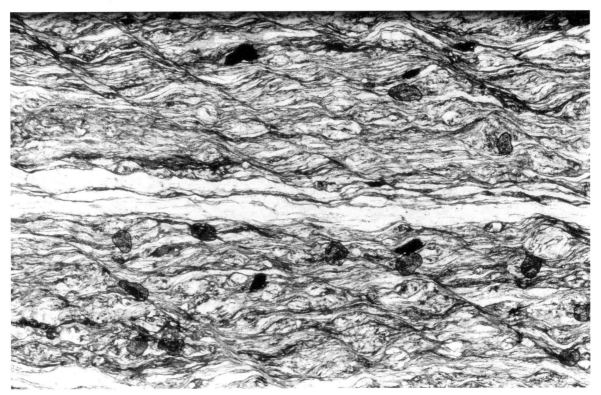

Fig. 5.14. C'-type shear band cleavage *(from upper left to lower right)* transecting the main foliation in a micaschist. Notice that the cleavage does not continue into the quartz ribbons in the *centre* of the photograph. Dextral shear sense. Menderes Massif, Turkey. Section parallel to the stretching lineation and normal to the foliation. Dark round patches are due to thin section preparation. Width of view 3.5 mm. PPL. (Photograph courtesy R. Hetzel)

only partly understood. It seems to develop late during shear zone activity after a strong mineral preferred orientation has already been established, and represents probably an energetically favourable flow partitioning in strongly anisotropic materials (Fig. 5.17; Platt and Vissers 1980; Platt 1984; Dennis and Secor 1987; Passchier 1991b). In an isotropic rock, two sets of conjugate shear bands would be expected around the shortening ISA; since the foliation in a mylonite lies between the extensional ISA and the fabric attractor, one of these potential shear band orientations makes a smaller angle with the foliation than the other. Strongly foliated mylonites may have a strong mechanical anisotropy which inhibits development of the steeper set (Fig. 5.17) and causes a decrease in the angle between the main set and the older foliation (Cobbold et al. 1971; Cobbold 1976; Platt and Vissers 1980).

The geometry of shear bands imposes a geometric limit on the possible flow regimes in mylonites during their growth; the segments between shear bands may have rotated synthetically or antithetically, dependent on the vorticity and volume change in a shear zone (Passchier 1991b). If microlithons between C'-type shear bands were rigid during C'-type cleavage development, the microlithons and shear bands must have rotated antithetically while the shear zone wall rock must have extended parallel to the zone (Fig. 5.17). There are indications that C'-type shear band cleavage is especially well developed in such 'stretching' shear zones (Passchier 1991b) and independent evidence from LPO analysis indicates that stretching shear zones may be common (Schmid 1994). If flow in a shear zone is a simple shear when C'-type shear bands form, the bands must have rotated synthetically and microlithons must have been deforming.

C-type shear band cleavage is part of a so-called C/S fabric (Fig. 5.13, 5.16) that consists of S planes (from French 'schistosité'), transected by planar distinct C-type shear bands or C planes (from French 'cisaillement', meaning shear; Berthé et al. 1979a,b; Vernon et al. 1983; Lister and Snoke 1984; Krohe 1990). C/S fabric is also written as S-C or C-S fabric in the

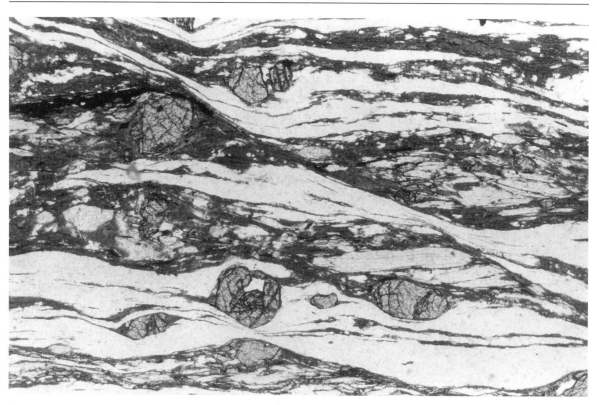

Fig. 5.15. C'-type shear bands in a quartz-feldspar-biotite-garnet mylonite, indicating dextral shear sense. Section parallel to the stretching lineation and normal to the foliation. Marsfjällen, Sweden. Width of view 4 mm. PPL

literature. The C-type shear bands in C/S fabric are parallel to shear zone boundaries (Figs. 5.9e, 5.13, 5.16) and relatively straight and continuous, unlike C'-type shear bands. C/S-fabric forms in weakly foliated mylonites with a small percentage of micas. It is most common in medium-grade shear zones and especially in deformed granites, where C-type shear bands anastomose around feldspar porphyroclasts. C-type

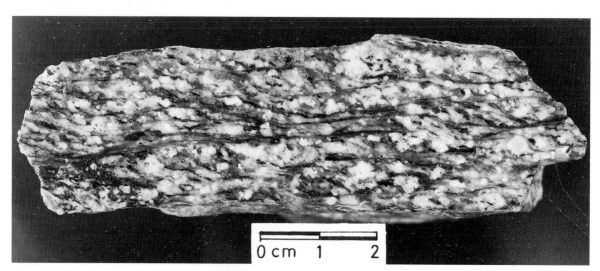

Fig. 5.16. Polished hand specimen showing a C/S fabric in granite. C-planes are *horizontal,* S planes trend *upper left to lower right* between C-planes. Shear sense is sinistral. Section parallel to the stretching lineation and normal to the foliation. South Armorican Shearzone, France

shear bands may nucleate at sites of high differential stress adjacent to feldspar porphyroclasts, and subsequently propagate and join up (Hanmer and Passchier 1991; Ildefonse and Mancktelow 1993).

C/S fabric probably reflects inhomogeneous simple shear. Contrary to C'-type shear band cleavage it may develop from the earliest stage of mylonite generation onward. The foliation in the microlithons probably continues developing while the shear bands grow, contrary to many C'-type shear band cleavages where the microlithons are probably rigid. C/S fabrics can be overprinted by C'-type shear band cleavage (Berthé et al. 1979b).

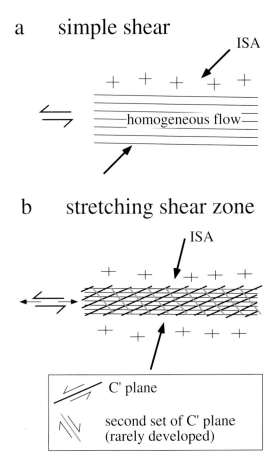

Fig. 5.17a,b. Schematic diagram showing the development of C'-type shear band cleavage with relatively rigid microlithons. The C'-type shear bands develop at a late stage of the shear zone activity after a foliation is well established. Shear bands can theoretically develop in two orientations, but only one, at a small angle to the foliation, is realised. Notice that the shortening direction must be relatively steep with respect to the shear zone and that the shear zone must be extending. Sinistral sense of shear

Lister and Snoke (1984) proposed a modification of the nomenclature and distinguished Type I and Type II C-S mylonites. Type I corresponds to C/S fabrics as described above, while Type II refers to sets of parallel shear bands without clear S planes. The principle example of Type II C-S mylonites used by Lister and Snoke (1984), however, refers to a stair-stepping of wings of small mica grains adjacent to mica-fish in quartzite mylonite (Chap. 5.6.7). They envisage that the wings represent C-type shear bands adjacent to the mica-fish. However, since such wings do not necessarily form by flow partitioning along shear bands (Chap. 5.6.7), we discourage the use of Type II C-S mylonite terminology.

Shear band cleavages have both internal and external asymmetry that can be used as shear sense indicators (e.g. Malavieille and Cobb 1986; Davis et al. 1987; Saltzer and Hodges 1988). The internal asymmetry is a sigmoidal shape of the older foliation between shear bands (Fig. 5.13,1); The external asymmetry is the angle between the enveloping surface of the older foliation and the shear bands (Fig. 5.13,2). C'-type shear band cleavage has an additional external asymmetry element since the shear bands are inclined to the shear zone in a characteristic way (Figs. 5.13,3, 5.14, 5.15). Shear sense in both C- and C'-type shear bands is synthetic with that of the main shear zone. The asymmetry of C'-type shear band cleavage is opposite to that of oblique foliation (Fig. 5.13).

5.6.5 Mantled Porphyroclasts

Porphyroclasts in a mylonite are commonly flanked by tapering grain aggregates which form a structural unit with the porphyroclast. If such aggregates have the same mineral composition as the porphyroclast, they are known as *mantles,* and the whole structure as a *mantled porphyroclast* (Fig. 5.9b). Mantled porphyroclasts are commonly composed of feldspar in a matrix of quartz-feldspar-mica, of orthopyroxene in peridotite and of dolomite in a calcite matrix. If the flanking aggregate consists of another mineral as the porphyroclast, it is known as a *strain shadow* (Chap. 6.3-6.5 and treated separately below).

Mantled porphyroclasts are interpreted to be a consequence of crystalplastic deformation and storage of dislocation tangles in the rim of a porphyroclast in response to flow in the matrix. The rim of the porphyroclast then recrystallises to a core-and-mantle structure (Box p. 37; White 1976). The fine-grained soft mantle can be deformed into *wings* (or tails) that extend on both sides of the porphyroclast parallel to the shape fabric in the mylonite (Passchier

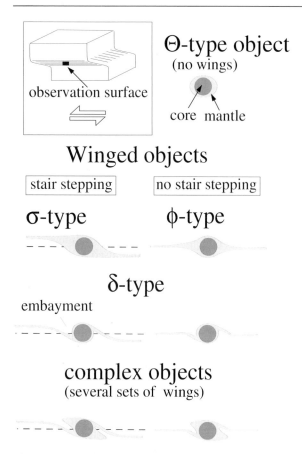

Θ-type object
(no wings)

core mantle

Winged objects

| stair stepping | no stair stepping |

σ-type   φ-type

δ-type

embayment

complex objects
(several sets of wings)

Fig. 5.18. Classification of mantled porphyroclasts. Sinistral sense of shear

and Simpson 1986). Wings are thought to stretch and change shape while the porphyroclast core remains rigid or continues to recrystallise in the rim, shrinking in size. Wing shape can be used as a shear sense indicator and as a rheology gauge (Chap. 8.3.4). Five types of mantled porphyroclasts have been distinguished in the literature (Hanmer 1984b; Passchier and Simpson 1986; Hooper and Hatcher 1988): Θ-type, φ-type, σ-type, δ-type, and complex objects (Figs. 5.18, 5.22, 9.5). Θ-type objects lack wings. φ-type objects have a mantle with orthorhombic symmetry (Passchier 1994). σ-type-, δ-type and complex objects have monoclinic shape symmetry. σ-type objects have wide mantles near the porphyroclast with two planar faces and two curved faces that define an internal asymmetry. The wings lie at different elevation on both sides. This difference in elevation is referred to as *stair-stepping* (Figs. 5.18, 5.19-5.22; Lister and Snoke 1984).

Passchier and Simpson (1986) distinguished σ_a- and σ_b-type porphyroclasts; the former occur isola-

ted in a mylonitic matrix; the second as part of developing C/S fabrics. δ-type objects have narrow wings and characteristic bends in the wings adjacent to the porphyroclast. As a result, two embayments of matrix material occur adjacent to the porphyroclast. Not all δ-type objects have stair-stepping (Fig. 5.18). Complex objects have more than one set of wings (Fig. 5.18).

σ_a-Type-, σ_b-type-, δ-type- and complex objects can be used as shear sense indicators using their internal asymmetry, and the stair-stepping of the wings. Stair-stepping is a useful shear sense indicator; the wings step up in the direction of movement of the upper block (Figs. 5.18, 5.19-5.22). However, care should be taken in inhomogeneous mylonite with many large porphyroclasts or low strain lenses; if a mantled porphyroclast lies between two large rigid objects, its asymmetry may reflect the relative movement of these two objects rather than the bulk shear sense in the shearzone. Therefore, mantled porphyroclasts are most reliable as shear sense indicators where they occur isolated in a fine-grained mylonitic matrix, e.g. in ultramylonite. δ-type- and complex objects mainly occur in high strain mylonites, while σ-type objects occur also at lower strain. φ-type objects are most common in high-grade mylonites. σ-type objects should not be confused with asymmetric strain shadows and strain fringes treated in Chapter 6.

5.6.6 Development of Mantled Porphyroclasts

Research into development of mantled porphyroclasts is still in progress, but this section serves to give an impression of the factors that play a role (Passchier and Simpson 1986; van den Driessche and Brun 1987; Passchier et al. 1993; Passchier 1994). Rigid objects in a non-coaxial flow will generally rotate with respect to flow-ISA, just as a paddle wheel inserted in a flowing river (Fig. 2.9). Even if the strain rate and vorticity of the flow are constant, the angular velocity of a rigid object may be fluctuating if the object is not a sphere (Ghosh and Ramberg 1976; Passchier 1987b). Elongate objects will accelerate and decelerate with changing orientation and, if the vorticity number is between that for pure and simple shear, may even become stationary in the flow when they exceed a critical aspect ratio (Box p. 119; Fig. 5.23; Ghosh and Ramberg 1976; Passchier 1987b). Rigid objects may also remain stationary with respect to flow-ISA if flow is strongly partitioned to form shear bands around the objects, as in the case of C/S fabrics (Passchier and Simpson 1986). σ_a- or φ-type objects

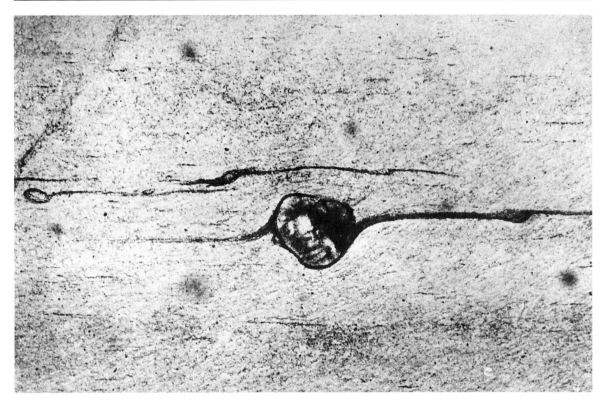

Fig. 5.19. Quartzite mylonite with a δ-type *(centre)* and small σ-type porphyroclasts of K-feldspar. All porphyroclasts show stair-stepping. A weak oblique foliation trends *from top right to bottom left.* Section parallel to the stretching lineation and normal to the foliation. Dextral shear sense. St. Barthélemy Massif, Pyrenees, France. Width of view 6 mm. PPL

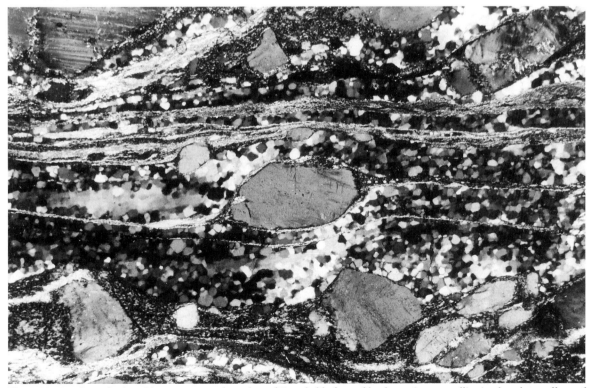

Fig. 5.20. Granite mylonite with a σ-type porphyroclast of K-feldspar *(centre)* in a matrix of recrystallised quartz. Feldspar porphyroclasts at the top are mantled by fine-grained dynamically recrystallised feldspar. The grain aggregate of quartz probably formed by dynamic recrystallisation but shows effects of static recrystallisation. Section parallel to the stretching lineation and normal to the foliation. Dextral shear sense. St. Barthélemy Massif, Pyrenees, France. Width of view 4 mm. CPL

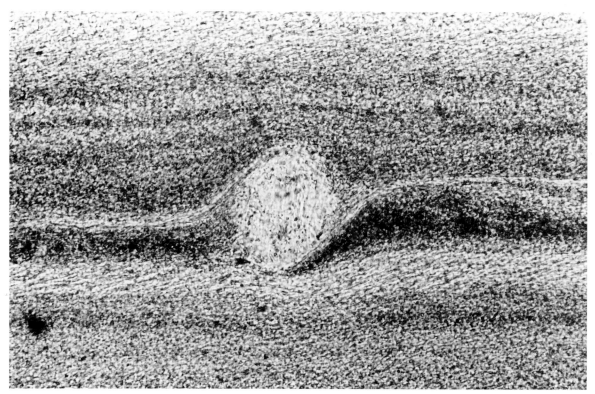

Fig. 5.21. δ-type mantled porphyroclast of K-feldspar in quartz-feldspar-mica mylonite. The object shows weak stair-stepping. A layer rich in white mica below the porphyroclast shows an oblique mica fabric. Section parallel to the stretching lineation and normal to the foliation. Dextral shear sense. St. Barthélemy Massif, Pyrenees, France. Width of view 0.3 mm. PPL

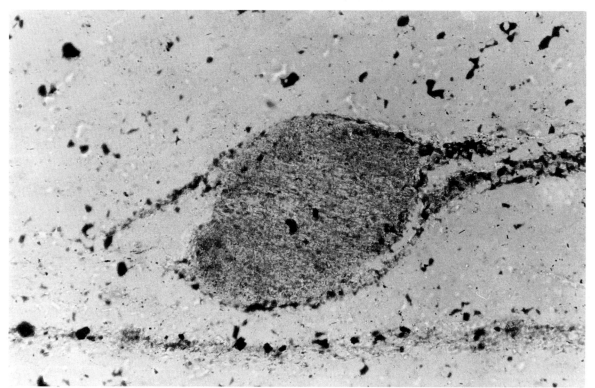

Fig. 5.22. Complex mantled porphyroclast of K-feldspar in quartzite mylonite. Section parallel to the stretching lineation and normal to the foliation. Dextral shear sense. St. Barthélemy Massif, Pyrenees, France. Width of view 2 mm. PPL

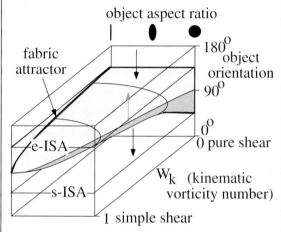
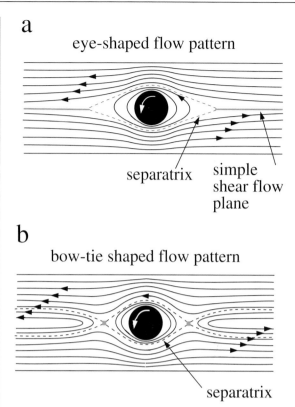

Fig. 5.24a,b. Perturbation of a simple shear flow pattern around a spherical rigid object in simple shear flow, in a plane normal to the vorticity vector. Two types have been reported: **a** eye-shaped and **b** bow-tie-shaped flow perturbations. A separatrix surface lies between elliptical displacement paths near the rigid object and open displacement paths further away

can form around stationary porphyroclasts, but no δ-type or complex objects (Passchier et al. 1993; Passchier 1994).

A porphyroclast in a flowing fine-grained matrix will cause a perturbation of the flow field, as shown in Fig. 5.24. With progressive deformation, particles adjacent to the porphyroclast move in ellipses, but further away the presence of the porphyroclast only causes a deflection of the displacement paths (Passchier et al. 1993). In simple shear, a boundary can be defined between the far field displacement paths and the elliptical paths, known as a *separatrix*. Experimental data (Passchier et al. 1993) show that the sepa-

ratrix around a spherical porphyroclast in simple shear flow can have an 'eye-shape' or a 'bow-tie shape' in a section normal to the rotation axis of the porphyroclast (Fig. 5.24). If a soft mantle exists around the porphyroclast, it will be deformed in the flow. The geometry of the deformed mantle depends, for a spherical porphyroclast, on the thickness of the mantle and the exact shape of the separatrix (Fig. 5.25). Wide mantles give rise to φ- or σ-type objects in eye or bow-tie shaped separatrices respectively (Figs. 5.20, 5.25c,f); thinner mantles to δ-type objects by wrapping of the wings around the rotating central porphyroclast (Figs. 5.19, 5.21, 5.25b,e); and very thin mantles give no wings at all (Θ-type objects, Fig. 5.25a,d; Passchier et al. 1993). Experimental evidence indicates that the shape of the separatrix depends on several factors such as the initial shape and orientation of the porphyroclast, the change of these factors with time, the rheology of the matrix, the vorticity and finite strain (Passchier and Sokoutis 1993; Pas-

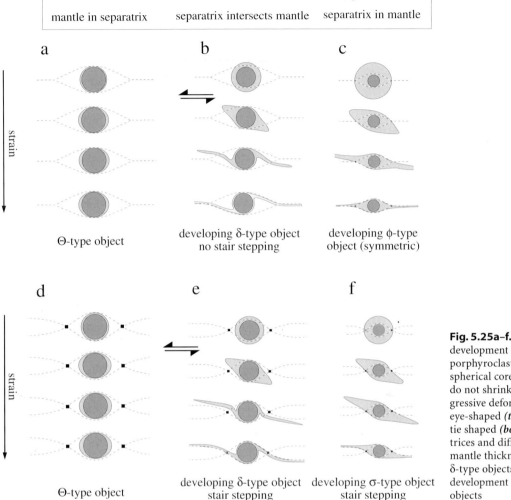

Fig. 5.25a–f. Idealised development of mantled porphyroclasts around spherical core objects which do not shrink during progressive deformation for eye-shaped *(top)*, and bow-tie shaped *(bottom)* separatrices and different initial mantle thickness. Note that δ-type objects start their development as σ-type objects

schier et al. 1993; Passchier 1994). It probably also depends on an 'isolation factor' of the porphyroclast in the shear zone, which is high when the porphyroclast is isolated in a relatively wide shear zone, and low if it lies in a relatively narrow shearzone or if porphyroclasts are close together (C. ten Brink, pers. comm. 1994). Despite these complications, a general trend can be given. For spherical porphyroclasts that do not change shape, a bow-tie-shaped separatrix seems to develop in non-Newtonian flow (power law flow; Chap. 2.12) and for a low isolation factor; an eye-shaped separatrix develops in Newtonian flow and if the isolation factor is high. Only a bow-tie shaped separatrix leads to stair-stepping (Passchier 1994). If the vorticity number is less than 1, stair-stepping will be less developed (Passchier 1988a). If the porphyroclast is recrystallising syntectonically, the separatrix

will shrink and σ-type objects will develop. If the porphyroclast has an elongate shape, the separatrix will change shape while the object rotates and secondary wings may form, resulting in complex objects (Figs. 5.18, 9.5); complex objects may also form where recrystallisation rate is irregular or if the porphyroclast starts recrystallising after a δ-type object was formed (Passchier and Simpson 1986; Passchier 1994). This effect is caused by the fact, that once a δ-type wing is established, no new material can be added from the porphyroclast to the wing; the material in the wing nearest to the porphyroclast is moving towards it, not away from it; if new recrystallised material is produced, new wings develop.

An important consequence of the model discussed above is that for exceptionally wide mantles and an eye-shaped separatrix, φ-type objects with approx-

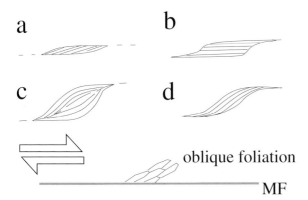

Fig. 5.26a–d. Schematic drawing of several common types of mica fish and their orientation relationship with mylonitic foliation (MF) and oblique foliation in a mylonite. All types show stair-stepping but have different internal symmetry. Convergence of lattice planes on an internal fault in **c** may be due to pressure solution

imately orthorhombic symmetry will develop at high strain in simple shear. Such conditions may occur at high metamorphic grade when diffusion-assisted deformation becomes important and may explain why many high-grade mylonites only have φ-type objects. φ-type objects therefore do not exclusively form in coaxial flow.

5.6.7 Mica-Fish

Single crystals of mica commonly have a lozenge shape and are known as mica fish (Figs. 5.9c, 5.26, 5.27; Eisbacher 1970; Choukroune and Lagarde 1977; Simpson and Schmid 1983; Lister and Snoke 1984; Goldstein 1988). They are most common in micaceous quartzite mylonite and ultramylonite. Mica fish lie with their long axis in the extensional quadrant of the deformation and show a steeper inclination to the fabric attractor than mylonitic foliation (Figs. 5.26, 5.27). Many mica fish have a monoclinic shape symmetry with one curved and one planar side that can be used as a shear sense indicator (Figs. 5.26, 5.27). Commonly, trails of small mica fragments extend into the matrix from the tips of isolated mica-fish (Fig. 5.27; Lister and Snoke 1984). These trails usually show stair-stepping (Chap. 5.6.5) which can also be used as a shear sense indicator. Basal planes of the micas are

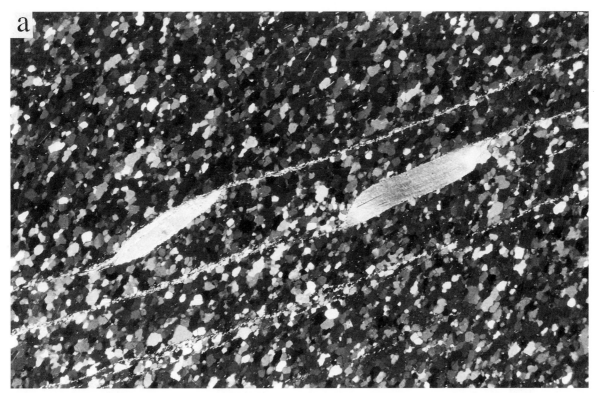

Fig. 5.27a–d. Mica fish of different type as shown schematically in Fig. 5.26 from a quartzite mylonite. Most mica-fish show stair-stepping of wings of mica fragments. Quartz in the matrix is dynamically recrystallised and developed an oblique foliation. Dextral shear sense. Minas Gerais, Brazil. Width of view **a, b, c** 4 mm; **d** 1 mm. CPL

Fig. 5.27b

Fig. 5.27c

Fig. 5.27d

usually in the direction of the long axis of the fish (Figs. 5.26a,c,d, 5.27b,c,d), but may be parallel to the planar sides (Figs. 5.26b, 5.27a). Little is known about the evolution of mica fish, but their development probably results from combined slip on the basal plane, rigid body rotation, boudinage and recrystallisation at the edges (Lister and Snoke 1984). Mica fish have been shown empirically to be reliable shear sense indicators.

Single mica grains can develop into mica fish, but polycrystalline mica layers in quartzite or marble can develop into polycrystalline *foliation fish*. These structures can have a similar shape as mica fish but are commonly bordered by shear bands (Fig. 11.7). They can be used as a shear sense indicator.

In some cases, other minerals such as kyanite and feldspars (Passchier 1982a) can show a similar geometry as mica fish, probably with a similar kinematic significance.

5.6.8 Quarter Structures

Porphyroclasts without mantles may show an asymmetric distribution of microstructures over the four quarters defined by the foliation and its normal; such structures have been named quarter structures (Fig. 5.28; Hanmer and Passchier 1991). Quarter structures are geometrical features that do not need to coincide with flow symmetry axes. Several types of quarter structures have been described and have been empirically established as shear sense indicator:

Quarter folds. Microfolds in the quarters that lie in the extensional direction are known as *quarter folds* (Fig. 5.28; Hanmer and Passchier 1991). Quarter folds probably develop by rotation of layering into the extension field of flow when passing the top of a porphyroclast during progressive deformation.

Quarter mats. Mica concentrations adjacent to a porphyroclast in the quarters that lie in the shortening direction are known as quarter mats (Hanmer and Passchier 1991). These probably form by preferential removal of quartz by solution transfer at stress concentration sites adjacent to a porphyroclast.

Asymmetric myrmekite. Myrmekite is commonly concentrated in shortening quarters in the rim of K-feldspar crystals (Chap. 7.8.3; Simpson 1985; Simpson and Wintsch 1989). These probably form by preferential proceeding of the K-feldspar breakdown reaction at sites of high differential stress (Simpson and

quarter structures

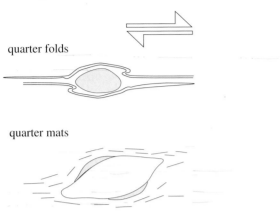

quarter folds

quarter mats

asymmetric distribution of myrmekite

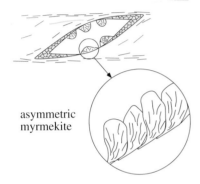

asymmetric
myrmekite

Fig. 5.28. Three types of quarter structures in mylonite that can be used to determine sense of shear. The structures are defined by an asymmetric distribution of fabric elements over the four quarters defined by the foliation and its normal. Myrmekite can also have an internal asymmetry that can be used to determine shear sense

Wintsch 1989). The arrangement of quartz lamellae in myrmekite may also show an internal monoclinic symmetry (Fig. 5.28 inset) which can serve as an independent, internal shear sense indicator (Simpson and Wintsch 1989).

5.6.9 Lattice-Preferred Orientation

The lattice-preferred orientation (LPO) of minerals commonly shows a monoclinic symmetry. Crystals with elongate shape such as mica and amphiboles can develop a monoclinic oblique fabric with respect to another foliation such as a layering, as described above. Moreover, the deviation in orientation of such minerals around the mean can be skewed. Such skew-

ness is difficult to measure optically, but has been detected in slates by X-ray goniometry (Chap. 9.8.6) and can be used to determine sense of shear (O'Brien et al. 1987).

Minerals with equant grain shape such as quartz, calcite, feldspar and olivine in mylonites commonly show a monoclinic symmetry of LPO with the symmetry axis normal to the mylonitic lineation and parallel to the main mylonitic foliation. LPO patterns in pole diagrams for a single crystallographic axis such as c- or a-axes in quartz can have an internal monoclinic symmetry defined by the shape of the pattern, and an external asymmetry with respect to foliations in the rock. Both asymmetries are useful shear sense indicators. Further details on LPO development and interpretation are given in Chapter 4.14–4.16. A method to measure quartz c-axes is presented in Chapter 9.10.

5.6.10 Vergence of Asymmetric Fold Sections

Cross sections through folds in mylonites parallel to the lineation commonly show a dominant vergence (Figs. 5.9, 11.6, 11.8). If the folds are sheath folds generated during mylonite formation and the section is strictly parallel to the movement direction, the vergence may be reliable as a shear sense indicator. In most cases, the three-dimensional shape of the folds is unknown and it is also unclear whether the folds are older or related to the mylonite formation. In those cases, folds cannot be used as shear sense markers.

5.6.11 Potential Shear Sense Markers

A number of structures in mylonites are potential shear sense markers, but they are either more cumbersome to use than the ones mentioned above, or the results obtained with them are not consistent. This is probably mainly because their development is as yet incompletely understood. In time, these structures may also be useful, but we advise not to rely exclusively on one of them at present. The most common ones are:

Deformed veins. If a large number of deformed veins of different orientation is present in a deformed rock, they can be used to obtain detailed information on the deformation process (Talbot 1970; Hutton 1982; Passchier 1990a; Fig. 5.29). This applies to intrusive veins in outcrop, but also to *microveins* that can be studied in thin section, formed by fracturing and pre-

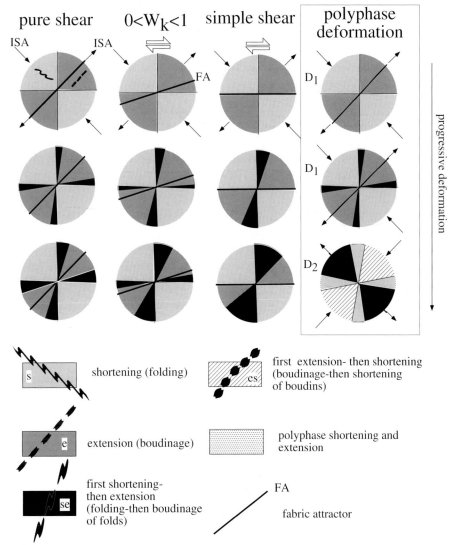

Fig. 5.29. Distribution of domains of deformed lines in space for four categories of progressive deformation. Notice how the distribution of the domains is dependent on the type of progressive deformation; in non-coaxial progressive deformation the distribution has monoclinic symmetry and can be used to determine sense of shear. The largest field of first shortened-then-extended lines *(se)* indicates the dominant rotation direction of lines, and therefore sense of shear (dextral). Only in the case of polyphase deformation are domains of first extension-then-shortening possible

cipitation of material from solution (Chap. 6). Such microveins have been studied in deformed pseudotachylyte (Passchier 1986b) and metachert (Wallis 1992a).

Veins can shorten, extend, or shorten and extend in sequence depending on vein orientation in the flow, and on flow parameters such as vorticity and volume change. If sufficient viscosity contrast exists between veins and matrix, veins can boudinage on extension, or fold on shortening. Figure 5.29 shows the distribution of domains of shortened (s), extended (e), first shortened-then-extended (se) and first extended-then-shortened (es) material line categories for different types of progressive deformation (see also Chap. 2.7; Fig. 2.11). Since veins do not start

folding or enjoying boudinage at the onset of deformation, and may unfold when being stretched, the boundaries of material line categories do not correspond exactly to domains of folding (f), boudinage (b), folding-then-boudinage (fb) and boudinage-then-folding (bf) in veins. Nevertheless, it is useful to plot the orientation of deformed veins against deformation category (f, b, bf or fb) and to compare its symmetry with the theoretically predicted patterns. At least sense of shear should be deducible; if the pattern is asymmetric, the sense of asymmetry indicates shear sense (Fig. 5.29). Complexly deformed veins are notably informative. Notice that first folded, then boudinaged veins (fb) can occur in any flow type, but veins with shortened or folded boudins (bf) are important: such a deformation sequence can *only* result from (1) a high rigid body rotation component of flow such as near rigid objects, or (2) polyphase deformation (Passchier 1990a). In most cases, the presence of folded or shortened boudins is due to polyphase deformation.

Complex indicators. Several microstructures with monoclinic shape symmetry do not exclusively occur in mylonites. These structures may be reliable shear sense indicators, but need close observation and classification before they can be applied. The most common examples are inclusion patterns in porphyroblasts (Chap. 7.6.8), tension gashes (Chap. 6.2), strain fringes and strain shadows (Chap. 6.3). The main problem with these structures is that they consist of several classes of geometries which are superficially similar but formed in different ways, commonly in opposite sense of shear (e.g. Chap. 7.6.8). Examples of these complex shear sense indicators are treated in Chapters 6 and 7.

Fragmented rigid grains. Large porphyroclasts of feldspar, pyroxene or other minerals may be transected by sets of micro-shear zones or faults, which cause relative displacement of the fragments (Fig. 5.30). The sense of movement of the fragments can be *antithetic* or *synthetic,* and depends not only on the bulk shear sense, but also on the shape of the original porphyroclast, on the kinematic vorticity number of flow, and on the initial orientation of the microfaults which may be partly controlled by crystallographic directions in the porphyroclasts (Chap. 3.12.4). Although attempts have been made to use these fabrics as shear sense markers (Simpson and Schmid 1983), they are still unreliable. Interpretation is usually as shown in Fig. 5.31.

Imbrication. The presence of a large number of rigid elongate crystals in a deforming material may result in their interference causing *tiling* or *imbrication* of the objects (Fig. 5.32; Fernandez et al. 1983). This type of structure seems to be common in phenocryst gra-

Fig. 5.30. Microfaults transecting feldspar porphyroclasts in a section parallel to the stretching lineation and normal to the foliation in granite mylonite. The faults do not continue into the mantle of recrystallised feldspar surrounding the por-phyroclasts. Dextral shear sense. Both synthetic *(bottom left)* and antithetic *(top right)* microfaults are present. St Bar-thélemy, Pyrenees, France. Width of view 9 mm. CPL

antithetic microfaults or shear zones in grains

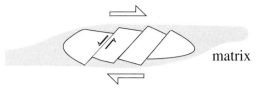

synthetic microfaults or shear zones in grains

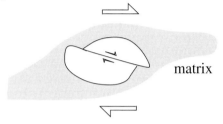

Fig. 5.31. Illustration of the two mechanisms of formation of stepped fragmented grains at similar bulk shear sense *(large arrows)*

nites deformed in the liquid state, and has been described macroscopically by Blumenfeld (1983) for feldspar grains in granitoid gneiss. The structure may theoretically also occur in fine-grained mylonite (Brunel 1986; Blumenfeld and Bouchez 1988). The asymmetry of imbrication should indicate shear sense, but reliability of this structure is still uncertain.

imbrication

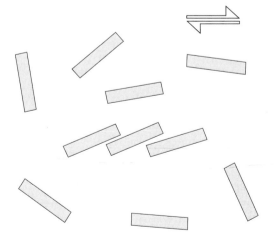

Fig. 5.32. Tiling of feldspar grains in a granite deformed in the liquid state

Tensional and constrictional stepover sites. In mylonites with a strong mica foliation deformed at low grade or high strain rate approaching the brittle deformation regime, small extensional fractures or micro-folds may occur between foliation-parallel but 'overstepping' micro-shear bands or faults (Fig. 5.33). If such locations systematically show the same stair-stepping of faults for constrictional or tensional stepover sites, they can be used as shear sense markers. Care should be taken, however, since slip on micro-shear bands may not be the only deformation in the sample, and need not be representative for bulk deformation; i.e. sense of shear on the micro-shear bands may be opposite to bulk shear sense.

'V'-pull-apart microstructures. Recently, Hippertt (1993) introduced a new potential shear sense indicator in the form of pull-apart structures that occur in the rim of feldspar porphyroclasts at low metamorphic grade. Fractures in the edge of the porphyroclasts may open to a V-shape and are filled with quartz or another mineral. In some mylonites these V-pull-apart microstructures have a persistent asymmetry that can be used to determine sense of shear.

stepped faults

extensional

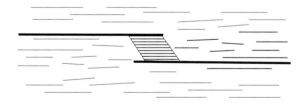

constrictional

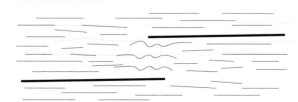

Fig. 5.33. Tensional and constrictional stepover sites in a mylonite. The tensional site is filled with fibrous material. The constrictional site shows microfolding of the foliation

5.7 Shear Sense Indicators in the Brittle Regime

5.7.1 Introduction

The internal fabric of gouge, cataclasite or breccia may contain microstructures that can be used to determine shear sense, as in mylonites. A problem in gouges and cataclasites is that with some exceptions (Tanaka 1992), penetrative lineations that could be used to determine the movement direction are lacking. Instead, *slickensides* (polished fault surfaces) occur that may contain parallel ridges or grooves (known as striations), linear aggregates of cataclased material or fibres (known as *slickenfibres*; Fig. 6.7) that are parallel or slightly inclined to the fault surface. Care should be taken when determining the movement direction along a fault in the field from striations or slickenfibres on slickensides, because they commonly only show the last movement stage on the fault. In any case, specimens for establishment of shear sense should be oriented with respect to the macroscopically determined movement direction.

Sense of shear can be determined in the field from displacement of markers as for ductile shear zones (Chap. 5.5.2) or from the shape of striations, slickenfibres or minor faults on slickensides (Petit 1987). If slickenfibres consist of calcite, the orientation distribution of deformation e-twins can be used to determine sense of movement on the fault (Laurent 1987). Other shear sense criteria in thin section are given below.

5.7.2 Incohesive Brittle Fault Rocks

Although it is usually difficult to sample and cut gouge or incohesive cataclasite, thin sections of such materials may give information on shear sense. A gouge normally consists of rock and mineral fragments in a matrix rich in clay minerals. This matrix may show a uniform extinction under crossed polars due to preferred orientation of the clay minerals; shear bands (Chap. 5.6.4) may also be present in the matrix. Both the extinction direction and shear bands can be used to determine shear sense as described for oblique foliation and shear bands in mylonite (Chap. 5.6.3, 5.6.4). Sets of subsidiary shear fractures with distinct orientation and movement sense, known as *Riedel shears* may also be present (Chester et al. 1985; Rutter et al. 1986; Evans 1990). They are subdivided

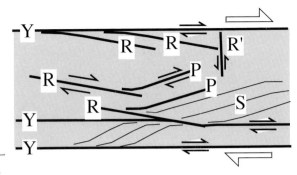

Fig. 5.34. Schematic diagram showing the characteristic geometry and shear sense of the most common types of Riedel shears *(R-, R'-, P- and Y-shears)* in a brittle fault zone. Shear sense is mostly established from deflection of older shears or, in foliated cataclasite or gouge, deflection of the foliation *(S)*

into R, R', P and Y shears, each with a characteristic orientation and shear sense (Fig. 5.34). Y shears act as boundary faults for the brittle fault zone or are parallel to the boundary. Riedel shears superficially resemble ductile shear bands but form by brittle fracturing and have a slightly different geometry and orientation.

Riedel shears are useful shear sense indicators. Since suitable displaced markers are usually rare, deflection of a foliation or of older Riedel shears by younger shears (e.g. P by R; Y by R as shown in Fig. 5.34) can be used to determine shear sense. Synkinematic veins of quartz and calcite are common in brittle fault rocks and occur in any stage of break-up from intact veins to rounded fragments (Chester and Logan 1987). Orientation of fibres in the veins (Chap. 6.2) or displacement of vein fragments can be used to determine shear sense.

5.7.3 Cohesive Brittle Fault Rocks

In most cohesive brittle fault rocks determination of sense of shear is difficult, except in foliated cataclasite. The most common shear sense indicators in foliated cohesive cataclasites are shear bands (Chester and Logan 1987; Petit 1987); these can be interpreted in a similar way as those in ductilely deformed rocks. Riedel shears may also be present (Fig. 5.34). Care has to be taken, however, with R shears; in many cases these are deflected towards Y shears in a sense as shown in Fig. 5.34 (top; Logan et al. 1979; Strating and Vissers 1994). This deflection is probably due to a gradient in the orientation of the stress field near Y-shears during development of R shears, which therefore obtain a curved shape (Strating and Vissers 1994). If many finely spaced R shears are present in a non-foliated cataclasite, they might be confused with foliation planes; in that case, use of the deflection towards Y shears as a shear sense indicator would give the wrong result (Fig. 5.34). However, R shears can be recognised because their spacing is dependent on the spacing of Y shears, which is not the case for foliation planes (Strating and Vissers 1994).

Deformed inherited micas can be used as kinematic indicators in some foliated cataclasites. Kanaori et al. (1991) describe inherited biotite grains in a cataclased granite which form cleavage steps or bio-

tite fish. Statistical analysis of the orientation of (001) in these micas against the main foliation trace allows determination of shear sense.

5.7.4 Pseudotachylyte

In pseudotachylyte, shear sense can rarely be determined in thin section. Displacement of markers is the best indicator, but this gives unreliable results (Fig. 5.12), especially since no slickensides are present as for gouge and cataclasite. In some pseudotachylyte veins, the orientation of injection veins or of fracture sets in the wall rock can be used to determine shear sense.

6 Dilatation Sites: Fibrous Veins, Strain Shadows, Strain Fringes and Boudins

6.1 Introduction

Many deformed rocks contain sites with a deviant mineralogy and fabric, interpreted as an effect of rearrangement of material by local dilatation and precipitation during deformation. Such 'dilatation sites' can be isolated and elongate (veins), flanking rigid objects (strain shadows) or occur in the neck of boudinaged layers or elongate crystals (Fig. 6.1). Strain shadows are also referred to in the literature as pressure shadows. Most veins and many strain shadows and boudin necks have sharp contacts with the wall rock and may form by precipitation of material from an aqueous solution in a fracture, as outlined below. Such sites are usually filled with polycrystalline material which may be massive, but commonly consists of rod-shaped crystals known as *fibres* (Figs. 6.1–6.3). Fibrous veins and strain shadows (the latter also known as *strain fringes;* Fig. 6.3) are some of the most complex microstructures to be found in rocks, and contain much information about deformation and deformation history (Figs. 6.1–6.3; Zwart and Oele 1966; Choukroune 1971; Durney and Ramsay 1973; Beutner and Diegel 1985; Etchecopar and Malavieille 1987). Strain fringes are also known as pressure fringes. Since the shape of the aggregates gives primarily information on strain distribution around an object, and not on forces, we advocate the use of the term strain fringe. The same applies to pressure shadow where we prefer the use of strain shadow. Some veins and strain shadows have fuzzy boundaries (Fig. 6.1). They may form by local alteration of the wall rock along a fracture *(replacement veins)* or rigid object, or by deformation and recrystallisation of veins with sharp boundaries (Chap. 6.5, 7.5 and 7.6.8).

The development of fibrous veins and fringes is associated with the circulation of fluids in rocks. Fluid pressure in rocks is usually between hydrostatic pressure (the pressure of a water column at a particular depth) and the smallest principal stress σ_3 (Chap. 2.11). Due to deformation, reduction of pore

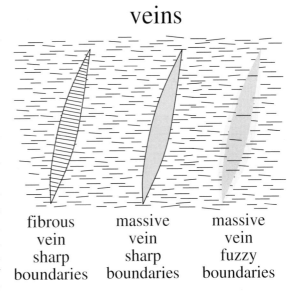

veins

fibrous vein
sharp boundaries

massive vein
sharp boundaries

massive vein
fuzzy boundaries

strain shadows

strain fringe   massive strain shadows

sharp boundaries

sharp boundaries

fuzzy boundaries

Fig. 6.1. Schematic drawing of fibrous and massive veins, strain fringes and strain shadows as treated in this text. Massive veins and strain shadows are filled by a polycrystalline aggregate with a granoblastic fabric

Fig. 6.2. Antitaxial vein of calcite fibres in a slate. A median line is visible. Appalachians, New York, USA. Width of view 10 mm. CPL. (Thin section courtesy Janos Urai)

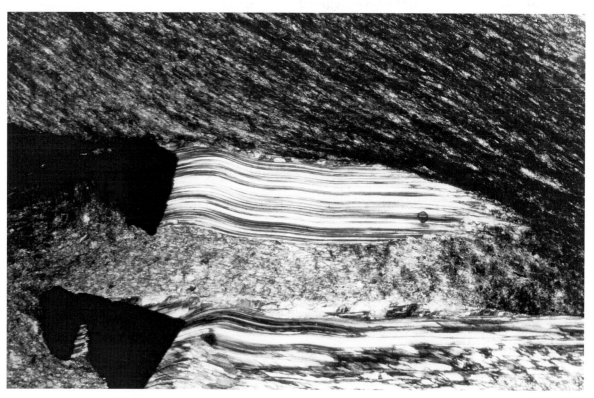

Fig. 6.3. Fibrous strain fringe of quartz developed alongside a pyrite grain. Individual fibres are undeformed but show bends which are interpreted to result from changes in the orientation of ISA with respect to the fabric in the wall rock. Lourdes, Pyrenees, France. Width of view 4 mm. CPL. (Photograph courtesy D. Aerden)

volume or metamorphic dewatering reactions, fluid pressure in rocks can approach σ_3 and if this value is reached, voids filled with fluid can open at any depth. Minerals can be precipitated in such voids, commonly as equidimensional crystals, but also frequently as aggregates of a fibrous nature, especially during deformation at upper crustal levels. Fibrous aggregates of quartz and calcite are particularly common, but mica aggregates also form (Williams 1972b; Passchier 1982a). In many cases, void-opening and filling is no unique event, but occurs repeatedly or continuously during a deformation phase. In such cases, the resulting *dilatant veins* or strain fringes contain much and detailed information on the deformation path, and are therefore some of the most useful structures to reconstruct tectonic events in thin section (e.g. Durney and Ramsay 1973; Ramsay and Huber 1983).

In microtectonic analysis, fibrous aggregates have a number of important applications:

1. The presence of fibrous aggregates indicates that fluid pressure was relatively high and that solution transfer operated during deformation. In rocks which contain fibres, pressure solution may have been important, and the possibility of volume change must be considered.

2. The presence of tension gashes (Chap. 6.2.1) implies that differential stress in the rock was relatively small (Etheridge 1983); if differential stress is high, a high fluid pressure will induce shear fractures rather than fibrous tension gashes.

3. The shape of veins and strain fringes and of the fibres in these structures can be used to determine shear sense and, in some cases, other deformation parameters.

6.2 Fibrous Veins

6.2.1 Introduction

The fibrous habit of quartz and calcite in veins is unusual for these minerals and appears to be due to a special growth mechanism (Fig. 6.4). Imagine a crack which forms in a crystalline aggregate of quartz or calcite. Immediately on opening, new crystalline material can be deposited on the existing crystals from solution in the fluid. If neighbouring crystals

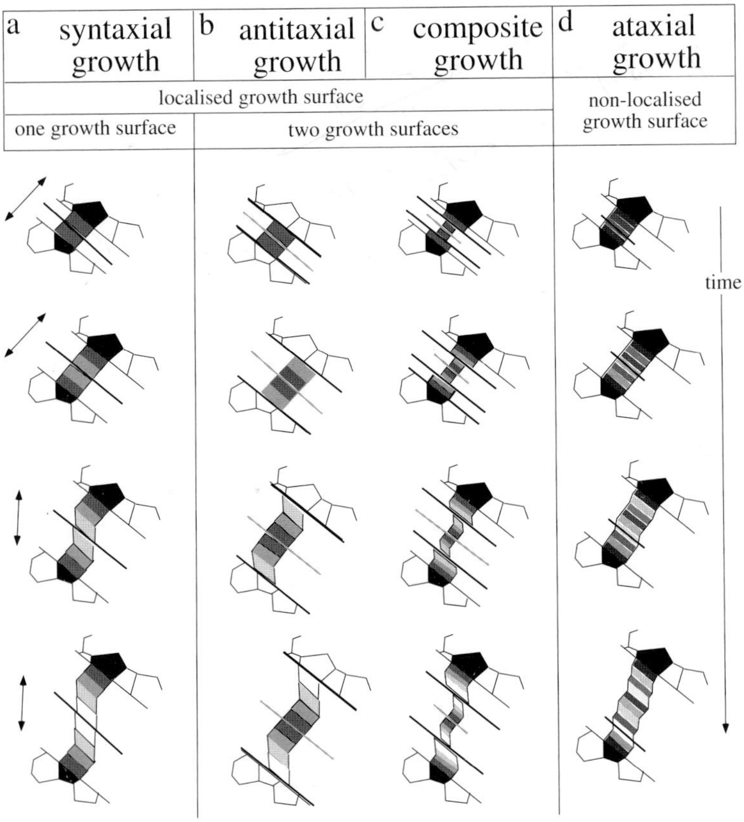

a syntaxial growth	b antitaxial growth	c composite growth	d ataxial growth
localised growth surface			non-localised growth surface
one growth surface	two growth surfaces		

time

Fig. 6.4a–d. Four types of fibre growth in veins common in nature. Youngest parts of the fibres are shown in the lightest colour. Growth surface is indicated by a ***bold dark*** line. **a** Syntaxial growth. Fibres are in continuity with the wall rock crystals; the oldest part of the fibres lies along the edge of the vein. A median line marks the final position of the growth surface. **b** Antitaxial growth; fibres grow from the centre outwards. The vein usually consists of other material then the wall rock. The oldest part of the vein is along the median line. Two growth surfaces occur, along the contact with the wall rock. **c** Composite growth, with a syntaxial and antitaxial component. Two growth surfaces are present at the contact between the vein segments where the youngest parts of the vein are situated. **d** Ataxial growth. Fibres are in continuity with crystals in the wall rock but lack a localised growth surface; growth is by repetitive fracturing at different sites. Young and old parts of the fibres can be mixed throughout the vein. No median line is present

grow at similar rates, the overgrowth obtains an elongate shape; crystals that grow slowly because they have an unsuitable crystallographic orientation will become thin and end while their neighbours make contact[2]. In the case of an isolated crack, fibrous growth occurs into the widening crack from both sides at the same rate. The result is a symmetric vein with a central plane where deposition of new material takes place. In thin section this plane appears as a clear line known as the *median line* (Fig. 6.4a). The median line is often marked by small opaque grains and a discontinuity in fibre fabric. Fibre growth as described here from the vein wall towards the vein centre is known as *syntaxial growth*, and the veins as syntaxial fibre veins (Ramsay and Huber 1983) or *syntaxial veins* (Fig. 6.4a).

Besides the scenario sketched above, veins can also be filled by growth of a mineral that is not the main constituent of the wall rock, e.g. calcite fibres in a quartzite. In that case, the growth usually occurs

along the contact of fibres and wall rock, i.e. on two sides (Fig. 6.4b). A weak median line defined by small grains of the fibrous mineral or fragments of the wall rock is normally present in the centre of the fibrous aggregate, indicating the initial nucleation site of the fibres. This type of growth is termed *antitaxial growth,* and the veins are called antitaxial fibre veins (Ramsay and Huber 1983) or *antitaxial veins* (Figs. 6.2, 6.4b). Single fibres in antitaxial veins can be continuous over the median line, in contrast to fibres in syntaxial veins. Composite veins are also possible, in which antitaxial fibres develop along the median plane of syntaxial fibres (Fig. 6.4c). A composite vein has three 'median' lines.

Veins may form by continuous growth of fibres into a void (either in a vein opened by a single event, or one that is opening faster than the crystal growth rate) or more likely by periodic sealing and fracturing known as *crack-seal growth.* If repeated sealing and fracturing occurs at the same site, this leads to development of synthetic, antithetic or composite veins with median lines as discussed above (Fig. 6.4a–c). Alternatively, fibrous veins may form by repeated

---

[2] We have simplified most drawings in this section by omitting this tapering effect and imagine all fibres to grow at the same rate.

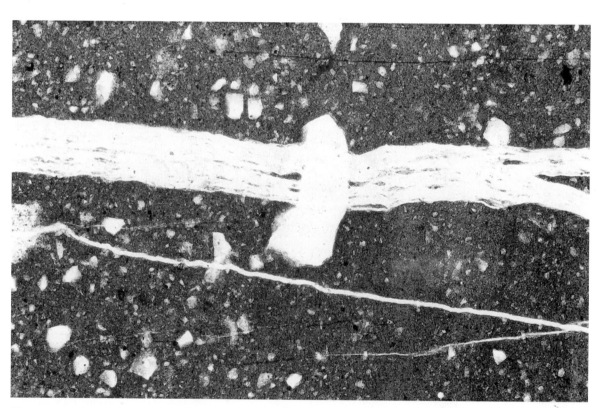

Fig. 6.5. Ataxial vein of quartz in fine-grained tourmalinite. A quartz grain in the tourmalinite *(centre)* has been cut by the vein and has been modified into a stretched crystal. Several planes of solid inclusions (tourmalinite fragments) occur in the vein and show that cracking was partly along the vein margins. Orobic Alps, Italy. Width of vein 4 mm. PPL

fracturing and growth at alternating different sites in the vein (Fig.6.4d). Such non-localised, 'ataxial' cracking and growth produce veins with jogged or smooth fibres without a median line that are in continuity with fragments of single crystals on both sides of the vein; such fibres and crystal fragments are known as *stretched crystals* (Figs. 6.4–6.6; Durney and Ramsay 1973). We use the terms ataxial fibre veins or ataxial veins for veins with such fibres (Figs. 6.4d, 6.5, 6.6). They are relatively common in nature. Some veins are not completely filled with fibrous material but contain also idiomorphic crystals; the latter may have formed in water pockets that were retained in the veins (Fisher and Bryne 1990; Henderson et al. 1990).

In many veins, fibres are imagined to be *displacement controlled,* i.e. they grow in the opening direction of the vein. Figure 6.6 shows fibre geometries in veins induced by the four common types of displacement-controlled fibre growth upon relative changes in movement direction of the wall rock (Chap. 6.2.2). Notice that syntaxial and antitaxial veins have mirror symmetry deflections due to their opposed growth directions. Composite veins show both senses. Non-localised fracturing in ataxial veins will usually give a 'mean' orientation without clear curvature.

The veins described above which lie at a high angle to the extension direction are also known as *tension gashes* (Fig. 6.7a); however, veins can also

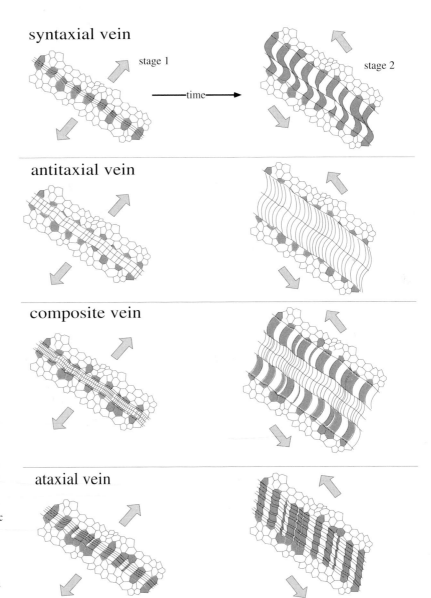

syntaxial vein

stage 1

—time→

stage 2

antitaxial vein

composite vein

ataxial vein

Fig. 6.6. Development of the four types of veins with displacement controlled fibres described in the text. A change in the relative orientation of the extensional ISA of the flow *(arrows)* and the vein can cause curvature of the growing fibres which can be used for kinematic analysis. Notice that the sense of curvature of the veins depends on the type of vein, and that ataxial veins develop straight fibres which give a mean displacement direction of the vein walls

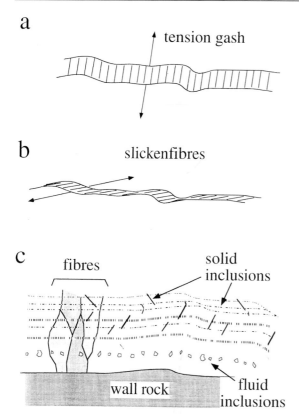

Fig. 6.7. a Development of a tension gash by extension at a high angle to the developing vein. **b** Development of slickenfibres by extension subparallel to the vein. **c** Various types of solid and fluid inclusions in a fibrous vein. None of the inclusions is necessarily parallel to the fibres. Surfaces of fluid inclusions are usually parallel to the vein wall, but solid inclusions may be both parallel to the opening direction of the vein, or occur in planes parallel to the vein wall. Some of the latter planes of solid inclusions consist of small fibrous grains normal to the vein wall

form at a small angle to the opening direction, e.g. along bedding planes in the case of flexural slip. In that case the fibres may be subparallel to the vein wall, and are known as *slickenfibres* (Figs. 6.7b, 6.8; Chap. 5.2.1).

Fluid and solid *inclusions* are commonly present in fibres at regular intervals. Some of these inclusions occur along distinct surfaces parallel to the edge of the vein and are interpreted to trace the position of the surface of fibre growth during the deformation (Figs. 6.7c, 6.8; Ramsay 1980b; Cox and Etheridge 1983). Surfaces of fluid inclusions may represent sudden changes in the opening rate or direction of a continuously or intermittently growing vein or result from a crack-seal process in or at the edge of the vein

(Fig. 6.7c). Solid inclusions, especially parts of the wall rock, are common in ataxial and antitaxial veins and may represent the action of a crack-seal mechanism along the vein boundary (Figs. 6.7c, 6.8); the void may temporarily seal and then reopen at approximately the same site, including fragments of the wall rock. In some antitaxial veins, sets of regularly spaced surfaces rich in small mica grains occur parallel to the wall rock, with individual micas oriented parallel to a foliation in the wall rock (Cox and Etheridge 1983); they are interpreted as overgrowths of micas on the vein wall rock, subsequently separated from the wall by cracking. Each mica-rich plane can be interpreted as representing a distinct growth and cracking event in a developing antitaxial vein (Cox and Etheridge 1983). From the spacing of such planes, individual crack openings in an ataxial vein have been estimated at 10 to 100 μm (Ramsay 1980b; van der Pluijm 1984; Cox 1987). Some isolated elongate fluid inclusions or fibres such as mica grains may lie oblique to the edge of the vein and to the surfaces of inclusions mentioned above (Fig. 6.7c); these may represent the opening direction of the vein. None of the inclusions is necessarily parallel to fibres, since fibres may or may not track the opening direction of a vein as discussed in Chapter 6.2.2.

6.2.2 Curved Fibres and Fibre Growth Direction

Fibres in veins are commonly curved. In some cases this curvature can be explained by fibre deformation or grain boundary migration (Williams and Urai 1989). However, in other cases, the curved fibres are strain-free and contain undeformed arrays of fluid inclusions or delicate banding visible in cathodoluminescence (Chap. 9.2) which would be destroyed or modified by grain boundary migration (Urai et al. 1991). The presence of such optically strain-free curved fibres has led to the suggestion that fibres may grow in a particular kinematic direction, and that the growth direction changes when kinematic axes rotate relatively to the rock volume in which the veins develop (Ramsay 1980b). Hence, the orientation of the opening vector of such dilating veins can be read from the orientation of the fibres; for simple vein geometries, this direction is considered to be parallel to the extensional ISA of the flow (Figs. 6.4, 6.6; Durney and Ramsay 1973; Wickham 1973; Wilcox et al. 1973; Philip and Etchecopar 1978; Casey et al. 1983; Ramsay and Huber 1983; Ellis 1986).

In non-coaxial flow, veins and new-grown fibres will rotate as material lines with respect to ISA, and

Fig. 6.8. Detail from an antitaxial slickenfibre vein of quartz and calcite (only quartz visible). The contact with the wall rock is parallel to the long axis of the photograph. Trails of solid inclusions trend *from top left to bottom right;* each trail probably represents a separate crack-seal event. Jogs in the trails are thought to indicate the opening direction of the vein *(horizontal)*. Fibres are oblique to both the solid inclusion trails and the movement direction, and trend *from bottom left to top right.* Orobic Alps, Italy. Width of view 5 mm. CPL

fibres that are growing in the (fixed) direction of the extensional ISA will therefore become curved. The curvature of these fibres corresponds to certain clearly defined geometries treated in the next section.

Fibre orientation is not in all cases associated with kinematic directions (Fig. 6.8). Comparison of fibre orientation with that of trails of phyllosilicates in the veins, or with off-set markers in the vein wall has shown that not all quartz or calcite fibres track the opening vector of the vein (Cox and Etheridge 1983; Cox 1987; van der Pluijm 1984; Williams and Urai 1989). In many cases, fibres simply grow normal to the wall rock of the vein in which they nucleate, and fill the available void without a change in growth direction. Williams and Urai (1989) have also shown that some curved, optically strain-free fibrous crystals are in fact recrystallised deformed fibres which initially were straight and orthogonal to the vein wall.

Urai et al. (1991) have suggested a solution for the bivalent growth behaviour of fibres. They assume that growth rate of fibrous crystals is isotropic along cracks where no rational crystal faces are present. If the growth surface of a vein is irregular in shape, e.g. because the original crack was not perfectly planar, fibre boundaries tend to migrate towards embayments in the growth surface that point towards the wall rock, and will become fixed there during further growth of the fibres (Figs. 6.9, 6.10). If opening and growth occurs by small steps and the void is closed between growth events, changes in displacement direction of the vein wall will be followed by the fibres; this is the origin of displacement-controlled fibres (Figs. 6.9, 6.10). However, if the vein opens rapidly or growth is slow, and the vein does not close between growth steps, fibres will continue to grow normal to the growth surface (Fig. 6.10); they are *face-controlled fibres*. Intermediate situations are also possible if growth steps are relatively large, or if the irregularities on the growth surface have a small amplitude below a critical value (Urai et al. 1991); fibres follow the movement of the wall rock to some extent in such cases, but do not track it completely. If the growth surface is flat, e.g. because the original crack was straight, the fibres

a   Closure of fluid-filled crack

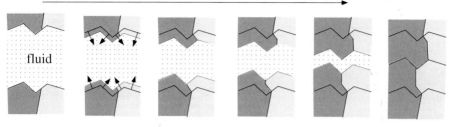

b   Fibres tracking embayments

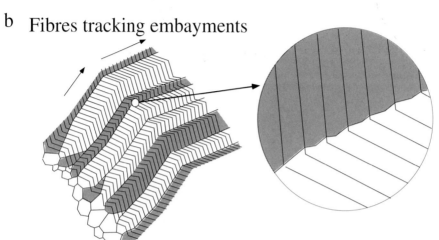

Fig. 6.9. a If a crack with irregular shape opens and crystals grow isotropically and at equal rate to fill the crack *(arrows)*, the grain boundary between them will be displaced normal to the crystal face till an embayment in the growth surface is reached that points towards the wall-rock; subsequently, this site in the embayment will be followed by the fibre boundary until the crack is filled. **b** This mechanism allows fibres to track the opening direction of the vein if growth and opening occur intermittently by small steps, as indicated. *Solid jogged lines* represent the vein wall at the onset of each opening increment

Opening of vein by large increments

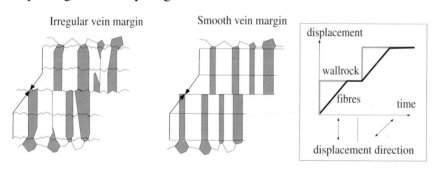

Opening of vein by small increments

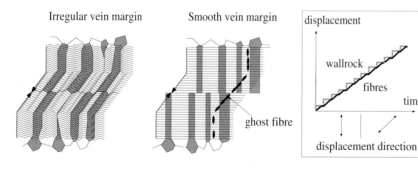

Fig. 6.10. Effects of vein-wall smoothness and opening rate of veins on fibre geometry, after Urai et al. (1991). Fibres will only be displacement-controlled (track the opening direction of the vein) if vein boundaries are irregular and if opening is by small increments *(bottom left)*; in all other cases, fibres tend to be face-controlled. Ghost fibres may track the opening direction in those cases

will in all cases be face-controlled; they grow normal to the growth surface and do not follow the movement of the wall rocks. This may be the case when a crack opens along a planar crystal face such as that of a pyrite cube (Figs. 6.10, 6.15). Domains of face-controlled fibres can contain *ghost fibres* (Ramsay and Huber 1983), usually solid inclusions or fibres of a deviant mineral, that cross the face-controlled fibres (Fig. 6.10). Ghost fibres are thought to track the opening direction of the vein. In the model of Urai et al. (1991), displacement-controlled fibres are therefore only possible under special circumstances of an irregular growth surface, isotropic crystal growth and small opening increments (Fig. 6.10). In many geometrical situations, the 'free' surfaces on both sides of an opening crack will move apart in the direction of ISA, and in that case the vein will track the ISA direction. It will be clear, however, that this does not necessarily apply in the case of complex vein shapes. This means that curved fibres may track the opening direction of the vein (Fig. 6.6), but not necessarily the instantaneous extension direction in the bulk rock (Chap. 6.3). It is therefore necessary to be careful when using fibrous aggregates for kinematic analysis; the nature of the fibre growth process should first be established.

We limit the treatment of veins, strain shadows and strain fringes in this chapter mainly to pure shear and simple shear progressive deformation histories. Obviously, other flow regimes and more complex histories involving volume change are also possible but cannot all be treated here. However, the end-member situations will in most cases allow assessment of at least shear sense, and permit establishment of the type of deviation from the ideal model.

6.2.3 Veins in Non-Coaxial Progressive Deformation

In brittle fault zones and some ductile shear zones, *tension gashes* develop in sets of veins that are arranged en-echelon (Fig. 6.11a; Olson and Pollard 1991). Large tension gashes in shear zones usually have a characteristic, curved geometry (Fig. 6.11a). In both coaxial and non-coaxial flow, tension gashes open approximately parallel to the direction of maximum instantaneous extension. If the veins form during progressive deformation, they may both become wider and propagate laterally outward parallel to the instantaneous shortening axis (one of the ISA). In coaxial progressive deformation, this has no implications for the shape of the vein, but in non-coaxial flow the older central part of a vein will rotate just like any

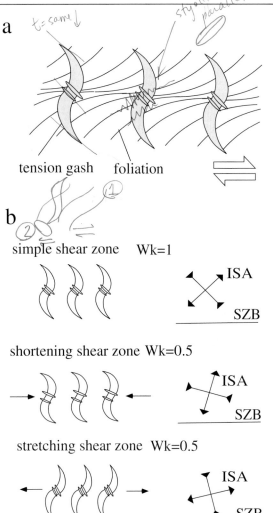

Fig. 6.11. a Schematic diagram of tension gashes in en-echelon arrangement in a shear zone. A second set of tension gashes develops in the centre of the older set. The sense of curvature for tension gashes and foliation in a shear zone is similar. **b** The orientation of the youngest parts (tips) of tension gashes with respect to the shear zone boundary *(SZB)* depends on the kinematic vorticity number *Wk* of the flow and on the orientation of the ISA with respect to the shear zone boundary. In absence of bulk area increase in the plane of section, shortening and stretching shear zones will have tips that make an angle with the shear zone boundary that is smaller or larger than 45°. For simple shear the angle will be approximately 45°

material line in the bulk flow (Fig. 5.29) while the tension gash still propagates outward along the instantaneous shortening axis. The older part of the vein is deformed in this process; antitaxial calcite veins commonly show deformation twins in the oldest parts of the calcite fibres that lie in the centre of the vein

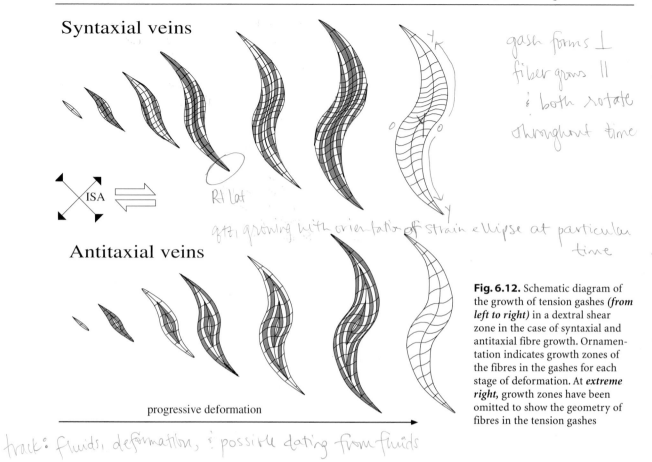

Syntaxial veins

*[handwritten: gash forms ⊥
fiber grows ||
& both rotate
throughout time]*

[handwritten: Rt lat]

[handwritten: ISA]

Antitaxial veins

[handwritten: qtz growing with orientation of strain ellipse at particular time]

progressive deformation

Fig. 6.12. Schematic diagram of the growth of tension gashes *(from left to right)* in a dextral shear zone in the case of syntaxial and antitaxial fibre growth. Ornamentation indicates growth zones of the fibres in the gashes for each stage of deformation. At *extreme right,* growth zones have been omitted to show the geometry of fibres in the tension gashes

[handwritten: track: fluids, deformation, & possible dating from fluids]

(Burkhard 1993). The younger, outer parts have rotated less, and this explains the curved shape of tension gash veins formed in non-coaxial progressive deformation (Fig. 6.12). The 'en-echelon' arrangement of tension gashes in many shear zones occurs because tension gashes start to develop where small cracks are formed at regular intervals along the central part of a shear zone. Because of their simple development mechanism, the shape of tension gashes is a reliable shear-sense indicator; S-shaped and Z-shaped gashes indicate sinistral and dextral shear sense respectively (Fig. 6.11a; Choukroune and Seguret 1968; Ramsay and Graham 1970; Beach 1975; Gamond 1983). In some cases, two generations of tension gashes are found, the younger one transecting the centre of the older one parallel to its tips (Fig. 6.11a). Such 'secondary' tension gashes are thought to form in response to rotation of the centre of the older gash into the extensional field of the flow (Chap. 5.6.11; Fig. 5.29). Similarly, stylolites are sometimes found at a high angle to developing tension gashes. Notice that a foliation in a shear zone will form oblique to the gashes, and that

foliation curvature due to a strain gradient has a similar geometry as the tension gashes, but with the low-strain (outer) parts of the foliation in the direction of the instantaneous extension axis (Fig. 6.11a).

If flow in a shear zone is by simple shear, the instantaneous shortening direction will lie at 45° to the shear zone boundary (Fig. 2.8) and the tips of the tension gashes will lie in this direction (Fig. 6.11b). If flow is between pure and simple shear ($0<Wk<1$; Chap. 2.5), the angle between the tips and the shear zone boundary will either be smaller or larger than 45°. Such structures are known as shortening- and stretching shear zones respectively (Chap. 5.6.4; Fig. 6.11b).

If fibres are present in curved tension gash veins, they may also have a complex shape that can be used to determine shear sense (Fig. 6.12). The pattern of curvature of the fibres depends on the nature of the fibre growth process. Antitaxial fibres have the same sense of curvature as the external shape of the tension gash; syntaxial fibres have the opposite sense of curvature (Fig. 6.12).

6.3 Strain Fringes

6.3.1 Introduction

Rigid objects in a coaxial or non-coaxial flow cause perturbations of the stress field and flow pattern. In the case of low temperature deformation and high fluid pressure, increased pressure solution may occur adjacent to the rigid object on the side of the shortening ISA, while extensional gashes may open on the contact of the object and the matrix on the side of the extensional ISA. New fibrous crystalline material may grow in these gashes and form *strain fringes* (Figs. 6.1, 6.3).

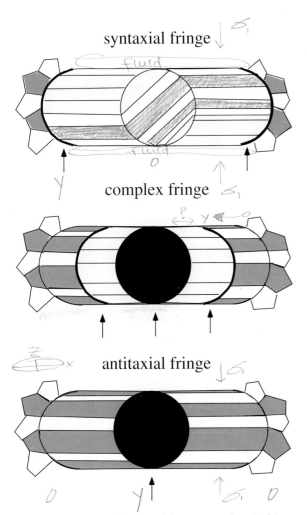

Fig. 6.13. Schematic drawing of three types of strain fringes that occur in nature. The core object of the syntaxial fringe is a crinoid stem fragment with deformation twins. *Arrows* indicate the position of growth surfaces

Because the presence of the rigid object (here referred to as the *core object*) complicates the nature of the flow around a developing strain fringe, its shape and internal structure differ considerably from that of a vein. Strain fringes carry information on flow and deformation history in both their internal and external shape, and are therefore useful as kinematic indicators. Strain fringes can be syntaxial, antitaxial or complex. Notice that in common practice, syntaxial fringes have the growth surface between the fringe and the wall rock, and antitaxial fringes between the fringe and the core object. This can be confusing since it may seem to be contrary to the terminology used for veins. (Fig. 6.13).

Syntaxial fringes have been observed around crinoid stem fragments as core object in limestones (crinoid-type fringes; Ramsay and Huber 1983) but are relatively rare. Complex fringes around pyrite crystals, with a calcite core and quartz rim, have also been observed. Most fringes are antitaxial (pyrite-type fringes; Ramsay and Huber 1983), probably because the core object is usually a mineral different from the matrix, such as pyrite in a quartz-feldspar rock. The rest of this section deals with these most common antitaxial fringes.

Strain fringes usually consist of quartz, calcite and locally also chlorite (Mügge 1930; Williams 1972b). The development of strain fringes has been studied for cubic and spherical core objects (Durney and Ramsay 1973; Ramsay and Huber 1983; Ellis 1986; Etchecopar and Malavieille 1987). The geometry of the fringe depends at least on the shape of the core object, the flow regime in the surrounding matrix, and whether fibre growth in the fringe is displacement-controlled (Fig. 6.14; Choukroune 1971; Ramsay and Huber 1983; Etchecopar and Malavieille 1987) or face-controlled (Fig. 6.15). In some fringes, both types of growth can be observed (Fig. 6.14b). Since the core object and the fringes may rotate while the fibres in the vein continue to grow at the object-fringe interface, the shape of the fibres in the fringe can be rather complex (Figs. 6.14, 6.18). If fringes are rigid, they may start to act as nuclei for second-generation fringes at the distal ends of the fringe (Fig. 3 in Choukroune 1971). In some cases, the fibres are also deformed and tend to lose information in the distal, oldest and most strongly deformed parts.

6.3.2 Fringes on Spherical Core Objects

The simplest type of fringe develops on spherical core objects. A common example are globular aggre-

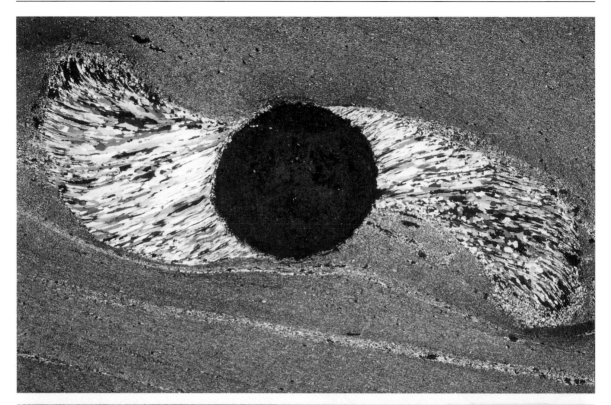

length f rate of time
edge of fringe
may go back
in soln

Fig. 6.14. a Strain fringes of quartz adjacent to a spherical pyrite framboid in chert. The shape of the fringes and fibres resembles that modelled for simple shear progressive deformation (Fig. 6.17). Dextral shear sense. Yilgarn Craton, Western Australia. Width of view 20 mm. CPL. **b** Detail of a fringe adjacent to another spherical pyrite framboid in the same outcrop. Most fibres are parallel and seem to be displacement controlled, but some small fibres radiate out from the central sphere and are face-controlled. Dextral shear sense. Yilgarn Craton, Western Australia. Width of view 12 mm. CPL

gates of pyrite with a raspberry-like external form known as *framboidal pyrites* (Fig. 6.14). Matrix material is pulled away from the rigid sphere by the flowing matrix and new fringe material is depositing in the gap. In coaxial progressive deformation displacement-controlled fibres are simply parallel to the long dimension of the fringe. Face-controlled fibres can be predicted to show inward curvature of fibres that gradually decrease in width Fig. 6.16).

In simple shear progressive deformation the situation is more complex (Fig. 6.17). The strain fringe is a stiff or even rigid object in the ductilely deforming matrix and in non-coaxial flow it will rotate as a whole while it is pulled away from the rigid core; continued growth of the fringe at the core object surface causes the fringe and the fibres to obtain a curved geometry. Since fringes become elongate with growth, their rotation rate tends to decrease with progressive deformation (Box p. 119; Ghosh and Ramberg 1976; Passchier 1988a). If the fringe is not rigid, it may deform internally while it is rotating and growing at one side. A non-deformed fringe can be recognised by the undeformed 'cast' of the core object at the distal part of the fringe (Fig. 6.14) and by fibres which

lack undulose extinction and grain boundary migration structures. Modelling of the interaction of fringe growth, rotation and deformation predicts patterns as shown in Fig. 6.17 (Choukroune 1971; Malavieille et al 1982; Etchecopar and Malavieille 1987). In all cases, the fringes are curved into an S-shaped spiral for dextral shear sense. If fibres are displacement-controlled, they will show a similar curvature as the outline of the fringe, but be inclined at a steeper angle to the flow plane (Figs. 6.14, 6.17). If fibres are face controlled, the fibres radiate outward. The curvature of the fibres will be mostly in the same sense as the curvature of the fringe, but fibres converge on the core object.

6.3.3 Fringes on Angular Core Objects

Most fringes in nature develop on angular rather than spherical core objects, especially around pyrite or magnetite crystals in fine-grained metapelites or carbonaceous slates at low metamorphic grade (Figs. 6.15, 6.18). Such fringes differ from those on spherical

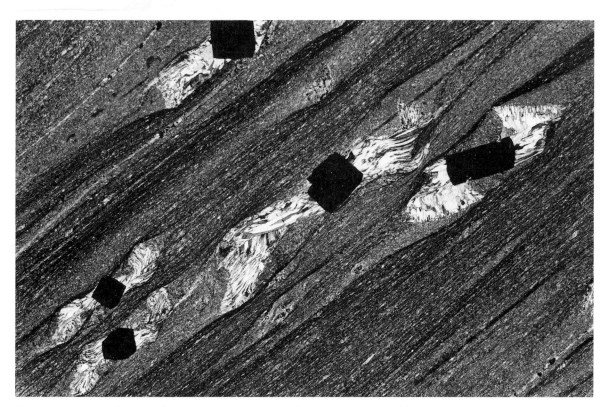

Fig. 6.15. Quartz and calcite fibres in strain fringes around pyrite grains in carbonaceous slate. The object at *right* is shown enlarged in Fig. 6.18. Lourdes, Pyrenees, France. Sense of shear sinistral. Width of view 20 mm. CPL. (Sample courtesy Henk Zwart)

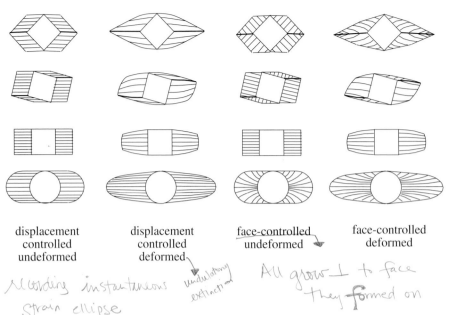

Fig. 6.16. Theoretical model of the development of strain fringes in coaxial progressive deformation around cubic and spherical core objects in the case of face-controlled and displacement controlled fibres. Rigid and deforming fringes are shown. In the case of cubic core objects, the shape of the fringe strongly depends on the original orientation of the core object with respect to the extensional ISA of the flow

displacement controlled undeformed

displacement controlled deformed

face-controlled undeformed

face-controlled deformed

[handwritten annotations: recording instantaneous strain ellipse; undulatory extinction; All grow ⊥ to face they formed on]

core objects, in that one, two or more crystal faces can be in contact with a fringe at any time; as a result, a dividing surface or *suture* may be present in the fringe, where it was attached to the corner between two faces of the core object (Figs. 6.15, 6.17). Figures 6.16 and 6.17 show the development of strain fringes around an angular core object in coaxial and non-coaxial progressive deformation. In the case of displacement-controlled growth and non-coaxial progressive deformation, the fibres are strongly curved in the outer, oldest parts of the fringe and are more straight on the inside. This is a result of decreasing angular velocity of the fringe when its aspect ratio increases (Box p. 119). In the case of face-controlled growth, curvature of the fibres is complex and directed towards the suture lines, which are therefore more prominent than in displacement controlled fibres. The shape of the sutures is usually less complex than that of the fibres and is more useful as a shear sense indicator; if the combined sutures of both fringes define an S shape, shear sense is dextral; if they define a Z shape, shear sense is sinistral. (Fig. 6.17). The external shape of the fringes is usually curved with a similar sense as the suture lines and as the external geometry of fringes around spherical core objects. However, the external geometry of angular core objects is less reliable as a shear sense indicator than that of spherical core objects; the orientation of the angular core object at the onset of fringe growth determines the final shape of the fringe.

In practice, the development of fringes may be even more complex than shown in Fig. 6.17, because the strict separation of fringes into those with dis-

placement-controlled and face-controlled fibres may be rather artificial. If the nature of fibres depends on the extension and growth rate, as suggested by Urai et al. (1991), then parts of a fringe could contain face-controlled fibres, and other parts displacement-controlled fibres (Fig. 6.14b). In practice, however, Fig. 6.17 is useful as a first approximation and serves to determine shear sense from fringes of this type.

In Fig. 6.17, all core objects are equidimensional and assumed to rotate at constant rate. Elongate core objects, however, can be expected to rotate at variable rate depending on their orientation in the flow (Passchier 1987b; Chap. 5.6.6). Such a 'pulsating' rotation rate will obviously influence the geometry of developing fringes. For example, in Fig. 6.15 most fringes on square pyrites show geometries as in the models of Fig. 6.17. However, the elongate pyrite at right in Fig. 6.15, (enlarged in Fig. 6.18), has unusual fringes that consist of two parts with almost orthogonal fibres. Fibres in both parts are not separated by a suture, but connected through a sharp bend. This bend may represent a sudden change in growth direction when the long axis of the elongate pyrite rotated rapidly from the shortening to the extensional quarter of the bulk flow: at this point fibres stopped growing along the long faces of the pyrite, which built the distal parts of the fringes and started growing on the short faces, building the proximal parts. The short faces are curved, but most fibres in parts of the fringes adjacent to the short faces are straight and parallel: this indicates that the fibres are mostly displacement-controlled in this part of the fringe.

[handwritten annotation at bottom: Calcite, qtz: Chlorite filler in strain shadows]

[handwritten margin notes: "Use for: Shear sense; specifically coaxial or noncoaxial... lots of asym leads to sym"]

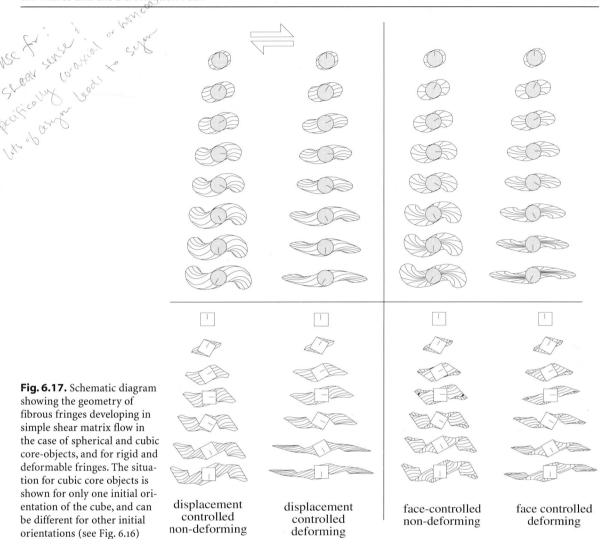

Fig. 6.17. Schematic diagram showing the geometry of fibrous fringes developing in simple shear matrix flow in the case of spherical and cubic core-objects, and for rigid and deformable fringes. The situation for cubic core objects is shown for only one initial orientation of the cube, and can be different for other initial orientations (see Fig. 6.16)

displacement controlled non-deforming

displacement controlled deforming

face-controlled non-deforming

face controlled deforming

6.4 Fibres and the Deformation Path

Strain fringes are informative structures and may be used to estimate sense of shear and finite strain (Chap. 8.2; Durney and Ramsay 1973; Reks and Gray 1982, 1983; Ramsay and Huber 1983; Beutner and Diegel 1985; Gray and Willman 1991). If fibres in a fringe are straight, the long axis of the fringe is thought to represent the X-direction of finite strain. If the total length of both fringes and the rigid inclusion is divided by the length of the inclusion, a minimum value for the principal stretch in direction X is obtained. With this method, only extension (stretch>1) can be

measured, not shortening. It is therefore only possible to determine a strain value in the case of plane strain and known volume change, or if stretch in the Y and Z directions are known by other means. Framboidal pyrites are assumed to have grown during early diagenesis, and fringes around such pyrites can therefore monitor more than just the tectonic strain (Durney and Ramsay 1973; Ramsay and Huber 1983). Euhedral pyrite in mineralised zones may have grown after diagenesis. If both types of pyrite are present in a rock, it should be possible to separate diagenetic and tectonic strain to some extent. Even so, the obtained finite strain is a minimum value, since fringes may not have formed continuously during the entire deformation history.

Many fibrous veins and fringes have curving fibres with a geometry that is more complex from that in

[handwritten notes at bottom: "Rotation rate doesn't have to be the same", "for in new text", "2 rates w/in fiber growth", "6.26 pg 181"]

Fig. 6.18. a Detail of Fig. 6.15 showing quartz-calcite-chlorite fringes around a pyrite grain in carbonaceous slate; **b** shows a detail of **a**. The assemblage resembles a face-controlled fringe with a suture formed in simple shear progressive deformation as shown in Fig. 6.17 but is slightly different, probably because this pyrite is elongate rather than square; the fibres have a sharp bend instead of a suture and may actually be displacement-controlled. Further explanation in text. Lourdes, Pyrenees, France. Width of view **a** 7 mm; **b** 2.5 mm. CPL

Fig. 6.19. Quartz fringe adjacent to a spherical pyrite framboid in chert. All fibres show a sharp bend, which is probably due to a change in the instantaneous extension direction during progressive deformation. Leonora, Yilgarn Craton, Australia. Width of view 10 mm. CPL

Figs. 6.12 and 6.17. Such fibres are interpreted to form by a deformation history with changing flow parameters. The irregular curves in fibres of Figs. 6.3 and 6.19, for example, can be explained as changes in the orientation of ISA with respect to the developing fringe and the foliation in the wall rock, provided the fibres are displacement-controlled. In fact, if fibres in fringes are displacement-controlled, they trace the displacement path (Box p. 9) of a particle on the surface of the rigid core object with respect to the wall rock. It should be possible to reconstruct the deformation path in the wall rock from the shape of fibres in fringes (Chap. 2.2; Durney and Ramsay 1973; Elliott 1973; Wickham 1973; Gray and Durney 1979b; Casey et al. 1983; Ramsay and Huber 1983; Beutner and Diegel 1985; Ellis 1986; Gray and Willman 1991; Hedlund et al. 1994). Two models have been proposed for this purpose, both of which assume that fibres track the extensional ISA; the most commonly used model (Durney and Ramsay 1973; Wickham 1973; Hedlund et al. 1994) assumes that fibres are rigid. The second model assumes that fringes deformed passively and homogeneously (Ramsay and Huber 1983; Ellis 1986).

In both models, the fibres are subdivided into small segments that represent incremental deformation steps, and progressive deformation is restored by repeated multiplication of deformation tensors derived from the fibre segments. The results of such *fibre trajectory analysis* are presented in diagrams that plot strain against a rotational component of the deformation (cumulative incremental strain history – CISH diagrams; Fig. 6.20). Ellis (1986) describes a method to analyse two fibres in each fringe, which allows reconstruction of the full deformation tensor. Thus, the paths of strain orientation, rotation and area change with increasing strain can be calculated and plotted. The results of such deformation path analyses have been used in studies of folding (Wickham and Anthony 1977; Beutner and Diegel 1985; Beutner et al. 1988; Fisher and Anastasio 1994; Hedlund et al. 1994), foliation development (Fisher 1990) and tectonic evolution of accretionary prisms (Sample and Fisher 1986; Fisher and Bryne 1990; Clark et al. 1993).

Fibre trajectory analysis has been successful in many cases and has a potential to become an impor-

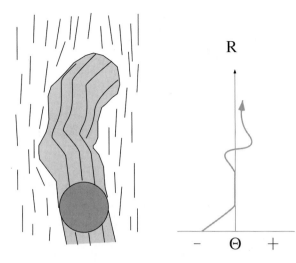

Fig. 6.20. Fringes with complex fibre shape *(at left)* can be used to reconstruct the deformation path in a volume of rock. The fibres can be used to construct diagrams as shown at ***right,*** which plot increasing strain ratio *(R)* against the angle (Θ) between the inferred orientation of the extensional ISA and the foliation

tant tool in kinematic analysis of rock deformation. It gives a unique insight in the deformation paths of rocks, while most other methods give only information on finite deformation or sense of shear. However, despite its frequent use (refs. cit.) there are problems with the basic assumptions in all available methods of fibre trajectory analysis, and more theoretical research on fibre development is needed before the methods will be accurate. Some of the main problems are the rigid-body rotation of fringes in non-coaxial flow; the difficulty to determine points of equal age on different fibres and uncertainty about the amount of ductile deformation taken up by fibres.

6.5 Non-Fibrous Strain Shadows and Strain Caps

Massive (non-fibrous) *strain shadows* are elongate domains on both sides of a core object in which the fabric is different from that in the rock matrix (Figs. 6.21a, 6.22). The boundary between the strain shadow and the matrix may be sharp, as for a fringe, but is more commonly gradual (Figs. 6.1, 6.21a, 6.22). Strain shadows are commonly enriched in soluble minerals such as quartz, carbonate and chlorite, whereas foliation forming minerals such as micas or chain-silica-

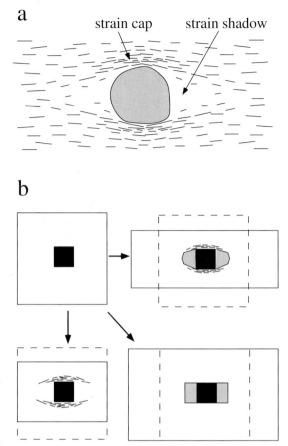

Fig. 6.21. a Geometry of strain shadows and strain caps around a rigid object in a foliated rock. **b** Schematic presentation of the development of three types of strain shadows, depending on strain and volume change as indicated by a *deformed square.* *Grey* strain shadows are formed by precipitation from solution. Notice that strain caps are not necessarily present (cf. Fig. 11.11)

tes are under-represented. If a foliation is present in the matrix, it is usually more weakly developed or absent in the strain shadow (Figs. 7.32, 11.11). The shape of massive strain shadows can be used as a tool to determine shear sense as in the case of strain fringes (Fig. 6.17). Obviously, more care is needed than in the case of fringes, especially if the core object is angular.

In foliated rocks, strain shadows and strain fringes are commonly associated with *strain caps,* domains enriched in micas or insoluble minerals, where the main foliation is strongly developed (Figs. 6.21a, 7.9, 7.39). Strain caps occur at opposite sides of the core object, in the quarters oblique to the strain shadow or fringe. Some strain fringes may develop their own strain caps if deformation is advanced,

Fig. 6.22. Non-fibrous strain shadow around a garnet porphyroblast in micaschist. Orós, NE-Brazil. Width of view 3.9
mm. Polarisers at 45°. Notice the presence of strain caps and the
gradual transition between the strain shadows and the matrix

when they may start to behave as independent core
objects.

The term strain shadow may suggest that strain
in the 'shadow' of the core object is relatively low, but
this is not generally correct. In fact, strain shadows
and strain caps are structures representing complex
partitioning of strain and volume change around a
core object, the exact nature of which is usually
unknown.

Massive strain shadows can be formed by non-
fibrous infilling of a void at the surface of a core
object as for strain fringes, by recrystallisation of a
strain fringe, or by redistribution of mineral phases
in response to inhomogeneous deformation around a
core object. This may happen at low fluid pressure by
pressure solution at the site of strain caps, solution
transfer, and redeposition of material at grain boundaries in the developing strain shadow without opening of distinct voids. Figure 6.21b shows schematically
some models for the development of different types
of strain shadows.

Mantled porphyroclasts superficially resemble
strain shadows (Chap. 5.6.5) but they have the same
mineral composition as the core object (porphy-

roclast), form by different mechanisms and have a
different kinematic significance as strain shadows
(Chap. 5.6.6: cf. Figs. 5.18 and 6.17). We therefore do
not include mantled porphyroclasts in the category of
strain shadows. It is preferable to reserve the terms
strain shadow and strain fringe for domains of material that have a different composition from the core
object. However, mantled porphyroclasts and strain
shadows are end members of a range of possible combinations; some strain shadows may be difficult to
distinguish from mantled porphyroclasts with wings
that have undergone chemical or mineralogical changes (Robin 1979; Wintsch 1986).

6.6 Microboudinage

Boudinage affecting elongate mineral grains at thin
section scale is often referred to as *microboudinage*
(Misch 1969, 1970; Vernon 1976; Allison and La Tour
1977; Masuda and Kuriyama 1988; Masuda et al. 1989,

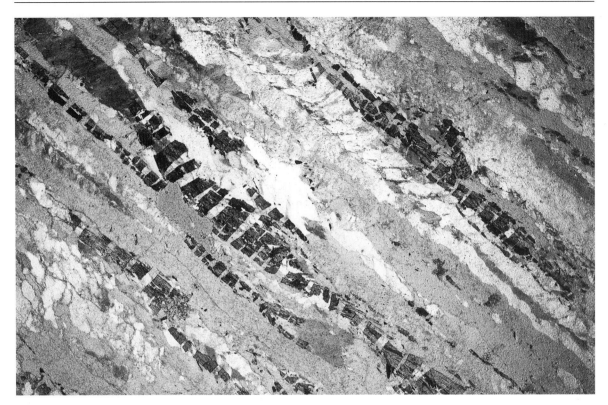

Fig. 6.23. Microboudinage of tourmalines *(dark)* in a quartzite. Notice boudinage both perpendicular and parallel to the elongate tourmalines *(chocolate tablet boudinage).* Quartz recrystallised in large grains invading the necks of the boudins, and was deformed again as testified by undulose extinction. Fortaleza, NE Brazil. Width of view 4.5 mm. Polarisers at 45°. (Specimen courtesy Michel Arthaud)

1990; Ji and Zhao 1993; Figs. 6.23, 6.24). The structures created in the necks of these boudins show many similarities with those in strain shadows and extensional veins.

Microboudins can help to establish metamorphic conditions during deformation, indicated by the mineral assemblage that grew in the necks of the boudins. In some cases, grain growth accompanies microboudinage to form zoned grains. Analysis of the zoning in these grains may also allow establishment of changing metamorphic circumstances during progressive deformation (Misch 1969, 1970; Figs. 6.24, 6.25).

Microboudinage can also be used as a strain gauge (Ferguson 1981,1987): the length of a boudinaged grain divided by the sum of the length of the boudins gives a minimum value for stretch along the long axis of the boudinaged grain. However, this axis does not necessarily coincide with the direction of maximum extension in the rock. It is also possible to use the length of boudin fragments to make estimates of differential stress (Lloyd et al. 1982; Masuda et al. 1990; Ji and Zhao 1993).

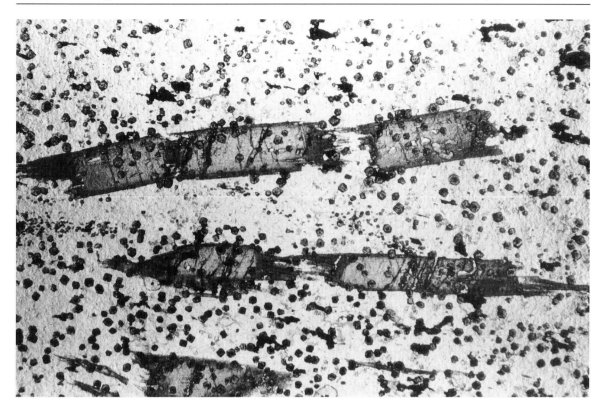

Fig. 6.24. Microboudinage of blue amphibole in a garnet bearing metachert. Notice how, after the boudinage of the light-
coloured cores, darker amphibole overgrew the cores and ten-
ded to mend the separated boudins. Metamorphic conditions
during boudinage can be estimated from the changing blue
amphibole composition (cf. Fig. 6.25). Sesia Lanzo Zone, Italian
Alps. Width of view 4 mm. PPL. (Sample courtesy Leo Minnigh)

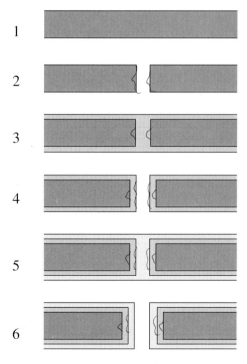

Fig. 6.25. Schematic deformation-growth sequence involved
in microboudinage of zoned crystals, showing a single site of
rupture. Although represented graphically as finite steps, both
stretching and accretion are thought to proceed essentially
simultaneously. (After Misch 1969, p 48)

7 Porphyroblasts and Reaction Rims

7.1 Introduction

A volume of rock involved in deformation and metamorphism will continuously undergo changes in structure and mineral content. This chapter treats mineral growth and replacement structures and the way in which their geometry can be used to reconstruct tectonic history. Two types of informative structures are treated: porphyroblasts and reaction rims.

Relatively large single crystals which formed by metamorphic growth in a more fine-grained matrix are known as *porphyroblasts* (Box p. 104). Porphyro-blasts are a valuable source of information on local tectonic and metamorphic evolution. Inclusion patterns in porphyroblasts can mimic the structure in the rock at the time of their growth (Fig. 7.1) and allow a reconstruction of the relative timing of mineral growth, reflecting metamorphic conditions, and deformation. Porphyroblasts are not equally common in all rock types and under all metamorphic conditions. Most common and most informative are Al-silicate porphyroblasts like garnet, biotite, staurolite, chloritoid, andalusite etc. grown under upper green-schist to amphibolite facies conditions in metapelites. Garnet, plagioclase, epidote and hornblende may form interesting porphyroblasts in metabasites. Apart from their inclusion patterns, porphyroblasts may

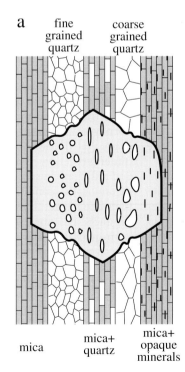

a   fine grained quartz   coarse grained quartz

mica   mica+ quartz   mica+ opaque minerals

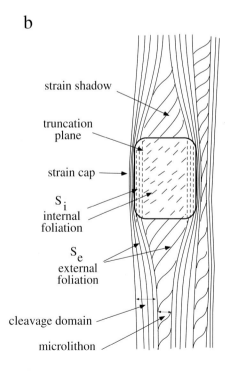

b

strain shadow

truncation plane

strain cap

S_i internal foliation

S_e external foliation

cleavage domain

microlithon

Fig. 7.1. a Diagram illustrating how an Al-silicate porphyro-blast may grow in a mica-rich matrix by substitution reactions involving minor volume change. Opaque minerals *(right hand side)* and quartz are taken up as inclusions and their preferred orientation and distribution is mimicked by the inclusions. Later deformation may affect the matrix but will not change the included structure if the porphyroblast remains undeformed. The inclusion patterns may undergo rigid body rotation but will retain a record of the structure in the rock at the time of porphyroblast growth. **b** Commonly used terminology for porphyroblasts

also record the metamorphic evolution from core to rim; either a growth zoning may be present, or inclusions of certain minerals may show P-T conditions different from the matrix.

Since porphyroblasts are such informative structures, it is usually advantageous to sample and study microstructures in available metapelites (and metabasites especially if they are garnet-bearing) in any area for large-scale tectonic studies. In order to evaluate the significance of porphyroblasts, we first describe why and how porphyroblasts grow and how they acquire inclusions. Important texts on the tectonic significance of porphyroblasts are Zwart (1962), Schoneveld (1979), Spry (1969), Vernon (1975, 1976, 1989), Bell and Rubenach (1983), Bell (1985), Bard (1986), Bell et al. (1986), Yardley (1989), Yardley et al. (1990), Barker (1990), Shelley (1993), and Johnson (1993a,b).

7.2 Porphyroblast Nucleation and Growth

The distribution and size of porphyroblasts in a metamorphic rock depend on the amount of nucleation sites and the rate at which the nuclei grow. The nucleation and initial growth stage of a new mineral in a metamorphic rock is hampered by the fact that small grains have a relatively high surface free energy and are therefore less stable than large ones (Poirier 1985). This unstable stage can be overcome at specific sites controlled by small irregularities such as strongly deformed grains or microfractures (Yardley 1989). If many suitable sites are available, many small porphyroblasts may form; if few suitable nucleation sites are present, isolated large porphyroblasts develop (Fig. 7.2). Thus, nucleation rate and growth rate are competing processes.

Some minerals nucleate on the crystal lattice of other ones in a particular orientation, e.g. sillimanite on muscovite, amphibole on pyroxene. This relationship is known as *epitaxy*. The special situation where the crystal lattices of both minerals are parallel is known as *syntaxy*.

Once a stable porphyroblast has formed, its radial growth rate is likely to decrease with time if its growth rate in terms of added mass is constant. Although little is known about the absolute growth rate of porphyroblasts, theoretical considerations and available radiometric dating give estimates for growth of a garnet 2 mm in diameter of less that 0.1

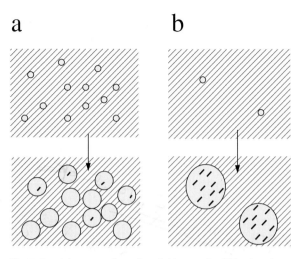

a   **b**

Fig. 7.2. a A large number of nuclei in a rock will lead to development of a large number of small porphyroblasts, each with few inclusions. **b** Few nuclei lead to few large porphyroblasts, which may contain a clear inclusion pattern and are therefore useful in fabric analysis

nucleation is a limiting stage
x/ size relates more to nucleation sites tha...

m.y. to 1 m.y. (Cashman and Ferry 1988; Christensen et al 1989; Burton and O'Nions 1991; Paterson and Tobisch 1992; Barker 1994).

7.3 Inclusions

The growth process of porphyroblasts is mainly controlled by diffusion, either in the solid state or through fluids present along grain boundaries. Elements necessary for growth that are not present have to be transported by diffusion to the surface of the porphyroblast. Minerals adjacent to the growing grain that do not or only partly participate in the mineral reaction have to be removed by dissolution and diffusion. In some cases, especially at high-grade metamorphic conditions, diffusion rates have been high enough to allow complete removal of reaction products and non-participating material, and clear, 'gem-quality' porphyroblasts result. In most cases, and especially at low to medium-grade metamorphism, minerals that do not participate in the reaction are not removed completely but are overgrown and enclosed by porphyroblasts as *passive inclusions*. If the rock adjacent to the growing porphyroblast had a compositional layering or a shape-preferred orientation of grains, this fabric may be partly preserved when grains are included in the porphyroblast; an

Fig. 7.3. Example of the process visualised in Fig. 7.1a. Post-tectonic porphyroblast of biotite *(top)* and staurolite *(below)* grew over a layered structure in a fine-grained schist. The structure is mimicked within the porphyroblasts. South Africa. Width of view 5.5 mm. PPL

inclusion pattern results which mimics the original fabric (Figs. 7.1–7.3). In this way, straight foliation traces can be included, but also more complex patterns such as folds or even complete crenulation cleavages (Figs. 7.4, 7.5). Opaque minerals and quartz are most commonly included in this manner, but zircon, monazite, apatite, rutile, sphene and epidote-group minerals are also common. Mica inclusions are rare but do occur in some Al-silicate porphyroblasts; they may have been included as excess phases of reactants. However, care is needed, since mica overgrowths may resemble inclusions (see below).

Microstructural observation of inclusions in porphyroblasts by numerous workers has led to the conclusion that they are mostly included in a passive manner, without being significantly displaced by the growing porphyroblast (Zwart 1962; Spry 1969; Vernon 1975, 1976, 1989; Bell 1981, 1985; Bard 1986; Yardley 1989; Yardley et al. 1990; Barker 1990). Deflection of matrix foliation around porphyroblasts (Fig. 7.5a) is therefore thought to form by deformation of the matrix around a rigid pre-existing porphyroblast (Zwart 1962; Vernon 1976; Barker 1990; Yardley 1989) and not by mechanical displacement

of the matrix by the growing porphyroblast as earlier proposed by Spry (1969) and Misch (1971). However, growing porphyroblasts can displace graphite and white mica in rare cases, as explained in Chap. 7.7.

Surfaces of aligned elongate inclusions within porphyroblasts are referred to as S_i (i for internal) whereas the foliation outside the porphyroblasts is called S_e (e for external; Fig. 7.1b). If deformation occurs after porphyroblast growth, S_i may have a different orientation from S_e.

The abundance of inclusions in Al-silicate porphyroblasts has been attributed to the limited mobility of Al-ions (Carmichael 1969). At greenschist and lower amphibolite facies conditions, Al-ions are far less mobile than Si, Fe, Mg, K or Ca-ions, unless the pH is extremely high or low, or if salinity is extremely high (Slack et al. 1993). This means that porphyroblasts of Al-silicates such as andalusite, cordierite, staurolite, chloritoid and garnet can be expected to grow at Al-rich sites such as mica layers and to have difficulty in replacing minerals that lack Al by an intact lattice: such minerals are included instead. This explains why Al-silicate porphyroblasts commonly

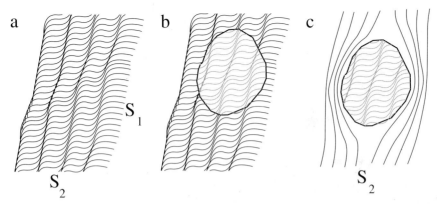

Fig. 7.4a–c. Diagrammatic sketch of the evolution of complex porphyroblast structures as shown in Fig. 7.5a,b. **a** S_2 crenulation cleavage develops, overprinting an older foliation S_1 (Chap. 4.8). **b** A porphyroblast overgrows the structure and mimics it in its inclusion pattern. **c** Continued deformation and/or recrystallisation and grain growth (transposition: Box p. 88) destroys the folds in the matrix where a more or less continuous foliation (S_2) develops. Only the relict structure included in the relatively rigid porphyroblast records the structural evolution in the rock

Fig. 7.5. a Micaschist with porphyroblasts of staurolite, biotite and andalusite. The large twinned crystal in the *centre* is staurolite with an inclusion pattern mimicking differentiated crenulation cleavage; a detail of the **right-hand rim** is shown in **b**. The light-coloured horizontal bands in the crystal are inclusion-poor zones representing the differentiated mica-rich limbs of microfolds (cf. Fig. 4.12) The dominant foliation in the matrix is a fine-grained foliation, strongly deflected around the staurolite porphyroblasts. This shows that since porphyroblast growth, crenulation cleavage in the matrix has been destroyed by a process as visualised in Figs. 7.4 and 4.17. (Example of syntectonic porphyroblasts: *F1* in Fig. 7.9). Rioumajou, Pyrenees, France. Width of view **a** 10 mm. Polars at 45°; **b** 2 mm. PPL

Fig. 7.5. b

(handwritten annotations:)
more continuous staur in mica rich area ; qtz rich area still has qtz ; mica now staurolite

(left margin handwritten annotations:)
mica rich ; crenulated ; MR ; rich

contain numerous inclusions when they grow in quartz and graphite-bearing pelitic rocks. Such porphyroblasts may even obtain a *skeletal shape* (Fig. 7.6) when they grow into Al-poor domains, for instance quartz-rich layers or strain shadows; they are unable to build a complete lattice at these sites, but rather follow grain boundaries. In many cases a compositional layering is included as inclusion-poor and inclusion-rich areas in porphyroblasts (Figs. 7.1, 7.3, 7.5b). This happens by overgrowth of mica-rich and quartz-rich domains (e.g. a differentiated crenulation cleavage). In extreme cases a porphyroblast grows only along layers of a specific composition and obtains an elongate shape, although its normal crystal habit may be more equidimensional. Figure 7.7 shows an example of elongate staurolite growing along pelitic layers in a metasediment. The shape of pre-existing but now substituted minerals may also remain visible as inclusion-poor areas within some porphyroblasts. These structures are known as *ghost structures* (Fig. 7.8).

Since the diffusion rate of ions is a function of temperature, inclusions become increasingly rare, more coarse-grained and less well-defined at higher metamorphic grade (upper amphibolite and granulite facies), and are seldom frequent enough to define S_i surfaces.

(handwritten annotation:)
↑T inclusions: rare, more c-g, less defined

7.4 Classification of Porphyro-blast-Matrix Relations

7.4.1 Introduction

Porphyroblasts with inclusion patterns contain information on the nature of early deformation and metamorphic events, and on the relative age of mineral growth and deformation. Zwart (1960, 1962) elaborated a scheme with nine diagnostic relations based on the idea that crystals may be older, younger or of the same age as specific deformation phases (Chap. 1.2). Here, we use a modified version of the Zwart scheme (Fig. 7.9). We use the terms pre-, syn-, inter- and post-tectonic, which describe the time relation between porphyroblast growth and one or two specific phases of deformation, normally represented in the matrix surrounding the porphyroblast by a foliation or by folding. As a shorthand notation, we also use symbols to show the time relationship of deformation and metamorphism as outlined in the Box of p. 161 and Fig. 7.10. Deformation phases (Chap. 1.2) are determined for individual thin sections; schemes of regional

Meta — Soild state Nxns

qtz replacing micas

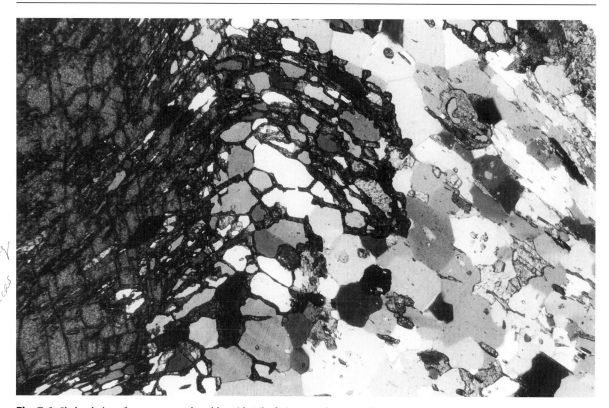

Fig. 7.6. Skeletal rim of a garnet porphyroblast (detail of Fig. 7.32) showing how quartz crystals of the strain shadow are incorporated into the growing crystal as slightly elongated inclusions. The curvature of S_i is caused by relative rotation between the porphyroblast and the matrix foliation (cf. Fig. 7.32). Baños, Equador. Width of view 2 mm. Polarisers at 45°

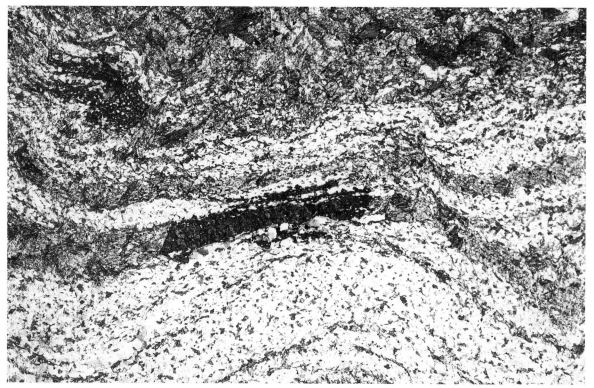

Fig. 7.7. Quartz-rich schist with elongate staurolite crystal (dark crystal in the *centre*) that grew along a mica-rich layer. Folding of the layering and layer-parallel foliation was probably later than the growth of the staurolite that contains a straight inclusion pattern. Pyrenees, Spain. Width of view 12 mm. Polarisers at 45°

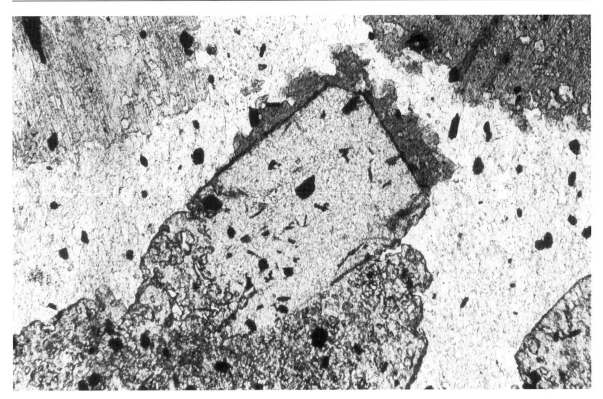

Fig. 7.8. Garnet biotite schist. The garnet crystal (*lower part* of the photograph) is very rich in inclusions except for an almost rectangular area in its upper part where only a few inclusions of opaque minerals are visible. The garnet apparently overgrew a biotite crystal in this area, the fringes of which are still visible at the outer contact. Since biotite has a similar Al concentration as garnet, the garnet crystal could substitute the biotite without incorporation of extra inclusions. Note also the more idiomorphic outline of the garnet crystal in this area. Once the biotite is completely overgrown its shape remains visible as a ghost structure of inclusion-poor garnet. Grenville Province, Canada. Width of view 2 mm. PPL

deformation phases have to be evaluated from schemes for individual thin sections (Fig. 7.10) combined with field observations (Chap. 7.9). For a correct interpretation of inclusion patterns it is desirable to determine their approximate three-dimensional shape by comparison of several parallel or orthogonal sections (Chap. 10.7). This applies specifically to inclusions with complicated patterns such as spiral-S_i garnets.

7.4.2 Pretectonic Porphyroblast Growth

Pretectonic porphyroblasts are rarely described (Zwart 1962; Fleming and Offler 1968; Vernon et al. 1993a, b) and seem to be uncommon in areas affected by regional metamorphism, except possibly in low-pressure/ high-temperature metamorphism. Even in the case of contact metamorphism, some deformation may predate porphyroblast growth. If present, inclusions in pretectonic porphyroblasts are ran-domly oriented (A, B in Fig. 7.9; Fig. 7.11) or show sector zoning (Chap. 7.7; Rice and Mitchell 1991). A primary compositional layering may survive as a ghost layering (Fleming and Offler 1968). It is incorrect, however, to interpret any crystal with random inclusions as pretectonic; in high-grade rocks, early foliations may be destroyed by grain growth, and subsequent porphyroblast growth may give rise to apparently pretectonic structures. Also, porphyroblasts with planar inclusion patterns may seem to contain randomly oriented inclusions in sections parallel to S_i (Fig. 10.2b). Pretectonic porphyroblasts may be surrounded by a matrix with polyphase deformation, as shown in case B in Fig. 7.9 (Vernon et al. 1993a).

Chlorite-mica stacks (Fig. 4.13), which are common in slates, may be one of the few examples of pretectonic (or early syntectonic) porphyroblasts. They occur as lens or barrel-shaped aggregates of chlorite and white mica in microlithons of slates, with (001) planes at a high angle to the foliation and commonly

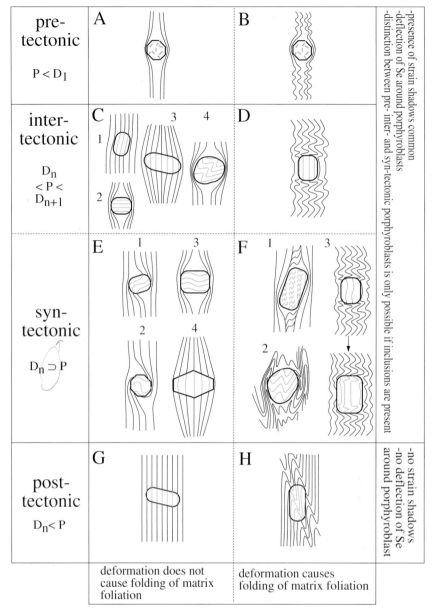

Fig. 7.9A–H. Schematic representation of pre-, inter-, syn-, and post-tectonic porphyroblast growth. The left-hand part of the diagram refers to deformation resulting in a single foliation or deformation of an earlier foliation without folding; the ***right-hand*** part considers deformation resulting in crenulation of an older foliation. Pretectonic porphyroblasts (**A** and **B**) show strong foliation deflection and randomly oriented inclusions. Intertectonic porphyroblasts (**C** and **D**) grew passively over a fabric in absence of deformation, and protect the resulting inclusion pattern from later deformation. Inclusion patterns are usually straight but more complex situations (**C4**) are also possible. **C2** and **E3** are known as millipede structures (Chap. 7.5). Syntectonic porphyroblasts (**E** and **F**) have grown during a phase of deformation. Inclusion patterns are usually curved and continuous with the fabric outside the porphyroblast, and show evidence of having been modified during porphyroblast growth. The distinction of syn- and intertectonic porphyroblasts is usually difficult since transitions occur and differences are subtle (cf. **C1** and **E1**; **C3** and **E4**; **C4** and **F1**). Post-tectonic porphyroblasts (**G** and **H**) have grown after cessation of deformation. The inclusion pattern is identical to and continuous with the external fabric. No strain shadows, strain caps or deflection of foliation are developed.

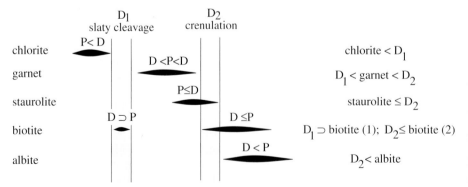

Fig. 7.10. Example of a relative age diagram for a single thin section of a micaschist. Chlorite is pre-D_1; garnet is intertectonic between D_1 and D_2. Staurolite is pre-syn D_2 and biotite has two growth phases; one syn-D_1 and the other syn-post D_2. Albite grows post-D_2. In the diagram, abbreviations are given ***at right***

parallel to bedding (Beutner 1978; Weber 1981; Craig et al. 1982; van der Pluijm and Kaars-Sijpesteijn 1984; Woodland 1985; Gregg 1986; Li et al. 1994). Some chlorite-mica stacks may have formed as detrital grains (Beutner 1978), but evidence exists for their original growth as crystals parallel to bedding in a diagenetic foliation at very low to low-grade metamorphic conditions, prior to deformation (Craig et al. 1982; Woodland 1985; Gregg 1986). Partial dissolution and new growth parallel to a developing microlithon of secondary foliation causes their final shape (Talbot 1965; Weber 1981; Gregg 1986; Clark and Fisher 1995; Li et al. 1994).

7.4.3 Intertectonic Porphyroblast Growth

The term intertectonic is introduced here for porphyroblasts that have grown over a secondary foliation, and are surrounded by a matrix affected by a later deformation phase that did not leave any record in the inclusion pattern of the porphyroblast (C and D

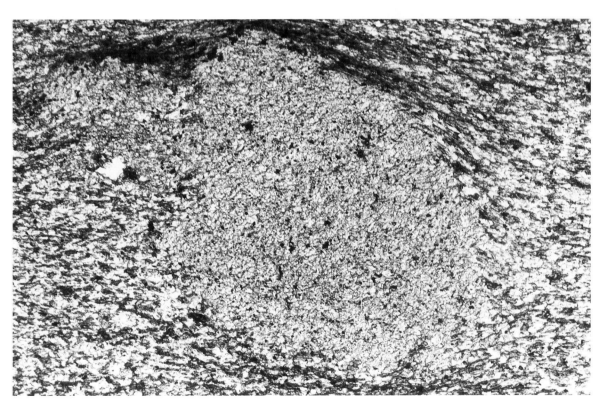

Fig. 7.11. Pretectonic porphyroblast of cordierite in cordierite-mica schist. The cordierite crystal has inclusions with random orientation showing that at the time of its growth the rock was a hornfels which lacked a directional fabric. Later deformation formed a foliation (S_1 *horizontal*) which is deflected around the cordierite crystal. Note the well-developed strain cap on top of the cordierite. Example of case A in Fig. 7.9. Leiden Collection. Width of view 2.5 mm. PPL

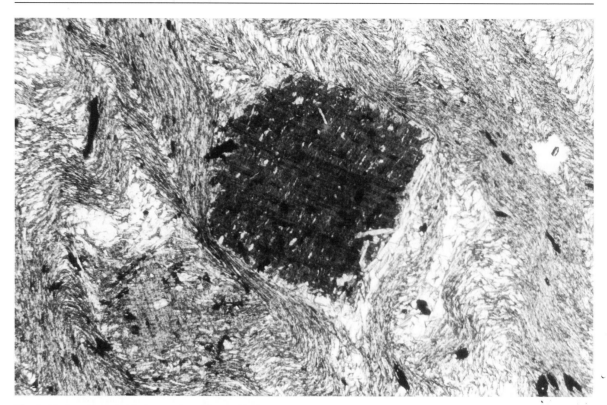

Fig. 7.12. Intertectonic biotite porphyroblast in biotite phyllite with approximately straight S_i (S_1) surrounded by a crenulation cleavage (S_2) that wraps around the crystal. This porphyroblast is labelled intertectonic since it grew after D_1 (including S_1) and before D_2. Its growth period may, however, overlap with both these phases since crystals grown very late during D_1 or very early during D_2 would show similar structures. Note mineral cleavage (001) within the biotite, almost perpendicular to S_i. Example of case D in Fig. 7.9. Concepción. Central-south Chile. Width of view 4 mm. PPL

in Fig. 7.9; Figs. 7.12, 7.13). Porphyroblasts with a straight S_i that is oblique to S_e can also be named *oblique-S_i porphyroblasts* and are discussed in Chap. 7.6.8. (C1 in Fig. 7.9; Fig. 7.14).

7.4.4 Syntectonic Porphyroblast Growth

Syntectonic porphyroblasts have grown during a single phase of deformation D_n and are the most frequently encountered type of porphyroblasts in nature. This is probably due to the fact that deformation has a catalysing effect on mineral nucleation and diffusion rates (cf. Bell 1981; Bell and Hayward 1991). A large variety of microstructures can form in this group (Prior 1987; Figs. 7.9, 7.32, 11.11). The principal controlling variables are finite strain, the ratio of growth rate to strain rate, and the stage of progressive deformation during which the porphyroblasts grew

(Barker 1994). The most characteristic syntectonic porphyroblasts form when growth and strain rates are of the same order of magnitude (Figs. 7.15, 7.32). Inclusion patterns are generally curved in syntectonic porphyroblasts, and random or straight in pre- and intertectonic porphyroblasts. S_i can be symmetrically arranged with respect to S_e, (E3, E4, F3 in Fig. 7.9) or show oblique-S_i or 'spiral' geometry (Chap. 7.6.8; E1 and E2 in Fig. 7.9). The latter is particularly common in garnet (Schoneveld 1979; Bell and Johnson 1989; Fig. 7.39). Included folds in porphyroblasts (C4, F and H in Fig. 7.9) are known as *helicitic folds*. Porphyroblasts with oblique and spiral-shaped patterns have been loosely referred to as *rotated porphyroblasts* (Chap. 7.6.8) but use of this term should be discouraged. The geometry indicates *relative* rotation of porphyroblast and S_e but determination of movement of either fabric element in an external reference frame is difficult (Ramsay 1962; Bell 1985; Johnson 1993a,b and Chap. 7.6.8).

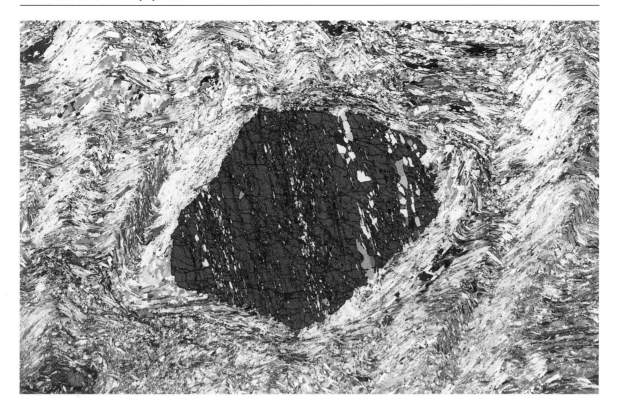

Fig. 7.13. Intertectonic garnet porphyroblast in garnet-mica schist. The garnet may be classified as intertectonic since it overgrew a straight secondary fabric ($S_i = S_n$) that has been deformed in the matrix by later deformation resulting in crenulation and relative rotation of about 90° of the garnet with respect to S_n. Since the continuity between S_i and S_e is almost completely destroyed by post-garnet deformation and grain growth in the matrix, an alternative explanation, considering S_i and S_n in the matrix as generated by entirely different phases, is also possible. Example of case D in Fig. 7.9. Tärnaby, Norrbotten, Sweden. Width of view 20 mm. Polarisers at 45°

7.4.5 Post-Tectonic Porphyroblast Growth

This group is easy to define by the absence of deflection of S_e, strain shadows, undulose extinction or other evidence of deformation which is common to pre- syn- and intertectonic porphyroblasts (G and H in Fig. 7.9). If inclusions are present, S_i is continuous with S_e (G in Fig. 7.9), even if folded (H in Fig. 7.9). Some care is needed with post-tectonic porphyroblast. It is not uncommon to find weak deformation effects, including strain shadows, in or around some crystals in a population of apparently post-tectonic porphyroblast. In fact, there are no reliable criteria to distinguish between very late syntectonic porphyroblasts and post-tectonic ones (Figs. 7.3, 7.20, 7.21).

7.4.6 Complex Porphyroblast Growth

A large number of combinations of the categories of porphyroblast-deformation relations mentioned above are possible, especially if a mineral has several growth phases. Relatively common are syntectonic crystals with post-tectonic rims, but combinations of porphyroblasts with pretectonic cores and syntectonic rims also occur (Fig. 7.17). These complex relations are easily overlooked but may be recognised by an unusual geometry or abrupt changes in the geometry of the inclusion pattern, especially if this is associated with zoning in the porphyroblast (Chap. 7.6.8).

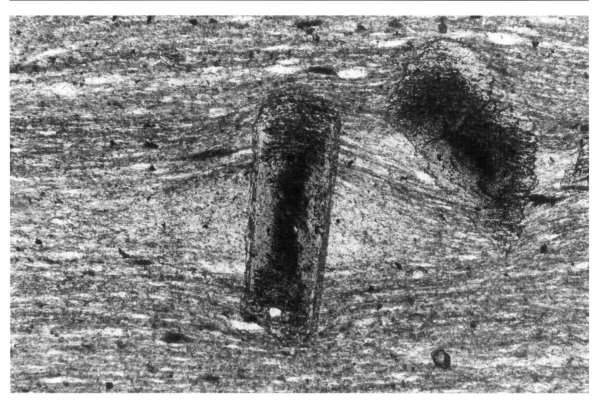

Fig. 7.17. Syntectonic chloritoid crystals (ottrelite variety) in slate. The central part of the main crystal does not contain any S_i, and the strain shadows next to this part seem to be free of cleavage, suggesting that the core of the crystal may be pretec- tonic. Only one phase of deformation can be recognised. Example of case E4 in Fig. 7.9. Curaglia, Switzerland. Width of view 1.8 mm. PPL

Fig. 7.18. Garnet porphyroblast in micaschist, syntectonic with respect to D_2. D_2 folds, traced by included opaque grains, are open in the garnet core, becoming tighter towards the rim. S_2 shows clear deviation around the lower part of the crystal. No strain shadows have developed, probably because the gar- net grew in a mica-rich band. The crenulation cleavage (S_2) and S_i (= S_1) are mainly defined by opaque minerals. Example of case F3 in Fig. 7.9. São Felix de Cavalcante, Goiás, Brazil. Width of view 3 mm. Polarisers at 45°

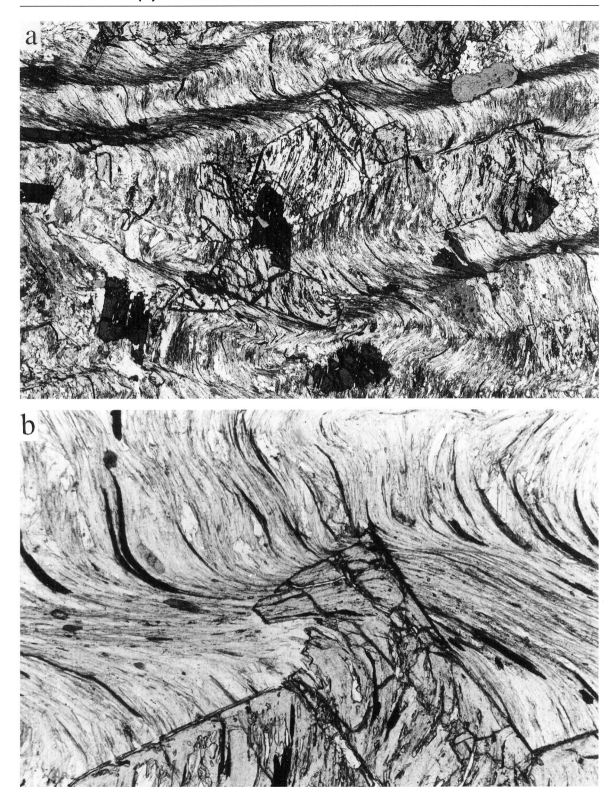

Fig. 7.19a,b. Garnet kyanite staurolite schist with S_2 crenulation cleavage and staurolite porphyroblasts that are syntectonic with respect to D_2. **a** Inclusions in the central light-coloured staurolite crystal show gentle folding, becoming tighter towards the upper rim. Lukmanier Pass, Switzerland. Width of view 9.6 mm. Polarisers at 45°. **b** Detail of central upper part of photograph **a,** showing the abrupt curvature of S_1 in the outer rim of the staurolite crystal. S_2 is deflected around the crystal that partly overgrows the mica-rich domains of S_2. Example of case F3 in Fig. 7.9. Width of view 2.4 mm. PPL

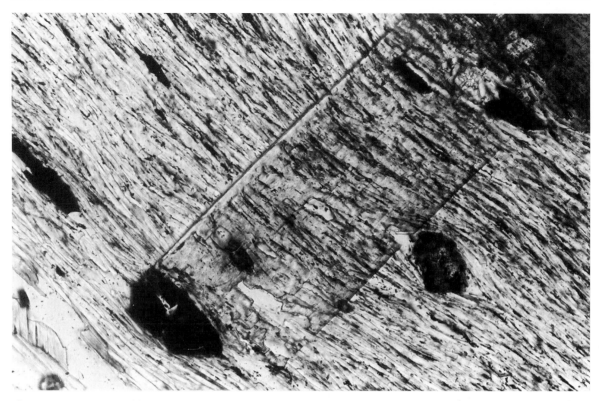

Fig. 7.20. Post-tectonic chlorite crystal overgrowing a slaty cleavage. The cleavage structure is perfectly continuous without any deflection or development of strain shadows. Older strain shadows around opaque grains are included without modification. Example of case G in Fig. 7.9. Araí, Goiás, Brazil. Width of view 0.6 mm. PPL

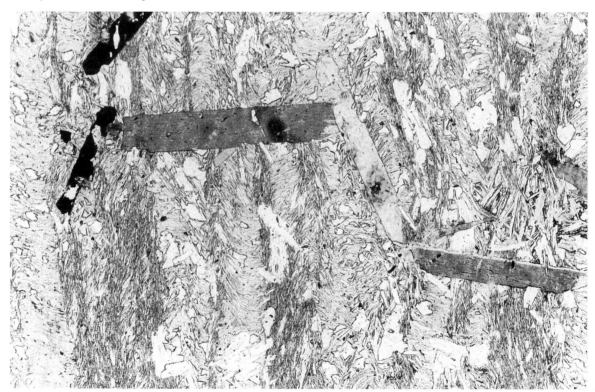

Fig. 7.21. Post-tectonic biotite porphyroblasts overgrowing a crenulation cleavage (S_2). Although no inclusion patterns have developed, the lack of deflection of S_2 and the lack of strain shadows show that the biotite crystals grew after the crenulation cleavage development. The opaque crystals at *left* are probably of the same age. However, very late syntectonic growth is also possible, as discussed in the text. Example of cases C2 and D in Fig. 7.26. Ouro Preto, Minas Gerais, Brazil. Width of view 1.8 mm. PPL. (Thin section courtesy Hanna Jordt-Evangelista)

7.5 Millipede and Deflection-Fold Microstructures

Bell and Rubenach (1980) and Bell (1981) have drawn attention to a microstructure in some inter- and syntectonic porphyroblasts which they named *millipede microstructure* (C2 and E3 in Fig. 7.9; Fig. 7.22a). The term refers to syn- or intertectonic porphyroblasts around which S_e is deflected in opposite directions (Fig. 7.23). In a related type of structure, S_e is deflected through isoclinal folding at both sides of a porphyroblast in a way as shown in Fig. 7.22b. This structure has been called *deflection-fold structure* by Passchier and Speck (1994; Fig. 7.24). Both structures are an effect of foliation deflection adjacent to a rigid porphyroblast. Structures similar to deflection folds and millipede structures can be reproduced

experimentally in homogeneous, non-partitioned flow around rigid objects (Ghosh and Ramberg 1976; Masuda and Ando 1988; Gray and Busa 1994). Bell (1981) claimed that deformation in rocks is generally partitioned into lenses ('pods') with little deformation or predominantly coaxial shortening, surrounded by an anastomosing network of shear zones (Fig. 7.25). He envisaged that porphyroblasts with millipede structures grow syntectonically in these pods until they impinge on the surrounding shear zones where they stop growing or dissolve. This does not seem to be generally valid, however; many millipede structures and deflection folds may be intertectonic, and may have grown over a straight foliation before a second foliation is developed; they should therefore be interpreted with care. The idea that porphyroblasts stop growing when they reach a shearzone or cleavage lamella seems also incorrect as illustrated in Fig. 7.19b (see also Figs. 11.14, 11.16).

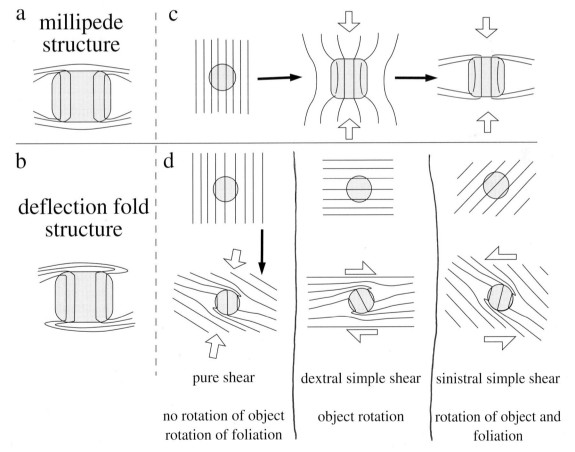

Fig. 7.22. a Millipede structure and **b** deflection fold structure for two inter- to syntectonic porphyroblasts. **c** Development of a millipede structure by coaxial flattening. **d** Three alternative ways to develop a deflection-fold structure

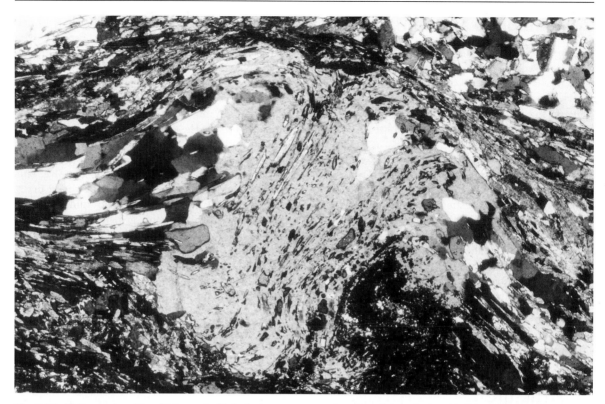

Fig. 7.23. Albite porphyroblast *(light grey)* with inclusion pattern characteristic of a millipede microstructure. S_i corresponds to S_1 and S_e to S_2. Garnet albite schist. Elephant Island, West Antarctica. Width of view 2.8 mm. CPL

7.6 Problematic Porphyroblast Microstructures

7.6.1 Inclusion-Free Porphyroblasts

The presence or absence of inclusions in porphyroblasts cannot be used to date them with respect to other fabric elements (Fig. 7.26). If porphyroblasts do not have inclusions, it is difficult or even impossible to date their growth with respect to deformation. The relative age can in some cases be determined by the intensity of deflection of S_e or from the presence of strain shadows, although care is needed (Fig. 7.26). If there is no deflection of S_e, porphyroblasts may be post-tectonic (C in Fig 7.26); if there is deflection of S_e or if strain shadows are present, porphyroblasts are pre-, inter or syntectonic (Figs. 7.26A and B, 7.40 at right). Care has to be taken since deflection may be caused by later deformation phases and late shortening normal to an earlier foliation (e.g. Bell 1986; Bell et al. 1986). Strain shadows are not always accompanied by deflection of S_e (e.g. Fig. 11.11)

Large, isolated elongate mineral grains such as micas and amphiboles which lie parallel to a foliation and which lack inclusion patterns can also be difficult to date relative to deformation (Fig. 7.26B and D). They may be inter-, syn-, or post-tectonic. Syntectonic porphyroblasts are, if elongate, usually well aligned with the foliation. Intertectonic porphyroblasts may have rotated towards the foliation plane and may be recognisable by slight but consistent obliqueness to the foliation and evidence of internal deformation or replacement along the edges (B in Fig. 7.26). Post-tectonic porphyroblasts are difficult to recognise if they have grown mimetically parallel to a pre-existing foliation. However, their post-tectonic nature can occasionally be recognised if some of the crystals overgrew the foliation obliquely (Fig. 7.21; D in 7.26).

7.6.2 Shape and Size of Inclusion and Matrix Grains

In many cases where a porphyroblast overgrew a structure without later deformation, the size and shape of inclusions differs little from those in the matrix (Figs. 7.1, 7.3, 7.6, 7.8, 7.27a). This is especially

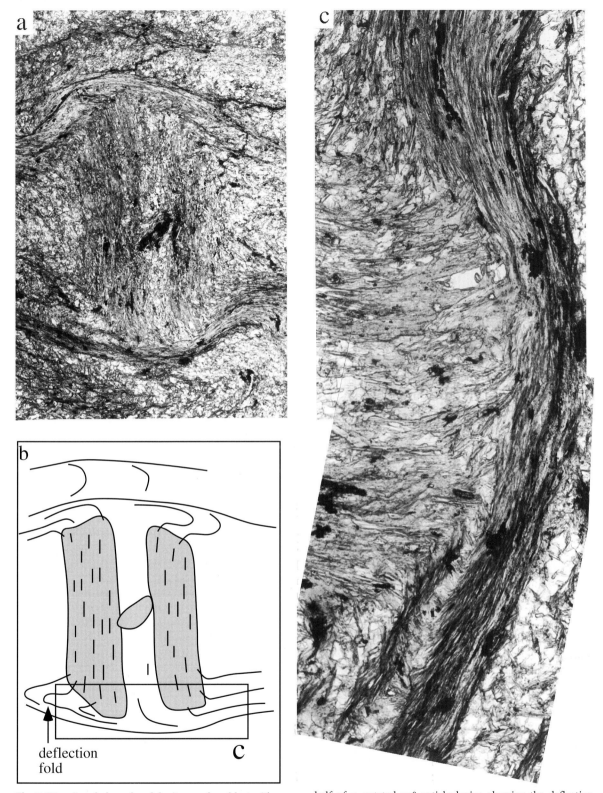

Fig. 7.24. a Spool-shaped andalusite porphyroblast with symmetric distribution of deflection folds on both sides. **b** Schematic drawing of the structure in **a. c** Enlargement of the lower half of **a**, rotated 90° anticlockwise, showing the deflection folds. Trois Seigneurs Massif, Pyrenees, France. Length of porphyroblast in **a** 2.9 mm. PPL

a   b

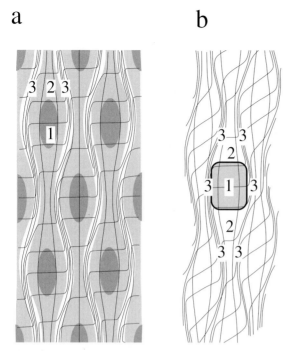

Fig. 7.25. a Deformation partitioning in bulk non-coaxial progressive deformation. **b** Deformation partitioning around a porphyroblast *(centre)* in bulk non-coaxial deformation. Millipede and deflection-fold structures are thought to develop by overgrowth of such partitioning patterns. *1* no strain; *2* coaxial progressive deformation; *3* non-coaxial progressive deformation. (After Bell 1985)

notable in the case of opaque minerals; structures like preferred grain shape orientation, crenulation cleavage and compositional layering can be perfectly preserved in this way as inclusion patterns. Since many porphyroblasts behave as rigid bodies during later deformation, the inclusion patterns, once incorporated, can remain unaffected by later deformation or modification by grain growth, dynamic recrystallisation and transposition that may affect the matrix. In this way porphyroblasts often preserve stages in the tectono-metamorphic evolution that would otherwise be lost (e.g. Figs. 7.4, 7.5). In some cases, inclusions in porphyroblasts may have another size and shape than matrix grains of the same mineral (Fig. 7.27b,c). Commonly, the inclusions are smaller and somewhat more rounded in shape than similar grains in the matrix. This may be caused by partial diffusion, or by a reaction involving the included mineral (Fig. 7.6). A decrease in size of included grains from core to rim can be similarly due to a gradual change in diffusion rate or porphyroblast growth rate. A sharp contrast in size between small inclusions and

large matrix minerals can be explained by progressive coarsening of the matrix after porphyroblast growth as a consequence of grain boundary area reduction (GBAR; Fig. 7.27b; Chap. 3.10). The presence of large inclusions compared to finer-grained matrix minerals, may indicate grainsize reduction in the matrix (Fig. 7.27c). This may for instance happen in mylonite by dynamic recrystallisation at a high differential stress (Chap. 5.3.4, 8.6.1).

7.6.3 False Inclusion Patterns

Some structures in porphyroblasts may resemble patterns of passive inclusions, but form in another way and can be a source of error. *Rutile needles* in biotite or quartz could be misinterpreted as passive inclusions, but usually lack a clear preferred orientation. Alteration (e.g. of feldspar to sericite) or exsolution structures along a crystallographic direction may also be difficult to distinguish from inclusion patterns. If a mineral is a solid solution of two or more phases, it can show exsolution when metamorphic conditions change. This is especially common for minerals which crystallised at high temperature. During retrogression, small grains of the minor phase form in the host crystal (Fig. 7.28, 7.29). The most common examples are found in feldspar, amphiboles, pyroxenes (Fig. 7.29) and spinel.

In the case of feldspars, the new phase may occur as elongate grains or lamellae with a strong preferred orientation within the host crystal, parallel to crystallographic directions. In K-feldspar, this exsolution structure is known as *perthite* (Fig. 7.28); in plagioclase as *anti-perthite*. In K-feldspar, deformation of old crystals may cause local enhancement of exsolution, especially when high-grade feldspars are deformed at low grade (Chap. 3.12.4).

In general, exsolution structures may be distinguished from passive inclusions by their composition and their fixed orientation with respect to a crystallographic direction.

7.6.4 Mimetic growth

Mimetic growth (Chap. 4.9.6) can be a problem in porphyroblast analysis. In some cases porphyroblasts of a mineral A may be mimetically replaced by a mineral B that inherits the inclusion pattern of A and the deflection pattern of the foliation in the matrix around it. This is a potential source of error; however, in our experience this replacement is seldom complete. Generally, it can be detected by the presence of

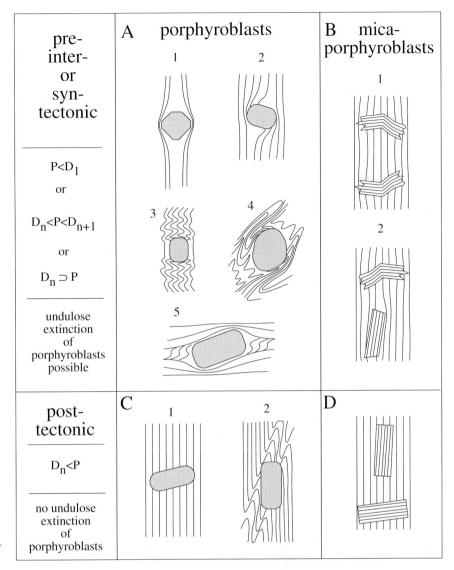

Fig. 7.26A–D. Schematic representation of pre-, syn-, and post-tectonic porphyroblast growth for porphyroblasts that lack passive inclusions. Only distinction of post-tectonic porphyroblasts is relatively easy. Distinction of pre-, inter- and syntectonic porphyroblasts is usually impossible, but they can commonly be distinguished from post-tectonic porphyroblasts by internal deformation features such as undulose extinction

relicts of mineral A, or by independent crystals of mineral B in the matrix that show the correct microtectonic relation. This kind of (partial) replacement structures can give important information on the metamorphic evolution and is treated in Chapter 7.8.

7.6.5 Deformed Porphyroblasts

The relations in Fig. 7.9 can also be recognised if pre-, inter- or syntectonic porphyroblasts show evidence of intracrystalline deformation such as microboudinage, undulose extinction and formation of subgrains. However, special attention is needed for crystals with helicitic folds; if an entire crystal is fol-

ded with the same wavelength and amplitude as the inclusion pattern, S_i may have been originally straight. Such crystals, recognisable by their undulose extinction, must not be mistaken for undeformed porphyroblasts containing true helicitic folds (Chap. 7.4.4).

7.6.6 Uncertain Age Relation of Host and Inclusions

In the previous sections, the recognition of passive inclusions (which developed entirely before growth of the porphyroblast) in porphyroblasts has been presented as a rather straightforward procedure. If

a

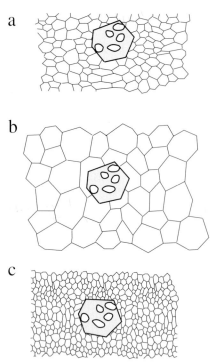

b

c

elongate inclusions of a certain mineral occur in groups in a porphyroblast and are not oriented parallel to a crystallographic direction, or even better, if they trace structures such as layering or folds in connection with similar structures in the matrix, they are most probably passive inclusions. Other inclusions that are probably included passively are quartz grains which form part of overgrown strain shadows (Figs. 7.6, 7.39a) and inclusions with identical size, shape and distribution as grains of the same mineral in the matrix. Using these passive inclusions, the age relation of deformation and porphyroblast growth can be established (Chap. 7.4). However, some care is needed; in some cases it may be difficult to determine the **growth sequence** of the minerals that form porphyroblasts and inclusions (cf. Flood and Vernon 1988; Barker 1994).

◄ **Fig. 7.27. a** Growth of a porphyroblast over matrix material. Inclusions are more rounded but of a size similar to those in the matrix. **b** After porphyroblast growth, grains in the matrix may become coarser by static recrystallisation and grain growth. **c** In some cases they may become smaller by dynamic recrystallisation due to deformation

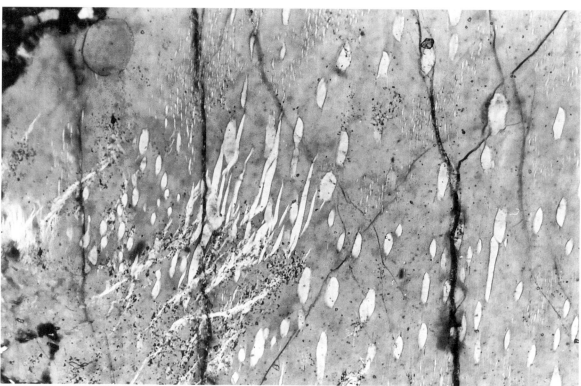

Fig. 7.28. Ellipsoidal and flame-shaped albite lamellae in perthitic K-feldspar from a granodiorite. Two sets of ellipsoidal lamellae of different size are present, possibly reflecting two stages of dissolution at different temperature (Chap. 8.9). The flame-shaped perthite-lamellae result from unmixing during greenschist facies deformation. The preferred orientation (N-S) is controlled by crystallographic directions. This microstructure should not be mistaken for passive inclusions. St Barthélemy Massif, Pyrenees, France. Width of view 0.6 mm. CPL

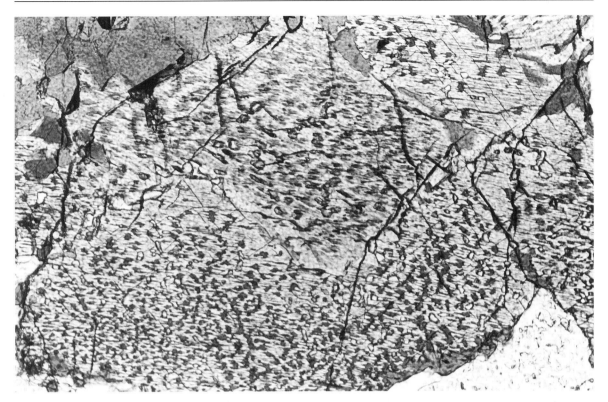

Fig. 7.29. Large clinopyroxene crystal showing substitution by hornblende in an exsolution-like structure that may be mistaken for passive inclusions. The crystallographic control of this type of false inclusions reveals their true nature. Retrograded granulite. Southern Minas Gerais State, Brazil. Width of view 1.8 mm. PPL

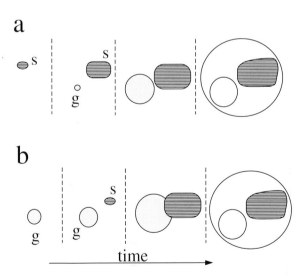

Fig. 7.30a,b. Sequence of events to show that it is difficult to estimate the relative age of two minerals from inclusion relations. In **a** staurolite *(s)* starts to grow and becomes included in garnet *(g)* because the latter mineral has a higher growth rate; in **b** garnet starts to grow, including staurolite that starts to grow later, leading to the same inclusion relationship

If isolated grains of mineral A are included in grains of mineral B, they may either have grown in B (e.g. as sericite in feldspar), or they may have been included during growth of the grains of B. The latter situation, however, does not necessarily mean that *mineral* B formed entirely later than mineral A. It is possible to establish from such relations that minerals A and B were stable or growing together for a period of time, but it is very difficult or even impossible to decide which mineral started and stopped growing first (e.g. garnet and blue amphibole in Fig. 6.24). The only possible exceptions to this rule occur if all grains of A are enclosed in the centre of grains of B, or if single grains of A are rimmed by coronas of B (Chap. 7.8). Figure 7.30 shows an example where either staurolite or garnet start growing. In the final stages of both situations, the garnet includes a staurolite grain in its rim, giving the impression that garnet is the younger mineral (Fig. 7.30). The inclusion of one mineral by the other is usually not a result of different age, but an effect of relative nucleation rate and growth rate of both minerals (Fig. 7.2). Minerals with

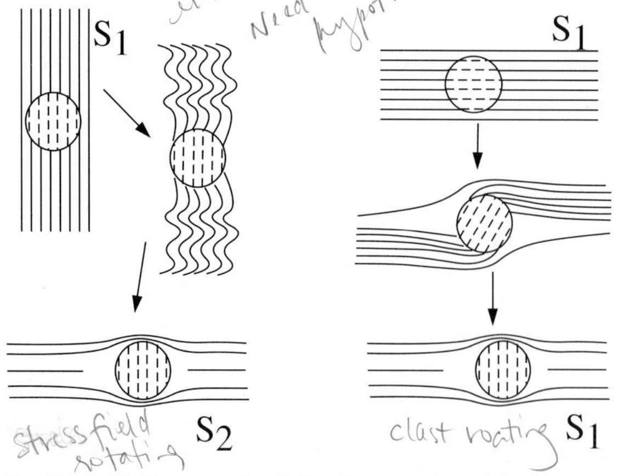

[handwritten margin note: need to see the connector, otherwise it may be incorrect. Need to have multiple hypothesis]

[handwritten annotations near figure: "S₂" labeled "stress field rotating"; "S₁" labeled "clast rotating"]

ROTATION AND REFERENCE FRAMES

Many publications on microstructures describe the rotation of porphyroblasts or other structures. Unfortunately, in many statements, no mention is made of reference frames, e.g. 'the shape of the inclusion pattern shows that garnet rotated'. Without further explanation, it is not clear if the garnet rotated with respect to a foliation, with respect to bedding, or with respect to the earth's surface. This example illustrates that, without a proper reference frame, rotations cannot be defined (Chap. 2.4; Box p. 12; Fig. 2.5). In all descriptions of rotation, a reference frame should therefore be given. Possible examples are the foliation in a rock; ISA; or geographical coordinates.

Fig. 7.31. If all connection is lost between S_i and S_e, they may either represent two different foliations S_1 and S_2 *(left)*, or early and late stages of development of a single foliation *(right)*

low nucleation rate and high growth rate engulf those with high nucleation rate (Fig. 6.24).

As a conclusion, the relation between periods of mineral growth and deformation can be established in most cases, using the relations shown in Figs. 7.9 and 7.26; however, the relative age of periods of mineral growth is much more difficult to establish.

7.6.7 Discontinuous S_i and S_e

If S_i is discontinuous with S_e (Figs. 7.5, 7.13, 7.31), deformation must have taken place after porphyroblast growth. However, it is certainly not correct to attribute S_i in such cases always to an earlier deformation phase, since it may well represent an earlier stage in the progressive development of the external foliation, S_e (e.g. Fig. 7.5).

7.6.8 Rotation of Porphyroblasts

Rigid objects suspended in a deforming matrix will under certain circumstances rotate with respect to the ISA of flow (Box p. 119; Fig. 5.23); this applies to elongate objects oriented oblique to shortening axes in coaxial progressive deformation, and to equidimensional and many elongate objects in non-coaxial progressive deformation (Fig. 5.23; Ghosh and Ramberg 1976; Masuda and Ando 1988). Equidimensional inter- and syntectonic porphyroblasts with oblique and spiral-shaped S_i patterns (Figs. 7.14–7.16, 7.32, 7.33) have therefore intrigued the imagination of many geologists as natural examples of objects that rotated with respect to ISA, capable of indicating sense of

shear (e.g. Zwart 1960; Rosenfeld 1968, 1970, 1985; Cox 1969; Powell and Treagus 1969, 1970; Spry 1969; Wilson 1971; Trouw 1973; Schoneveld 1977, 1979; Powell and Vernon 1979; Olesen 1982; Lister et al. 1986; Vernon 1988; Miyake 1993). Two basic types can be distinguished: those with a straight S_i (*oblique-S_i porphyroblasts;* Chap. 7.4.3), and those with a curved or spiral-shaped S_i (*spiral-S_i porphyroblasts*). The sequence of events leading to the development of oblique-S_i porphyroblasts (Figs. 7.14, 7.34a, 11.14; Passchier and Speck 1994) seems clear: (1) creation of a foliation S_e; (2) growth of the porphyroblast; (3) deformation that causes relative rotation of the porphyroblast and S_e. Such porphyroblasts are intertectonic, or syntectonic if the porphyroblast growth rate exceeded strain rate significantly. An intuitive explanation of the oblique-S_i porphyroblasts in Fig. 7.34a is *dextral* rotation of the porphyroblast with respect to a stable S_e and to flow ISA in a dextral non-coaxial flow (Figs. 7.22d centre, 7.34b). However, Ramsay (1962) pointed out that a pre-existing foliation at an angle to ISA will rotate with respect to the ISA in coaxial flow, while an equidimensional porphyroblast in the same setting may remain stable. The structure in Fig. 7.34a can therefore also be explained by *sinistral* rotation of S_e with respect to ISA and to a stationary porphyroblast in coaxial flow (Fig. 7.22d left, 7.34c) or with respect to a more slowly rotating (Fig. 7.22d right) or even stationary (Fig. 7.34d) porphyroblast in sinistral non-coaxial flow. These alternative interpretations would, of course, give an entirely different tectonic significance to the structure. Bell (1985) and Passchier and Speck (1994) have shown that these alternative explanations are indeed feasible in at least some cases. Careful investigation of the geometry of oblique-S_i porphyroblasts is therefore needed before an attempt is made to use them as shear sense indicators.

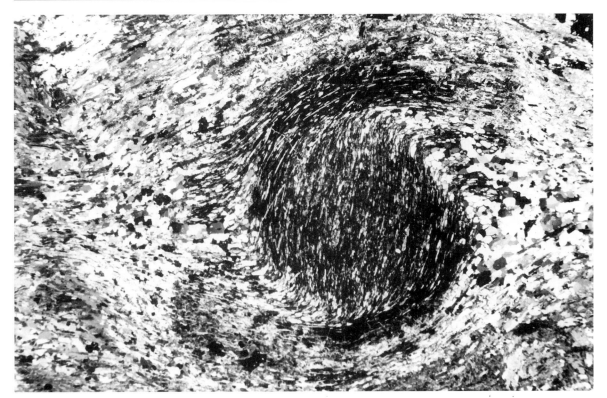

Fig. 7.32. Syntectonic garnet in micaschist showing almost 90° of sinistral rotation with respect to S_e. The central part of the garnet has approximately straight inclusions whereas close to the rim a deflection plane marks the transition to the outer part. Apparently the deformation responsible for the garnet rotation occurred relatively rapidly during growth of the part containing the abrupt bend. The outer rim grew over the matrix, apparently after the rotation had stopped (cf. Fig. 7.39a). Note the strong differentiation in the outer rim between strain shadows rich in quartz where the garnet grew in a skeletal way (enlarged in Fig. 7.6), and garnet rims at the upper and lower part where the garnet grew with relatively few inclusions, apparently over strain caps. Baños, Equador. Width of view 20 mm. CPL

Spiral-S_i porphyroblasts as presented in Figs. 7.15, 7.16, 7.32, 7.33 are relatively common in garnet, staurolite (Busa and Gray 1992; Gray and Busa 1994), albite and several other minerals, but well-developed spirals of S_i with a relative rotation angle exceeding 180° (also known as *snowball structures* (Figs. 7.16, 7.33) seem to be restricted to garnet (e.g. Rosenfeld 1970; Wilson 1971; Trouw 1973; Schoneveld 1977, 1979; Powell and Vernon 1979). Porphyroblasts with open spirals can in some cases be explained as helicitic folds which have been overgrown, but this is unlikely for porphyroblasts with spiral angles exceeding 180°; such structures have traditionally been interpreted as syntectonic porphyroblasts that were rotating with respect to S_e and ISA of bulk flow during porphyroblast growth (refs. cited). Data that seem to support this latter interpretation were given by several authors (e.g. Passchier et al. 1992). Powell and Treagus (1969, 1970) have shown that inclusion patterns in spiral-S_i garnets are not cylindrical in three dimen-

sions, but commonly mirrored around a plane through the centre of the porphyroblast and normal to a twofold symmetry axis (Fig. 7.36a,b). They also demonstrated that central sections normal to the symmetry axes in such crystals show larger rotation angles than side sections (cf. Fig. 7.36c). Interestingly enough, some cross sections through spiral-S_i porphyroblasts (Fig. 7.36c – R/FA section at right) strongly resemble millipede structures (Chap. 7.5; Gray and Busa 1994).

Busa and Gray (1992) studied oblong staurolite porphyroblasts that lie parallel to S_e with a variable orientation of the long axis within S_e. They found a three-dimensional geometry of S_i similar to that described by Powell and Treagus (1969, 1970), with the symmetry axis of the S_i-spiral parallel to the long axis of the porphyroblast, despite the variable orientation of the porphyroblasts in space. They also found a systematic relation between the 'rotation angle' of S_i and the orientation of long axes of the porphyro-

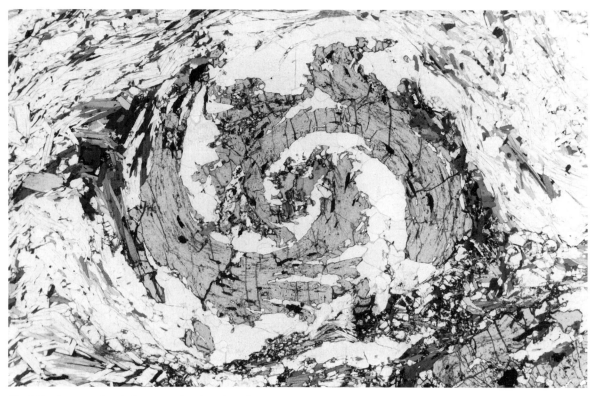

Fig. 7.33. Syntectonic spiral-S_i garnet in micaschist, showing a double spiral of inclusions. One spiral consists of coarse quartz grains that nearly divide the garnet into two parts; the other spiral consists of fine graphite inclusions in massive garnet.

Notice the tight folds in garnet and graphite at *lower centre* and *top left* which have been predicted in the model of Schoneveld (1977) as shown in Fig. 7.37. Aiuruoca, Minas Gerais, Brazil. Width of view 10 mm. PPL

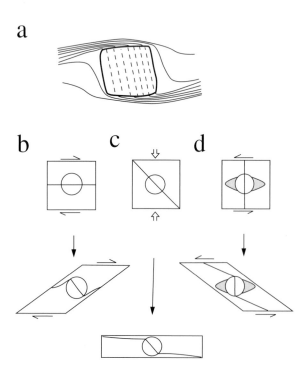

blasts. Such a three-dimensional geometry of the S_i pattern agrees well with theoretically predicted S_i patterns formed by syntectonic growth of a porphyroblast that was rotating with respect to S_e and ISA of bulk flow (Schoneveld 1979; Masuda and Mochizuki 1989; Gray and Busa 1994).

Schoneveld (1979) discussed garnet crystals in which two sets of spiral inclusion trails are present, one of quartz inclusions, and one of opaque inclusions (Fig. 7.33). He modelled these spiral S_i trails as resulting from the inclusion of quartz from strain shadows and opaque grains from strain-caps during rotation of the growing porphyroblast with respect to

Fig. 7.34. a Intertectonic porphyroblast with straight S_i oblique to S_e (oblique-S_i porphyroblast). This structure can form by: **b** dextral rotation of the porphyroblast with respect to a less-rotating foliation in dextral non-coaxial flow; **c** rotation of the foliation around a stationary porphyroblast in coaxial flow and **d** sinistral rotation of the foliation with respect to a stationary porphyroblast in sinistral non-coaxial flow. The porphyroblast can be stationary in non-coaxial flow **d** if it lies in, and is coupled with a non-deforming or coaxially deforming microlithon *(grey)*

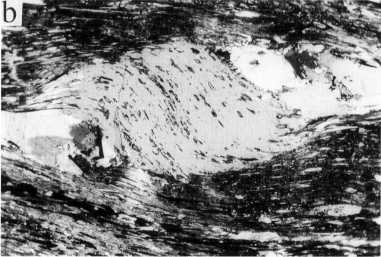

Fig. 7.35. a Syntectonic albite porphyroblasts with sigmoidal S_i pattern and asymmetric strain shadows of quartz. The asymmetry of the strain shadows indicates dextral shear sense, which implies that the albite rotated in a clockwise sense with respect to the kinematic frame during its growth. **b** Detail of **a**. Sanbagawa Belt, Japan. Width of view **a** 2.5 mm; **b** 1 mm. PPL. (Photographs courtesy S. Wallis)

the ISA of bulk flow (Fig. 7.37). Schoneveld (1977) has shown how the ratio of growth rate versus rotation rate of porphyroblasts can determine the shape of spiral trails of quartz and opaque inclusions (Fig. 12 in Schoneveld 1977). This model, elaborated in three dimensions, has been tested in natural examples and seems to explain observed structures in a satisfactory manner (cf. Powell and Vernon 1979; Johnson 1993a,b; Gray and Busa 1994; Fig. 7.38).

Wallis (1992b) presented an interesting structure where the geometry of an s-shaped inclusion pattern in albite porphyroblasts and the asymmetry of flanking quartz strain shadows on these porphyroblasts can both be explained by dextral rotation of the porphyroblasts with respect to ISA of dextral noncoaxial flow in the matrix (Fig. 7.35).

Despite the microstructural and theoretical support for a 'rotational' origin of spiral-S_i porphyroblasts mentioned above, Bell (1985), Bell et al. (1986) and Bell and Johnson (1989) have questioned the development of spiral-S_i garnets by porphyroblast rotation with respect to ISA of bulk flow, and advocated the theory that porphyroblasts do not rotate in a reference frame fixed to geographical coordinates. In many spiral-S_i garnets Bell and Johnson (1989) identified so-called *truncation planes* where the spiral inclusion pattern is interrupted (Fig. 7.1b, 7.39b). They interpreted S_i on both sides of a truncation plane as representing separate deformation phases, and reinterpreted the spiral fabrics as successively overgrown helicitic folds during up to eight subsequent deformation phases, included without rotation of the por-

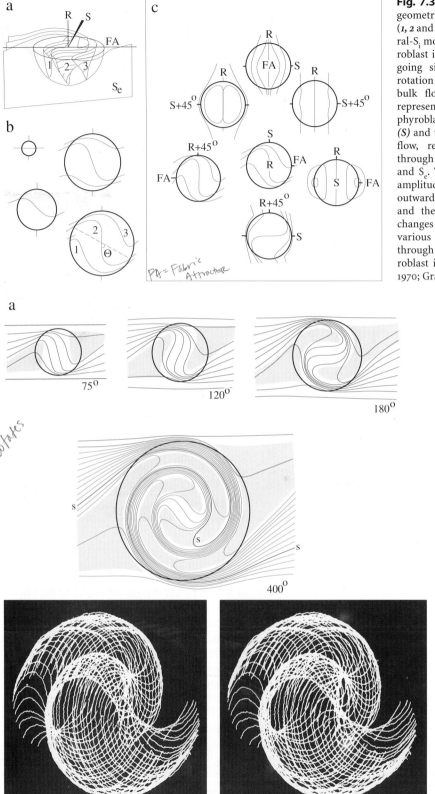

Fig. 7.36. a Schematic diagram of the geometry of three S_i inclusion surfaces (**1, 2** and **3**) in a spherical syntectonic spiral-S_i model porphyroblast. The porphyroblast is embedded in a matrix undergoing simple shear and grew during rotation over 90° with respect to ISA of bulk flow. Orthogonal reference axes represent the rotation axis of the porphyroblast **(R),** the pole to the flow plane **(S)** and the fabric attractor **(FA)** of bulk flow, respectively. **b** Serial sections through the model normal to the R-axis and S_e. The angle Θ, which defines the amplitude of the curve of S_i, decreases outward from the centre of the sphere and the trend of the inclusion trails changes systematically. **c** S_i patterns for various orientations of section planes through the centre of the model porphyroblast in **a**. (After Powell and Treagus 1970; Gray and Busa 1994)

Fig. 7.37. a Diagram traced from photographs of an experimental model of the development of spiral-S_i garnet inclusions, from Schoneveld (1977). Four stages in the development of a porphyroblast are shown. The *lines outside and inside the porphyroblast* indicate S_e and S_i. The foliation surface marked s is shown in three dimensions in **b**. A double spiral develops in the blast, one of densely spaced lines where the porphyroblast overgrows the mica-rich strain caps (usually formed by opaque inclusions); and a second one where the blast overgrows the strain shadow (marked in *grey;* usually formed by quartz). The amount of rotation (in degrees) is shown under each diagram (cf. Fig. 7.33). After Schoneveld (1977). **b** Stereoscopic representation of a non-central S_i surface in a model garnet with a rotation angle of 400°, marked as *s* in lower part of **a.** (Schoneveld 1979)

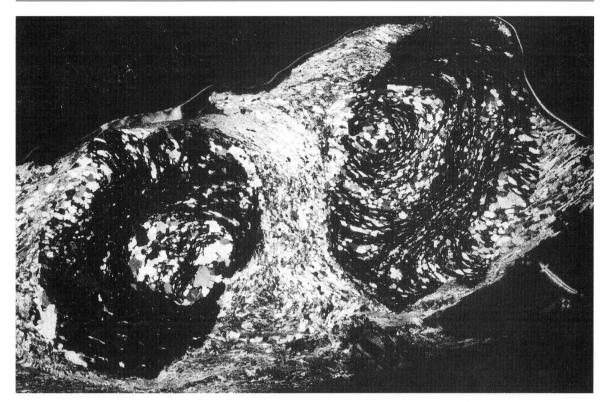

Fig. 7.38. Two garnet porphyroblasts in a garnet-mica schist containing inclusion patterns similar to the pattern at *right* in Fig. 7.36c (section normal to the S-axis of Fig. 7.36). In fact, the section is slightly inclined to the R (rotation) axis (Fig. 7.36a). Leiden Collection. Width of view 45 mm. CPL

phyroblast with respect to geographical coordinates. However, the truncation planes can also be explained by overgrowth of strain caps by the porphyroblast (Fig. 7.39; Chap. 6.5; Passchier et al. 1992). Since strain caps in metapelites are mica-rich, Al-silicate porphyroblasts tend to overgrow their own strain caps (Fig. 7.32). Pulsating growth of a rotating porphyroblast, alternating with periods during which mica-rich strain caps develop can cause development of sharp *deflection planes* (Fig. 7.32, 7.39a). If porphyroblast growth is temporarily alternating with local dissolution, truncation planes as reported by Bell and Johnson (1989) can also be formed during progressive deformation (Fig. 7.39b).

The model of Bell (1985) and Bell and Johnson (1989) has led to considerable debate (Bell et al. 1992;

Fig. 7.39a,b. Development of deflection planes and truncation planes around a syntectonic periodically growing porphyroblast in non-coaxial progressive deformation. The foliation and the porphyroblast rotate with respect to each other. **a** Strain caps and strain shadows develop around the porphyroblast during progressive deformation. After mica-rich strain caps are developed, they are overgrown by the porphyroblast, forming a deflection plane (e.g. Fig. 7.32). **b** If development of a syn-

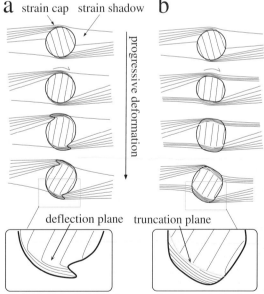

tectonic porphyroblast is temporarily interrupted by local dissolution in the strain caps, renewed growth over the strain caps causes development of truncation planes. The geometry of deflection and truncation planes is shown in the *enlarged insets*

ROTATION OR NON-ROTATION
OF SPIRAL-S_i PORPHYROBLASTS

Discussions by Bell (1985), Bell and Johnson (1989), Passchier et al. (1992) and Johnson (1993a,b) have shown that it
is difficult to find reliable criteria to determine whether spi-
ral-S_i porphyroblasts rotated with respect to kinematic axes
of bulk flow, or with respect to geographical coordinates.
Here we list some criteria which might be of help.

A rotational interpretation is likely to be correct if:
- S_i spirals in a porphyroblast are continuous and linked
  with S_e (Figs. 7.16, 7.32, 7.36, 7.37), especially if the sense of
  rotation of the porphyroblast is confirmed by other
  sense of shear markers (Busa and Gray 1992; Fig. 7.35).
- S_i spirals in three dimensions have gradually decreasing
  amplitude towards the rim of the crystal in both directions from the core of the crystal along the symmetry
  axis of the spiral (Figs 7.36b, 7.37b; Powell and Treagus
  1969, 1970; Busa and Gray 1992).
- included "folds" in S_i have an axial surface trace that is
  strongly curved (Figs. 7.16, 7.33, 7.37).
- S_i spirals that can be interpreted as included strain shadows are present (Fig. 7.37a; Schoneveld 1977, 1979)
- the relative rotation angle of the porphyroblast exceeds
  180°
- in elongate crystals, the symmetry axis of the S_i-spiral in
  the crystals is parallel to the long axis, even in sets of
  porphyroblasts with variable orientation of the long
  axis (Busa and Gray 1992).

*An interpretation of a spiral-S_i inclusion pattern as an over-
growth of helicitic folds is likely to be correct if:*
- more than one wavelength is included (Jamieson and
  Vernon 1987; cf. Figs. 11.16, 11.19).
- the included folds are comparable to matrix folds (cf.
  Fig. 11.19).

7.7 Crystallographically Deter-
mined Inclusion Patterns

Passive inclusion as described in Chap. 7.3–7.5 is not
the only process that controls the inclusion of foreign
matter in a porphyroblast. In some porphyroblasts
the distribution and shape of the inclusion density
pattern are associated with crystal habit (Figs.
7.40–7.43). Characteristic microstructures are *textural
sector zoning* and *re-entrant zones* (Fig. 7.44; Rice and
Mitchell 1991). Textural sector zoning (Figs. 7.40, 7.42,
7.44a) probably develops by differences in growth rate
and diffusion rate at different crystal faces or from
preferential adsorption of impurities at certain
crystal faces (Frondel 1934; Barker 1990). If textural
sector zoning develops on two pairs of faces only, it is
known as *hour-glass zoning* (Figs. 7.42, 7.43). Re-
entrant zones are bands of inclusions, commonly
with a preferred orientation, that follow the bisectrix
of dominant crystal faces and are characteristic of
chiastolite (Figs. 7.41, 7.44b). They commonly show
feather-edge structures, also a growth feature (Figs.
7.41, 7.44; Rice and Mitchell 1991). Re-entrant zones
are thought to form if a crystal only incorporates
inclusions (mostly graphite) along the crystal ribs,
while the same material is dissolved or displaced
along crystal faces (Spry 1969; Harvey and Ferguson
1973; Ferguson 1980; Ferguson and Lloyd 1980; Rice
and Mitchell 1991). In the latter case, *cleavage domes*
may form, accumulations of displaced material
(usually graphite) along crystal faces (Figs. 7.3, 7.40,
7.44b, 7.45). Observations by Rice and Mitchell (1991)
suggest that an isotropic stress field (no or very small
differential stress) is needed for inclusion displacement and accumulation of graphite. This would occur
during contact metamorphism as in the thermal
aureole of an intruding batholith in the absence of
deformation.

Another controlling factor for inclusion orientation is crystal cleavage (Vernon 1976) that may influence both abundance and orientation of inclusions,
especially in micas (Fig. 7.46).

Crystals with textural sector zoning or re-entrant zones commonly contain *growth inclusions*
(Figs. 7.41, 7.44b, 7.45). Unlike the passive inclusions
treated above, growth inclusions form by new growth
at the growing crystal face of the porphyroblast. They
are usually recognisable by their strict parallel or
orthogonal orientation with respect to porphyroblast
crystal faces, and oblique orientation with respect to
passive inclusions (Figs. 7.41, 7.44b). In some cases,

Busa and Gray 1992; Passchier et al. 1992; Visser and
Mancktelow 1992; Gray and Busa 1994), and although
most evidence now seems to indicate that spiral-S_i
porphyroblasts form by syntectonic rotation with
respect to ISA of bulk flow in the rock, some structures have not yet been satisfactorily explained by the
available models and development of spiral-S_i porphyroblasts may still hide some surprises.

Schoneveld (1979) has described a number of
garnets that are rotational with relation to a progressively developing crenulation cleavage. This leads to
fairly complicated inclusion patterns that, judging
from the literature, are not very common in nature.
Examples are shown in Figs. 11.14 and 11.16. In the Box
above, a short list of criteria is given that may help to
distinguish between porphyroblasts that rotated with
respect to an external foliation, and those that formed
by overgrowth of helicitic folds.

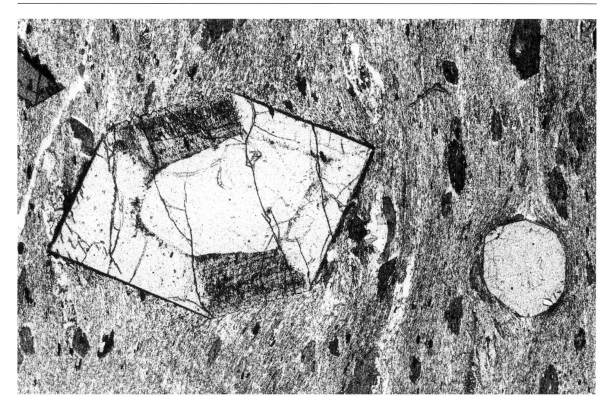

Fig. 7.40. Staurolite garnet biotite schist with a staurolite crystal *(at left)* that shows textural sector zoning and cleavage domes. S_i in the sectors mimics S_e rotated over about 30°. The foliation is strongly deflected around the garnet crystal without inclusions at the *right-hand side* of the photograph. Based on the deflection patterns, it can be concluded that garnet grew first, then staurolite and finally biotite (the *dark patches* in the matrix), all during the deformation phase that produced the foliation (syntectonic). Orós, NE Brazil. Width of view 10 mm. PPL

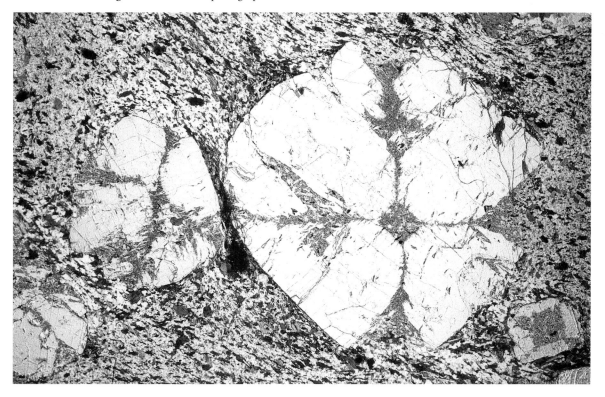

Fig. 7.41. Biotite schist with porphyroblasts of chiastolite showing re-entrant zones with feather-edge structures. Density of inclusions is controlled by crystal habit. Growth inclusions occur in the larger crystal. Laraquete, central Chile. Width of view 16 mm. Polarisers at 45°

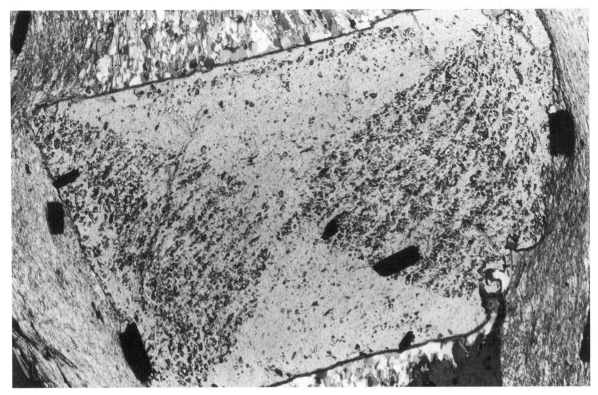

Fig. 7.42. Chloritoid crystal with textural sector zoning in hour-glass shape, controlled by crystal habit. A shape orientation of S_i is visible in two sectors, suggesting a relative crystal rotation of 60° with respect to the matrix. Leiden Collection. Width of view 4 mm. CPL

Fig. 7.43. Layered chloritoid schist with almost euhedral chloritoid crystals that show both hour-glass zoning and a rhythmic concentric layer-zoning of inclusion-rich and poor areas. A gentle crenulation has developed by D_2 which is also present in the crystals, indicating that they grew late syn-D_2. Açunguí, São Paulo State, Brazil. Width of view 17 mm. PPL

a

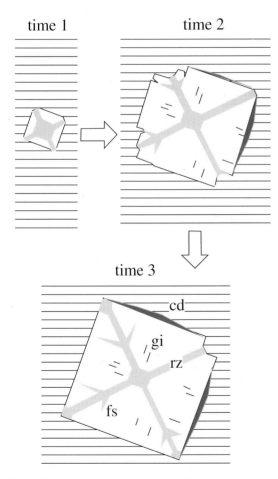

b

Fig. 7.44. a Development of porphyroblast with textural sector zoning with preferred orientation of passive inclusions (S$_i$). **b** Development of porphyroblast with re-entrant zones *(rz)*, feather-edge structures *(fs)* and growth inclusions *(gi)*. Cleavage domes *(cd, black)* occur on two sides

healed fractures may resemble passive inclusions and form a possible source of error.

Some porphyroblasts (e.g. garnet; Fig. 7.47) contain inclusion-rich cores surrounded by rims that are almost inclusion-free or vice versa. This may reflect changes in diffusion rate and crystal growth rate due to changing metamorphic conditions, possibly related to a growth interval. However, it may also be due to a change in the porphyroblast-forming reactions, if a new reaction becomes active consuming the mineral that forms inclusions.

7.8 Reaction Rims

7.8.1 Introduction

A change in metamorphic conditions can give rise to porphyroblast growth, or to partial **replacement** of some minerals by others. Such replacement usually occurs along grain boundaries and causes development of *reaction rims* (Fig. 7.48). Reaction rims are invaluable tools in the reconstruction of a sequence of metamorphic reactions. They can be monomineralic or polymineralic and can be divided into several geometric types. If they form closed rings around grains (shells in three dimensions), they are known as *coronas* (Fig. 7.48c–f). Monomineralic coronas are also known as *moats* (Figs. 7.48c, 7.49); polymineralic ones composed of an intergrowth of small elongate new grains are known as *symplectitic coronas* (Figs. 7.48d, 7.51–7.55). The structure of lamellar or vermicular fine-grained intergrown material is known as *symplectite* (Figs. 7.48d, 7.51–7.55).

Reaction rims form in several metamorphic settings in response to both retrograde and prograde metamorphic reactions. Substitution of andalusite by sillimanite is obviously prograde, while most coronas and symplectites are retrograde. Reaction rims form because progress of reactions generally depends on the presence of a fluid phase along grain boundaries for the transport of ions to and from the reaction site. Reaction rims are most common in high-grade rocks, eclogites and ultramafic rocks. This is probably due to the limited availability of aqueous fluids in these rocks, which inhibits reactions to reach completion.

Another type of reaction rim is formed by chemical *zoning* within a mineral. This may be visible by a gradual or abrupt change of the extinction angle or of the colour of pleochroic minerals; in other minerals it may only be detectable with a microprobe.

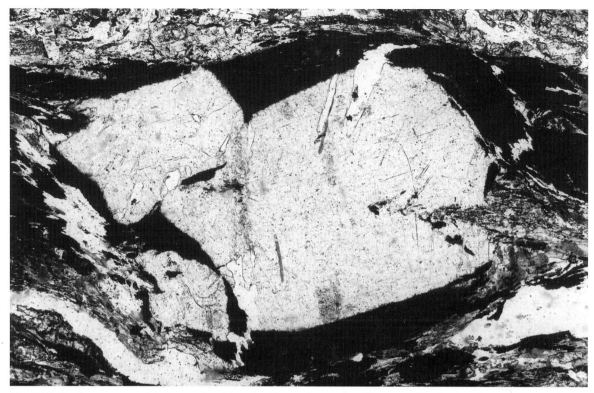

Fig. 7.45. Two intergrown andalusite porphyroblasts in mica-schist, with cleavage domes of graphite. The porphyroblasts are almost free of inclusions, but graphite is a major constituent of the micaschist matrix. Some growth inclusions are visible in the porphyroblast. A weakly developed re-entrant zone is visible at *lower right.* Menderes Massif, Turkey. Width of view 2.5 mm. PPL. (Photograph courtesy R. Hetzel)

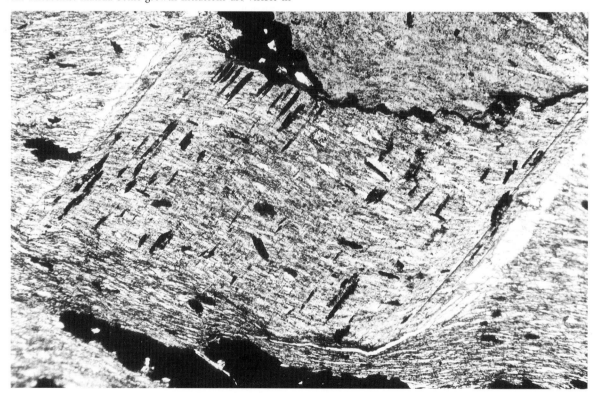

Fig. 7.46. Biotite porphyroblast in biotite schist with inclusions of opaque minerals in two almost orthogonal directions; the straight NE-SW ones are parallel to, and probably controlled by the crystal cleavage, whereas the curved NW-SE ones constitute S_i (passive inclusions). The centre of the crystal shows a clockwise rotation of about 25° with respect to S_e. Strain shadows are visible at the *left* and *right hand side* of the biotite crystal where the matrix with opaque grains was apparently detached from the crystal (Chap. 6.3). Rioumajou, Pyrenees, Spain. Width of view 4 mm. PPL

Fig. 7.47. Part of adjacent hornblende *(at left)* and garnet *(at right)* porphyroblasts in garnet-hornblende schist. The garnet has a sharply defined inclusion free idiomorphic rim, indicating changing conditions during its growth. S_i is more fine-grained then the matrix. The inclusions in the hornblende porphyroblast are similar in orientation and shape to those in the garnet, suggesting the contemporaneous growth of both minerals. Note the presence of secondary white mica along the contact of garnet and hornblende, suggesting a retrograde reaction consuming hornblende. Kittelfjäll. Västerbotten, Sweden. Width of view 4 mm. Polarisers nearly crossed

Zoning can form in at least two different ways: (1) as *growth zoning* reflecting changing PT conditions during growth, and (2) as *reaction zoning* in a pre-existing crystal by an ion-exchange reaction along the rim. Reaction zoning of an element A usually follows the outer rim of a zoned crystal and may advance further into the crystal, where it is in contact with another mineral rich in A, or along fractures. Growth zoning may also follow the outer rim or have a more complex shape due to growth-coalescence of smaller grains. Growth zoning can be truncated by grain boundaries if the crystal has been subject to erosion due to recrystallisation or pressure solution. In some cases, reaction zoning of an element A may even be superposed on growth zoning of an element B (Tucillo et al. 1990).

7.8.2 Coronas and Moats

If two dispersed minerals A and B in a rock react to form new minerals, these may form local isolated reaction rims along grain boundaries of A and B (Fig. 7.48a,b). However, if a mineral A breaks down to other minerals along its outer rim, or if it reacts with a mineral B that is abundant in the surrounding matrix, the newly formed minerals may form a ring-shaped corona around A. (Figs. 7.48d, 7.49). In high-grade rocks, several coronas may be superimposed on each other as concentric shells as double or composite coronas (Figs. 7.48e,f, 7.51, 7.52). Careful monitoring and analysis of corona structures can allow detailed reconstruction of the pressure-temperature-time (PTt) path in a rock sample (Chap. 1.3). A special form of coronas are *atoll garnets;* ring-shaped garnets, usually filled with quartz and white mica. Atoll garnets possibly form as coronas on biotite or cordierite, where the core mineral is later replaced by an aggregate of other minerals. However, an origin by growth along grain boundaries in coarse-grained quartz-mica aggregates has also been proposed (Bard 1986).

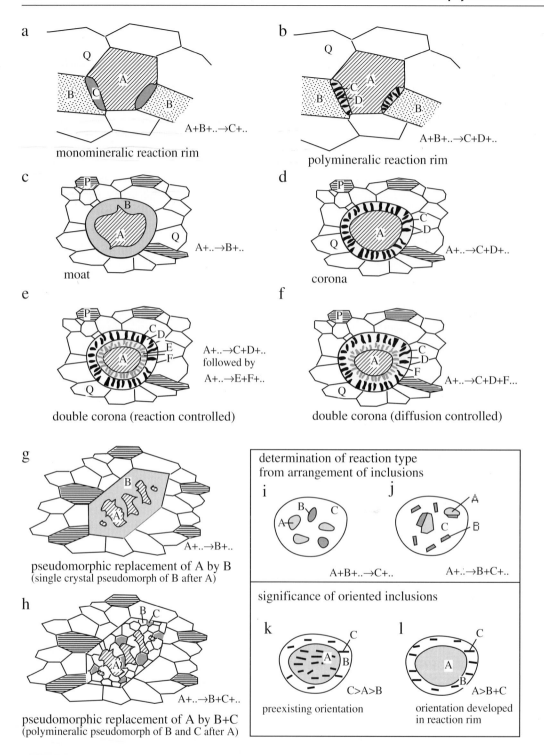

Fig. 7.48a–f. Various types of reaction rims. Likely reactions causing the rims are given below each drawing. *A–F* are minerals involved in reactions, *P* and *Q* are not involved. The equations are open since phases other than the ones shown may be involved in the reactions as well. *i* and *j* show how reaction type can be established to some extent from the arrangement of

inclusions. *k* and *l* show the significance of oriented inclusions in a reaction rim; the relative age of minerals *A, B* and *C* is given. In *k* the alignment of *C* is due to passive inclusion of aligned grains of *C* in *A,* and subsequent growth of *B*; in *l, C* grew with a preferred orientation in response to a high differential stress. Further explanation in text

Fig. 7.49. Corona of garnet *(black)* separating plagioclase (centre) from clinopyroxene and hornblende in the matrix. Such monomineralic coronas are also known as moats. Retro- grade granulite. Southern Minas Gerais, Brazil. Width of view 2 mm. CPL

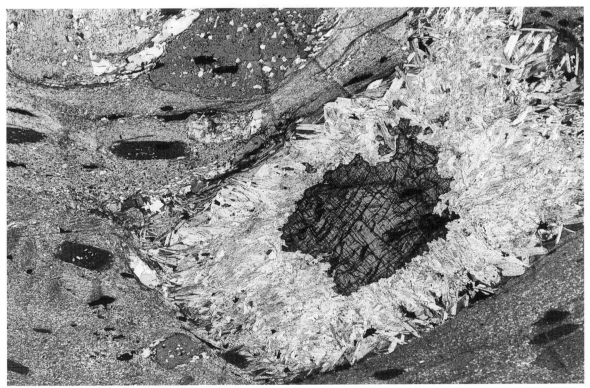

Fig. 7.50. Reaction rim composed mainly of muscovite around a staurolite crystal in staurolite biotite schist. The reac- tion rim forms a pseudomorph after staurolite. Pyrenees, Spain. Width of view 16 mm. CPL

7.8.3 Symplectites

If two or more minerals are present in a corona, they may form a *symplectite* in which the minerals form an intergrowth of lamellae that may be straight, curved or vermicular (Figs. 7.51–7.55). Symplectites are thought to develop due to relatively rapidly proceeding reactions, or lack of a fluid phase to transport material towards and away from the reaction site. Nucleation sites of symplectite may be stress-controlled as well as P-T overstepping controlled (Simpson and Wintsch 1989).

Most symplectites are *reaction symplectites* that form by reactions of the type A + B+.. $\Rightarrow$ C + D + .. or A + .. $\Rightarrow$ C + D + .., where C+D+.. form the symplectite (Figs. 7.48b,d, 7.55a,c). Discontinuous precipitation reactions of the type A $\Rightarrow$ A′ + B. constitute a special type that will be loosely referred to as *exsolution symplectites* (Fig. 7.55b,d). They develop when two grains of a supersaturated solid solution A with

different orientation but identical chemistry are juxtaposed along a grain boundary. The grain boundary migrates into one of the grains and leaves a symplectite of A′ + B behind (Fig. 7.55b). Exsolution symplectites can potentially be used as a temperature gauge (Chap. 8.9).

Symplectites may be affected by grain boundary area reduction (GBAR; Chap. 3.10) which causes the lamellae to neck and obtain a globular shape. Such symplectites have been named *globular symplectites* (Fig. 7.55c,d). They are particularly common in high-grade rocks; all examples in Figs. 7.51–7.54 can be classified as globular symplectites. Symplectites that are not or little affected by GBAR and in which lamellae are elongate with parallel boundaries are known as *lamellar symplectites* (Fig. 7.55a,b). They are commonly formed during metamorphic retrogression, especially in eclogites.

Kelyphite or *kelyphytic structure* is the name for a symplectitic corona structure around olivine, commonly in several concentric layers, which may con-

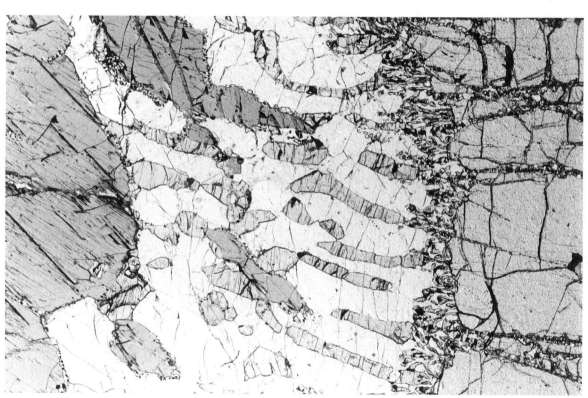

Fig. 7.51. Double symplectitic corona between hornblende *(left)* and garnet *(right).* The *left-hand,* coarse corona consists of plagioclase and orthopyroxene. The narrow corona at *right* consists of plagioclase, orthopyroxene and spinel. Notice that the narrow orthopyroxene-plagioclase-spinel corona occurs only along the garnet and along cracks in the garnet, but not near hornblende. Therefore, the coarse corona is thought to reflect a first reaction hornblende + garnet → orthopyroxene + plagioclase and the narrow corona represents a second reaction garnet → orthopyroxene + plagioclase+spinel. In this way, the sequence of reactions can be established in a thin section. Bolingen Island, Prydz Bay, Antarctica. Width of view 7 mm. PPL. (Photograph courtesy P. Dirks)

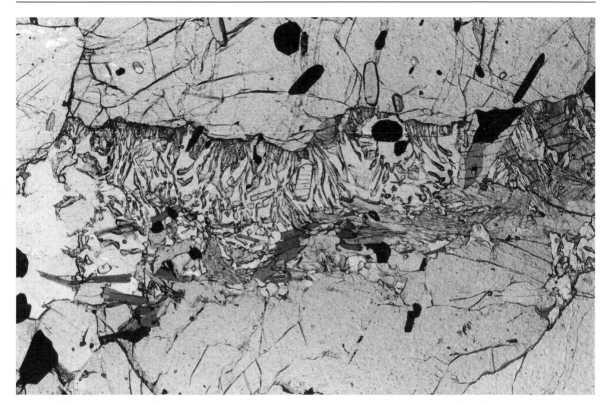

Fig. 7.52. Zoned corona between garnet *(top)* and orthopyroxene *(bottom).* The upper symplectitic corona adjacent to garnet consists of cordierite and orthopyroxene. The lower corona consists mainly of saphirine. Central Sri Lanka. Width of view 7 mm. PPL. (Photograph courtesy P. Dirks. Thin section provided by L. Kriegsman)

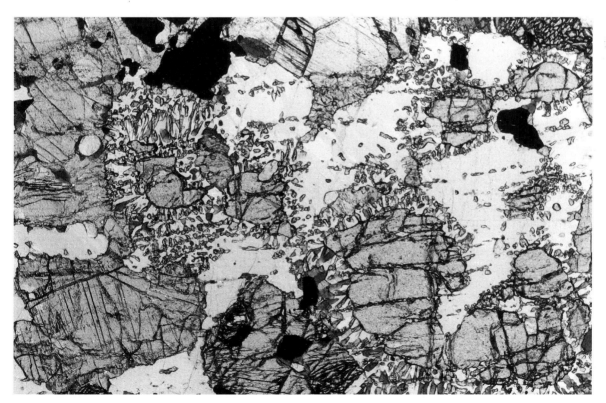

Fig. 7.53. Symplectitic coronas of plagioclase, orthopyroxene and hornblende between garnet and clinopyroxene grains, reflecting the reaction garnet + clinopyroxene + H2O → plagioclase + orthopyroxene + hornblende. Notice that some orthopyroxene grains are aligned in the coronas parallel to cracks in the garnet relics: the coronas probably developed initially along cracks. The cracks therefore predate the reaction. Bolingen Island, Prydz Bay, Antarctica. Width of view 5 mm. PPL. (Photograph courtesy P. Dirks)

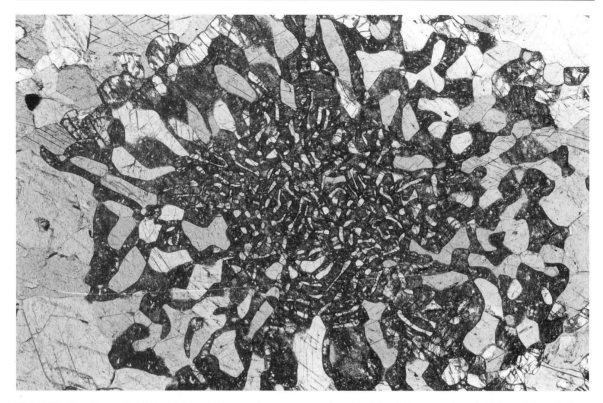

Fig. 7.54. Pseudomorph of plagioclase-orthopyroxene symplectite after garnet. The grain size of the symplectite decreases inwards. Wu Li Dong, N-Shanxi, China. Width of view 9 mm. PPL. (Photograph courtesy P. Dirks)

tain orthopyroxene, clinopyroxene, amphibole and spinel or garnet. Spinel or garnet may be in symplectitic intergrowth with hornblende or orthopyroxene. Amphibole-plagioclase symplectites have also been called kelyphitic if they form clearly defined coronas.

A *myrmekite* is a bulbous symplectite of vermicular quartz in plagioclase. It is common in high-grade metamorphic and igneous rocks, mostly as breakdown product of K-feldspar during retrograde metamorphism (Smith 1974; Phillips 1974, 1980; Shelley 1993). Myrmekite may develop at stress-concentration sites during progressive deformation (Simpson and Wintsch 1989) and in that case can serve as a shear sense indicator (Chap. 5.6.8).

7.8.4 Establishing the Nature of Reactions

In coronas and symplectites it is important first to establish which components are likely to be new minerals, and which are old grains. An important principle is that silicates usually have slow diffusion through the crystal lattice, and that reactions therefore mainly occur at grain boundaries where grains

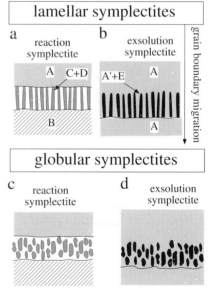

Fig. 7.55a–d. Symplectites can be subdivided into reaction **(a, c)** and exsolution **(b, d)** symplectites, depending on the reactions that take place. Another possible subdivision is in lamellar **(a, b)** and globular **(c, d)** symplectites. Globular symplectites are thought to develop from lamellar ones through grain boundary area reduction, especially at high metamorphic grade

are in contact with each other or with the scarce metamorphic fluid. It is therefore usually assumed that a corona or symplectite grows from the outside inwards, and that large grains with irregular shape, completely surrounded by another mineral, are older than this surrounding material (Figs. 7.48, 7.50). In exsolution symplectites, growth is thought to proceed from the grain that is in crystallographic continuity with one of the phases of the symplectite, towards the second grain (Fig. 7.55b). Replacement commonly also takes place along cracks in old grains, and old grains therefore may be split into various fragments (Figs. 7.48g,h, 7.51). If replacement of the old grain is advanced, its remnants can be recognised by the fact that they all have the same lattice orientation (Fig. 7.48g,h), and by concave-inward boundaries with the new mineral (Fig. 7.48c,g). If old grains of two minerals are not in contact, they are likely to have reacted with each other to form the corona or symplectite (Fig. 4.48i). It is important to realise that contacts may be missed in thin sections with few observation sites (Fig. 10.2i). If old grains of two minerals are in contact, one of them is probably not involved in the reaction (Fig. 7.48j). New grains form either the corona or part of a symplectite, or are finely dispersed in the corona. New grains may be aligned, but will lack the identical lattice orientation of old grain fragments. Small grains in a corona with a weak preferred orientation may have grown as new grains in the corona when it was subject to a high differen-

tial stress (Chap. 4.9.7), but may also be relics of inclusions in an old grain that has been replaced. This can usually be decided by the presence of relics of the old grain (Fig. 7.48k,l). If *double coronas* are present (Fig. 4.48e,f), it can be more difficult to establish a relative age. It is sometimes assumed that the outer rim is youngest, but there are other possibilities. With changing metamorphic conditions, reactions may also occur between the included old grain and its corona (Fig. 7.56a), between the corona and phases outside (Fig. 7.56b), or between coronas. The old grain may also be replaced inward by a new corona while the first corona is unaffected (Fig. 4.48e), or the reaction may change while the corona grows due to increasing length of the diffusion path (Fig. 7.48f, 7.56c). Especially if Al-rich minerals are involved, this possibility should be investigated. In all cases, interpretations based on geometrical arguments should be checked to see if proposed reactions are chemically and thermodynamically possible.

Reaction rims are interesting sites for geothermometry and geobarometry since they form under conditions other than the original mineral assemblage and therefore may define different stages along a PTt path (Chap. 1.3). However, there are some potential pitfalls; old grains and new grains may be strongly zoned, in which case it may be difficult to decide which compositions should be used for thermo-barometry; careful reconstruction of the growth of the reaction rim structures is useful in such cases.

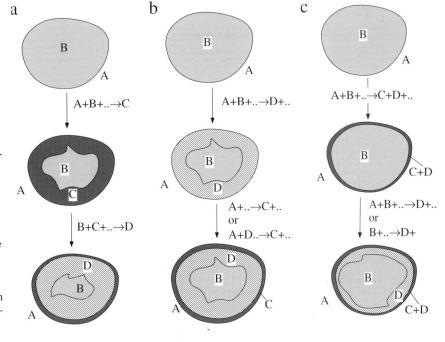

Fig. 7.56a–c. Three mechanisms to form double coronas. *A–D* are minerals. The equations are open since phases other than the ones shown may be involved in the reactions as well. A second corona forms: **a** from reaction between the core mineral and the first corona; **b** by growth on the outside or reaction of the first corona with minerals in the matrix; or **c** by a change in the reaction that causes breakdown of the old grain

Moreover, the composition of old grains may have been modified during the reactions. This can usually be determined if zoning in old grains is carefully monitored by SEM observation or by a fine grid of measurement points over the grain in a microprobe. If zoning is parallel to the edges of the old grain, it is probably modified during the reaction. If the zoning is truncated by reaction rims, especially along cracks, it is probably original. Finally, care should be taken with the assumption that only old grains and reaction rims took part in a reaction; reactions may be rather complex and may also involve minerals that are not directly in contact with the reaction rims or that have completely disappeared.

7.8.5 Pseudomorphs

If a crystal is largely or completely replaced by another mineral or an aggregate of minerals, the new minerals may preserve the shape of the original grain (Fig. 7.48g,h). Such an aggregate is known as a *pseudomorph;* for example, if chlorite replaces garnet we speak of a 'chlorite pseudomorph after garnet'. Pseudomorphs can be recognised if relics of the old mineral grain are still present (Fig. 7.48g,h), or if the old grain was euhedral with a characteristic crystal shape. It is sometimes difficult to decide in an aggregate of minerals which ones are involved in a reaction and in which direction the reactions were proceeding. Figure 7.50 shows an example of a partial muscovite pseudomorph after staurolite, and Fig. 7.54 a complete pseudomorph of plagioclase and orthopyroxene after garnet.

A distinction can be made between prograde and retrograde pseudomorphs according to the minerals involved. For example, a staurolite pseudomorph after chlorite is prograde, while a chlorite pseudomorph after garnet is retrograde. Since pseudomorphs show the subsequent stability of at least two metamorphic minerals, they are important for the reconstruction of PT-evolution.

7.8.6 Relation with Deformation

As mentioned above, some symplectites may form in response to deformation. In general, however, it may be difficult to decide whether pseudomorphs or coronas have replaced a mineral before, during or after a phase of deformation. In principle, the criteria mentioned in Chap. 7.4 can be used, but unfortunately reaction rims rarely contain passive inclusions. Intracrystalline deformation of the new minerals in

the aggregates can be used to decide about relative age. For example, if undeformed chlorite replaces strongly deformed biotite grains, the chlorite is likely to be post-tectonic. Figures 7.51 and 7.53 show interesting examples where the relative age of intracrystalline fractures and symplectite can be established.

7.9 Reconstruction of Tectono-Metamorphic Evolution

Porphyroblast-matrix relationships and reaction rims may help to unravel the tectono-metamorphic evolution in an area (see also Chap. 1). Figure 7.57 shows a schematic evolution in space and time to illustrate the different relationships that may be expected between mineral growth and deformation. The following course of action could be undertaken in an area with a history as shown in Fig. 7.57a.

Fig. 7.57. a Diagram showing three evolutionary stages of a subduction complex at an active continental margin, culminating in terrane collision. Five sample locations, α to ε, are indicated. They are progressively involved in successive deformation phases and metamorphism. γ represents a mafic intrusion. **b** Diagram showing relationships between porphyroblast growth (*dark grey,* minerals *A–G*) and deformation (*coarse stipple,* deformation phases D_1–D_4) in time and space for the region illustrated in **a**. The sequence of events starts with sedimentation *(solid line at left),* followed by diagenetic compaction *(diagonal lines).* Deformation phases are continuous in space, except along major fault zones such as at terrane boundaries; they can be diachronous and even joining in space (e.g. D_1 and D_2). D_1 at α represents early deformation related to the genesis of this terrane; D_1 at β to ε reflects the subduction movements and is therefore strongly diachronous; D_2 at δ and ε represents ductile obduction or backthrusting related to the shape of the continental margin. The arrival of the terrane causes renewed deformation propagating outwards from the collision area, labelled D_2 at sites α to γ, and D_3 at δ and ε. Finally, D_3 at α to γ and D_4 at δ and ε reflect orogenic collapse and associated uplift. Metamorphic evolution is presented in a simplified way as growth of single minerals rather than mineral associations. Such growth can also be diachronous, but can be discontinuous both at major faults and at lithologic contacts. *A* is a high T/low P mineral related to arc activity, whereas *B* is a high P/low T mineral related to subduction. *C* may be a medium P/T mineral and *D* is a retrograde mineral. Minerals *E*, *F* and *G* reflect a similar history in the mafic intrusion, with somewhat different growth periods. **c** Shows the sequence of events at site ε as an example of the terminology used, and shows how structural and metamorphic analysis of individual samples can help to unravel the tectonic evolution of a region

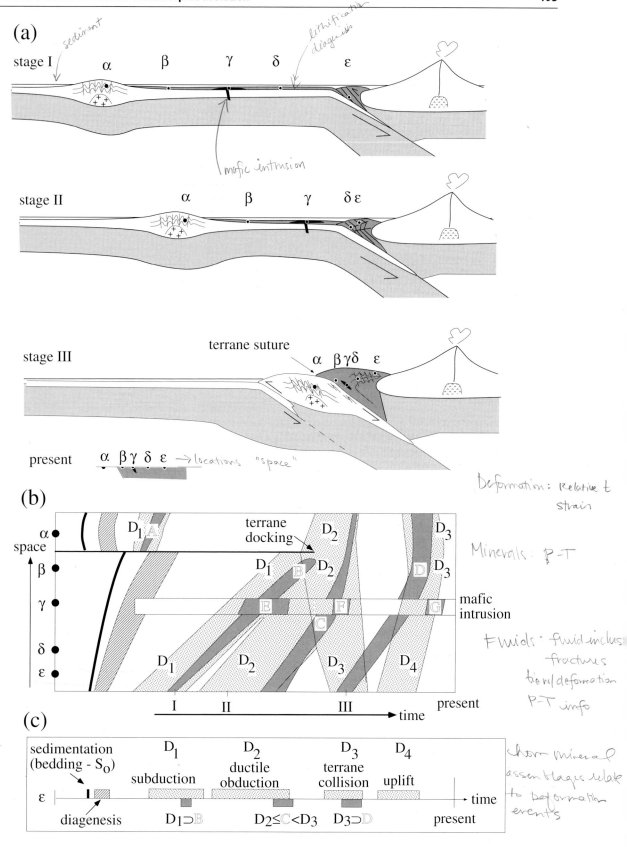

(a)

stage I   *sediment*   α   β   γ   δ   *lithification diagenesis*   ε

mafic intrusion

stage II   α   β   γ   δ ε

stage III   *terrane suture*   α   β γ δ   ε

present   α β γ δ ε → *locations   "space"*

(b)

Deformation: Relative t strain

space   α • D_1 A   terrane docking D_2 D_3

        β • D_1 B D_2 D D_3

Minerals: P-T

        γ •   E   F   G   mafic intrusion

        δ •   C

        ε • D_1 D_2 D_3 D_4

Fluids: fluid inclus. fractures tie w/deformation P-T info

                       I   II   III   present
                                                    → time

(c)

how mineral assemblages relate to deformation events

sedimentation D_1 D_2 D_3 D_4
(bedding - S_0)   ductile   terrane
           subduction   obduction   collision   uplift

        ε |

diagenesis $D_1 \supset B$ $D_2 \leq C < D_3$ $D_3 \supset D$ present
                                                                    → time

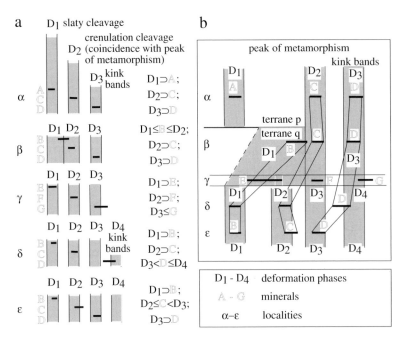

Fig. 7.58a,b. Diagram illustrating how data on relative age of minerals and deformation can be used in reconstructions of tectono-metamorphic history. The scheme is based on the imaginary evolution of Fig. 7.57. **a** Relative age of mineral growth with respect to each phase of deformation is established for hand specimens α–ε and plotted in mineral-time diagrams as shown. Notice that generally space is left between phases for intertectonic growth. Only in β D_1 and D_2 are continuous as may be indicated by the inclusion pattern in mineral B. Labelling can be done for minerals A–G as shown at right. If field-data are available, the schemes represented in **a** can be correlated into a diagram like **b**. Comparison of diagram **b** and Fig. 7.57b shows that only a coarse reconstruction is possible, unless more samples are analysed and absolute age data are added to the diagram. Nevertheless, the basic tectono-metamorphic history of Fig. 7.57 is contained in diagram **b**

1. Define in each outcrop or tectonic domain (Fig. 7.57α–ε) the sequence of deformation phases that can be recognised in thin sections from overprinting relations (Chap. 4.11.2). The phases have to be properly defined, for example as 'responsible for slaty cleavage, for crenulation cleavage, relative rotation of porphyroblasts, kink bands' etc. The phases may be labelled D_1, D_2, D_3 if field relations indicate that no earlier deformation phases were present. If this is not clear, labels like D_n, D_{n+1} etc. can be used.

2. Plot the deformation phases on a horizontal relative time axis, leaving some space in between for possible intertectonic growth, unless there is evidence for continuity (Figs. 7.10, 7.58a).

3. Determine the growth period for each mineral species and plot it with horizontal bars or dashed lines where in doubt (Figs. 7.10, 7.58a). 'Pillows' may be used to indicate main growth versus subsidiary growth (Fig. 7.10).

4. The terms pre-, syn- and post-tectonic have to be clearly defined with respect to a specific deformation phase or episode. For example, in Figs. 7.57c and 7.58a, mineral C in locality ε grew syn- to post D_2 and pre D_3.

5. Use field data and geometrical arguments to correlate deformation phases in different thin sections and from different sample locations (Fig. 7.58b).

At this stage it is clear that the reconstruction that can be reached with porphyroblast analysis alone is insufficient for a complete understanding of the tectonic evolution; the scheme of Fig. 7.58b is only a coarse approximation of the true pattern in Fig. 7.57b. Additional data related to the PTt evolution of each sample site, absolute age dating, nature and chemistry of igneous intrusions, and sedimentary environment of protoliths all play an equally important role in the final reconstruction.

8 Natural Microgauges

8.1 Introduction

Structural geologists have long used the macroscopic and microscopic geometry of the fabric of deformed rocks to determine a sequence of tectonic and metamorphic events, finite strain, or sense of shear. However, the geometry of deformed rocks stores a wealth of quantitative information that can be retrieved using the characteristic geometry of some microstructures. Since such microstructures can be used to determine parameters such as stress, temperature etc., we introduce the term *natural microgauges.* This chapter gives some examples of presently available microgauges and possible future developments, and will hopefully stimulate readers into research on the subject. Microgauges can only be calibrated if the effects of all parameters that cause their geometric evolution are understood. At present, the study of microgauges is in its infancy and much theoretical and experimental work remains to be done. Finally, the limits and problems of the methods are indicated since the creation of numbers from rocks tends to give a (possibly) misplaced sense of confidence.

8.2 Strain Gauges

In many tectonic applications it is desirable to determine finite or tectonic strain. In order to express strain in simple values, it must be homogeneous (Chap. 2.5). In practice, natural strain will always be inhomogeneous at most scales of observation, but it may be considered homogeneous in small volumes of fine-grained rock with a homogeneous fabric (Fig. 2.6). The presence of a straight, homogeneous (continuous) foliation is a good indication for homogeneous strain at the scale of a thin section.

For a full description of three-dimensional homogeneous finite strain, six numbers are needed; three to describe the orientation of the strain ellipsoid, and three to describe strain magnitude. Strain magnitude can be expressed by three principal stretch values, or by two strain ratios and volume change. In the second case, the two strain ratios describe the *shape* of the strain ellipsoid (as given in a Flinn plot, e.g. Fig. 4.40), and volume change describes its *size.*

Three-dimensional strain can be determined when data from several thin sections in different orientations are combined. It is important to cut these thin sections parallel to principal strain axes X, Y and Z, if possible. Many foliations are approximately parallel to the XY plane of finite strain (Chap. 4.10.2), and stretching or mineral lineations (Chap. 4.1) are generally parallel to X. If thin sections are cut normal to the lineation, parallel to the foliation, and parallel to the lineation but normal to the foliation, this will approximately correspond to YZ, XY and XZ sections. In thin section, two-dimensional finite strain can be completely described by three numbers representing the orientation of the strain ellipse and strain magnitude (Chap. 2.6). Strain magnitude can be expressed as two principal stretch values, or a strain ratio and area change. Methods to measure strain are mentioned in most structural geology textbooks. Below, we give an outline of some methods that can be applied in thin section to allow the reader to determine whether his material is suitable for strain analysis, and to make the best choice between different methods.

In some cases, strain ratio can be measured directly using objects with known original shape such as spherulites and oolites. However, it is important that the measured objects have the same rheology as the matrix in which they lie; for example, feldspar grains in a quartzite at low metamorphic grade cannot be used since they are stronger than quartz and therefore show only part of the tectonic strain. If objects were not initially spherical, the R_f/ϕ method can be used; the elliptic ratio of objects (R_f) is plotted against their orientation (ϕ) and the geometry of the resulting graphs is compared with standard patterns to determine strain (Ramsay and Huber 1983).

If the exact original shape of objects is not known, but if the statistic mean is assumed to approach a spherical shape as for detrital grains in a quartzite, measurement of the dimensions of a large number of grains can be used to determine the strain geometry (Dayan 1981, Law et al. 1984). Care must be taken in this case that the original outline of the grains can still be seen, that no sedimentary shape fabric was present, and that only old, non-recrystallised grains are measured. In a passively deformed grain aggregate without grain boundary migration, strain can also be determined from the orientation of the deformed grain boundaries using the method of Panozzo (1984) explained in Chapter 9.7.2.

If the shape of objects such as grains in a sandstone has been affected by pressure solution, the Fry method (Fry 1979) or centre-to-centre method (Erslev 1988) should be used. In these methods, the distances between grain centres measured in different directions in a deformed aggregate are compared; if these distances were statistically equal before deformation (as in a well sorted sandstone), strain can be calculated. In recrystallised quartzite, however, it may be dangerous to use such techniques since the present centres of grains do not normally coincide with the original centres.

Foliations which are thought to have developed by mechanical rotation of fabric elements can, in principle, be used to estimate strain ratios and the geometry of finite strain (Oertel 1983, 1985). This applies to feldspar phenocrysts in a granite and mica grains in a slate (Oertel 1983, 1985). The degree of preferred orientation of inequant grains is thought to reflect the intensity of deformation; the higher the strain, the more pronounced the preferred orientation becomes. This preferred orientation can be measured by goniometer (Chap. 9.8.6). Some care should be taken since mineral grains are not passive material lines; at low strain, the fabric in mica-rich aggregates may actually be stronger than that predicted by a model of passive rotation of material lines (Means et al. 1984). This is probably due to folding of micas normal to the shortening direction; material lines in this orientation will shorten but will hardly rotate (Fig. 4.15,1). At high strain values, the fabric may be less intense than the theoretical prediction because micas do not stretch passively and rotate more slowly than passive lines because of their low aspect ratio (Fig. 4.15,1; Means et al. 1984). Another point is that different minerals in a foliation may rotate at different velocities (Kanagawa 1991). Fabric intensity in slates can therefore be used only as an approximate measure of strain (Etheridge and Oertel 1979; Siddans 1977; Gapais and Brun 1981; Kanagawa 1991). The fabric of feldspar phenocrysts in granitoids may be more reliable (cf. Chap. 5.6.11).

Strain analysis is also possible using lattice preferred orientation patterns (LPO patterns). LPO patterns cannot be used to determine individual strain ratios or volume change, but carry information on the shape of the strain ellipsoid; the LPO pattern in a single thin section can give information on the full three-dimensional strain geometry (Fig. 4.40; Lister and Hobbs 1980; Wenk 1985). An LPO pattern is easily re-equilibrated, however, and may reflect only the last part of the deformation history (Law 1990). Comparison of the LPO pattern with another method of strain analysis in the same rock may help to decide if strain geometry changed during the deformation history.

One disadvantage of the determination of strain ratios as described above is that even if ratios in three perpendicular directions are known, only the geometry of the strain ellipsoid can be determined, but not its size. This means that volume change cannot be determined in this way. Volume change is difficult to measure in rocks. Most techniques compare the chemistry of undeformed and deformed rock volumes, assuming that they were originally identical and that the undeformed volume did not change its composition (e.g. Mancktelow 1994). Unfortunately, these assumptions are not always valid (Chap. 4.10.3). Alternatively, volume change can be determined if stretches in several directions, or a combination of stretches and strain ratios, can be measured. Examples of structures that can be used to determine stretch values in thin section are deformed microveins (Chap. 6.2), strain fringes (Chap. 6.3) and microboudinage of crystals (Chap. 6.6). Sets of folded or boudinaged microveins can be used to determine stretch values provided that layer parallel shortening or extension in the veins is minimal. This is the case if little difference in layer thickness exists between limbs and hinges of folds as in some ptygmatic folds, or between the centre and edge of boudins. If many deformed veins in different orientations are present in a sample, they can be used to determine principal strain values, sense of shear (Chap. 5.6.11) and even the kinematic vorticity number (Chap. 8.3.2). Care has to be taken, however, that area change and volume change are not confused (Box p. 82) and that a three-dimensional reconstruction of the strain is made wherever possible.

An interesting method to determine principal stretch values and thereby volume change was proposed by Brandon et al. (1994) for sandstones which deformed by pressure solution and solution transfer, and where quartz grains with strain fringes show no effects of intracrystalline deformation. Thin sections are cut parallel to principal strain axes to show where fringes are developed (principal stretch>1), and where grains have been dissolved (principal stretch<1). The mean original diameter of grains can be determined in the direction of fringe growth since it did not change in that direction. Principal stretches >1 can now be determined from the length of grains with their fringes, divided by the mean undeformed diameter; principal stretches <1 are found from the mean diameter of dissolved grains in the direction of that principal strain axis, divided by the mean undeformed diameter.

A method to determine finite strain in shear zones was devised by Ramsay and Graham (1970). They showed that the curvature of a foliation into a shear zone reflects a gradient in finite strain from its peak in the core of a shear zone outwards; it develops because foliations rotate from a position between the instantaneous extension axis and the fabric attractor towards the latter with increasing strain (Chap. 5.5.3). The orientation of the foliation can be used as a strain gauge, since the angle between the foliation and shear zone margin diminishes systematically with increasing strain; however, it is a function of W_k and A_k of flow as well (Chap. 2.5.2). Only if W_k and A_k can be estimated, e.g. if flow in a shear zone was by simple shear ($W_k = 1$, $A_k = 0$), is it possible to calculate principal stretch values at any site in the zone from the orientation of the foliation. The total displacement over the shear zone can also be determined by integration of the strain profile (Ramsay and Graham 1970; Ramsay and Huber 1983). In practice, this method is reliable only at relatively low strains. At high strain values the angles become very small and difficult to measure accurately.

8.3 Vorticity Gauges

8.3.1 Introduction

Several methods have been proposed to establish the kinematic vorticity number W_k of flow in rocks, i.e.

the ratio of pure shear to simple shear (Chap. 2.5.2; Passchier 1988a; Means 1994). A useful tool in such reconstructions is the Mohr diagram for stretch (Means 1982; Passchier 1988b, 1990b). The methods are still in the phase of development. A short outline of the presently available methods to determine W_k in rocks is given below.

8.3.2 Deformed Sets of Veins

The stretch history of a particular material line in homogenous flow depends not only on its initial orientation with respect to ISA, but also on W_k, the kinematic dilatancy number A_k and finite strain. In simple deformation histories, lines undergo extension (e), shortening (s), or a transition from extension to shortening (e–s) and vice versa (s–e) (Figs. 2.11, 5.29). Finite strain affects the shape of the patterns, but not the relative size of the (e–s) and (s–e) fields. If the relative sizes can be established in a rock, they are a measure of W_k and A_k (Passchier 1991a). Veins which become folded or boudinaged can be used for such an analysis provided that a large range of orientations is present (Fig. 5.29). The method has been applied to rocks by Passchier (1986b), Passchier and Urai (1988) and Wallis (1992a).

A problem of the vein-set method is that boundaries between material line fields (Fig. 5.29) will not coincide with boundaries between fields of folded and boudinaged veins, and a calibration is necessary which is, at present, difficult. The method will only work for deformation histories with flow conditions that remained constant or underwent little change. The method is therefore at best semi-quantitative and has been mainly used to determine sense of shear (Fig. 5.29).

8.3.3 Lattice-Preferred Orientation

The geometry of LPO patterns such as those for quartz and calcite is a function of finite strain, strain geometry, active slip systems and W_k (Chap. 4.13). LPO patterns can therefore be used to distinguish between coaxial and non-coaxial progressive deformation (Law et al. 1986; Law 1987), and to determine W_k (Lister and Williams 1979; Wenk et al. 1987; Ratschbacher et al. 1991; Erskine et al. 1993). First attempts to measure W_k by such analysis have been made but as yet the results are rather inaccurate. Platt and Behrmann (1986) and Wallis (1992a) combined high quality strain data with the degree of quartz LPO pattern asymmetry to find W_k; Vissers (1989) combined the rotation angle of garnet porphyroblasts with garnet aspect ratio and quartz LPO pattern asymmetry; and Ratschbacher et al. (1991) used the orientation of the c-axis maxima of calcite LPO patterns.

8.3.4 Mantled Porphyroclasts, Fibrous Veins and Fringes

The rotational behaviour of rigid objects in non-coaxial flow depends, amongst other factors, on the shape of the objects and W_k of the bulk flow (Ghosh and Ramberg 1976; Passchier 1987b; Masuda et al. 1995a; Box p. 119). The geometry of the deformed mantle of porphyroclasts is influenced by this rotational behaviour (Chap. 5.6.6; Passchier 1987b, 1988a; Passchier and Sokoutis 1993). Consequently, the shape of porphyroclast mantles and the orientation distribution of the long axis of porphyroclasts, together with their aspect ratios can theoretically be used to determine W_k (Ghosh and Ramberg 1976; Passchier 1987b; Masuda et al. 1995). However, a large gap still exists between the available simple and mostly two-dimensional models and the complex deformation history and three-dimensional geometry of natural mantled porphyroclasts.

The geometry of fibres in veins and fringes contains much information on W_k (Etchecopar and Malavieille 1987; Passchier and Urai 1988). Figures 6.11, 6.12, 6.14, 6.16 and 6.17 show that major differences exist between fibrous veins and fringes formed in pure shear and in simple shear. While these geometries have not been calibrated, they can only be used to distinguish end members of the flow range, but potentially these microstructures are powerful vorticity gauges. A pioneering attempt to use these structures was published by Passchier and Urai (1988).

8.3.5 Porphyroblasts

Rosenfeld (1970) and Ghosh (1987) suggested methods to determine W_k from comparison of the actual amount of rotation of a porphyroblasts and the theoretically expected rotation angle for finite strain measured in the rock. Although this is an attractive method, it will only work if porphyroblasts are equidimensional, rotated freely in the rock and if the strain is known for the period of porphyroblast rotation.

8.3.6 Tension Gashes and Foliations in Shear Zones

The tips of tension gashes are thought to develop in the direction of the shortening ISA, and in combination with the orientation of the shear zone in which they form, they can be a useful vorticity gauge (Chap. 6.2.3; Fig. 6.11b). Similarly, the deflection of foliations into shear zones can be used as a vorticity gauge, since the orientation of the foliation is a function of strain, W_k and A_k of the flow (Chap. 8.2). If strain is known independently and A_k can be estimated (e.g. in plane strain volume-constant flow it is zero), the orientation may be used to determine W_k in the shear zone.

8.3.7 Oblique Foliations

Theoretically, the angle between an oblique foliation and the fabric attractor is a function of W_k, strain rate and recrystallisation rate (and therefore probably of temperature). The angle can therefore be used to determine W_k and is expected to be maximal for simple shear. A problem with this method is that several other factors may influence the angle, and that finite strain should be sufficiently high to rotate fabric elements into parallelism with the fabric attractor (Chap. 2.9). For example, some oblique foliations make an angle with the fabric attractor that exceeds 45°; such orientations are difficult to explain with the available theory.

8.3.8 Al-Cr Zoning in Spinel

Ozawa (1989) showed that many spinel grains in peridotite have an asymmetric sector zoning of Al and Cr, with Al concentrated in the direction of the stretching lineation, and Cr in the direction of the normal to the foliation in the peridotite. He suggests that Cr concentrated in the σ_1 and Al in the σ_3 direction due to unequal diffusivity of these ions when the spinel grains deformed by solid-state diffusion creep. In fact, the sector zoning is more likely to lie in the direction of ISA and may be useful to determine sense of shear and W_k if sector symmetry planes are oblique to the shape fabric in the peridotite.

8.3.9 W_k History

A problem with all determinations of W_k is that it may have been variable over a volume of rock and may have changed with time; in such cases a mean value is established with the methods given above, which is difficult to interpret. One possible solution to this problem is to measure W_k in a rock using several different gauges which re-equilibrate at different rate during the deformation history. For example, quartz fabrics are thought to reequilibrate relatively quickly, while deformed veins will record the whole deformation history if they predate deformation; if both methods give different values, this may indicate the trend of change in W_k during the deformation history (Passchier 1988a, 1990a; Wallis 1992a). Detailed reconstructions of deformation paths, including W_k history, are possible using fibrous veins and fringes (Ramsay and Huber 1983; Ellis 1986). However, none of these methods is as yet very accurate.

8.4 The Concept of Palaeostress Gauges

Although several methods have been proposed to determine the orientation and magnitude of stress in a rock during deformation (also referred to as *palaeostress*), it is important to realise that stress is not preserved, only its effects. Moreover, stress is only defined at a point, and usually varies in size and orientation from point to point in a rock, and also changes strongly with time. Stress leaves traces in a rock only when permanent deformation is realised and stress gauges are claimed to capture the properties of the stress field during this time. However, in inhomogeneous materials, such as rocks on the grain scale, stress was probably strongly variable from crystal to crystal, and even within individual crystals, and must have changed with time. Probably, stress gauges measure some kind of 'mean value' for stress; however, it is important to remain critical about the meaningfulness of such mean values. Microgauges to measure 'palaeostress' in deforming rocks are divided into three main types; 1. gauges for the orientation of stress principal axes; 2. gauges for differential stress; and gauges for mean stress or pressure.

8.5 Gauges for the Orientation of Palaeostress Principal Axes

8.5.1 Calcite Twins

Calcite e-twins ($\{01\bar{1}2\}$) have been proposed as a tool for determination of the orientation of palaeostress principal axes (Turner 1953; Laurent et al. 1981; Dietrich and Song 1984; Borradaile and McArthur 1990; Shelley 1992; Burkhard 1993). Since movement on twins can take place in only one direction, data on the presence of twins, the orientation of twins and crystallographic c-axes in a large number of grains can give an impression of the orientation of principal shortening and extension directions. Therefore, the quantity that is really measured is *strain* accommodated by the twins. Only in isotropic materials that undergo coaxial deformation will the orientation of stress and strain axes coincide. Hence, calcite twins can only be used to measure the orientation of principal axes of palaeostress in rocks that deform coaxially. Only straight twins can be used, which restricts use of the method to low temperature deformation (Chap. 8.9). In all cases, there will be a number of grains that do not fit in the determined directions of palaeostress axes (Groshong et al. 1984; Pfiffner and Burkhard 1987). The percentage of deviating grains can be taken as a measure of the reliability of the method in a particular case. Attribution of the deviating grains to other phases of deformation with a different orientation of the stress field is probably not realistic. Methods of determination of palaeostress orientation using twins have also been proposed for dolomite (Christie 1958), pyroxene (Raleigh and Talbot 1967), olivine (Carter and Raleigh 1969) and plagioclase (Lawrence 1970).

8.5.2 Deformation Lamellae

Quartz deformation lamellae (Box p. 32 top) have been interpreted as planes of high resolved shear stress and can therefore be used to determine palaeostress directions in a way similar to calcite e-twins

(Carter and Raleigh 1969; Law 1990; Twiss and Moores 1992). Since calcite e-twins can only accommodate movement in a single direction, they are probably more reliable as microgauges than quartz deformation lamellae. The same objections and restrictions to application of the method mentioned for calcite twins are valid for deformation lamellae

8.6 Differential Stress Gauges (Palaeopiezometers)

8.6.1 Dynamically Recrystallised Grain Size

The size of dynamically recrystallised grains in a deforming material (Fig. 3.24) is a function of differential stress and has been proposed as a *palaeopiezometer*, i.e. a method to measure the magnitude of palaeostress (Mercier et al. 1977; Etheridge and Wilkie 1979, 1981; Christie and Ord 1980; Schmid et al. 1980; Koch 1983; Ord and Christie 1984; Ranalli 1984; Twiss 1986; Hacker et al. 1990, 1992; Michibayashi 1993). Dislocation density and subgrain size have also been proposed as palaeopiezometers and seem to give good results in metals. However, they can only be

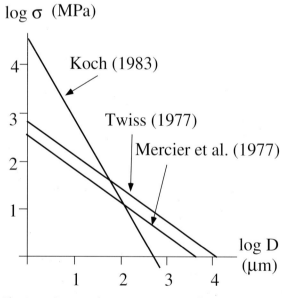

Fig. 8.1. Diagram of grain size against differential stress for quartz. Three published graphs are shown (After Michibayashi 1993)

determined in a TEM, and seem to be sensitive to changes after deformation due to recovery. They are therefore less applied in geological samples (with complex, non-controllable histories) than in metals; dynamically recrystallised grainsize is usually preferred.

For a particular differential stress during progressive deformation, each mineral has particular mean size of recrystallised grains, although water content may influence this grain size (Bell and Etheridge 1976) and grains formed by SR recrystallisation tend to be smaller than those formed by GBM recrystallisation (Chap. 7.3.1; Drury and Urai 1990; Twiss and Moores 1992). Some observations also suggest that GBM recrystallisation gives more accurate results than SR recrystallisation (Hirth and Tullis 1992). Notice that mean grain size is mentioned; even amongst recrystallised grains, there can be a significant range in grain size. Grain size can be estimated with the mean linear intercept method (Smith and Guttman 1953; Dehoff and Rhines 1968) or, more accurately, with image analysis techniques (Panozzo 1984). Most data on stable grain size and associated differential stress are available for quartz and olivine (Mercier et al. 1977; Post 1977; Ross et al. 1980; Karato 1984) and calcite (Schmid et al. 1980). Typical graphs of grain size against differential stress for quartz are given as an example in Fig. 8.1 (Michibayashi 1993). Estimates for differential stress in rocks based on grain-size palaeopiezometers range from a few MPa in high temperature deformation to 100–200 MPa in some low-temperature mylonite zones.

Grain size reduction in mylonites is due to the fact that differential stress in active ductile shear zones can be high, especially at low temperature; consequently the stable recrystallised grain size is small. However, extremely fine-grained rocks such as cherts may undergo grain growth during dynamic recrystallisation in a shear zone to reach the stable grain size (Masuda and Fujimura 1981). Figures 3.24 and 5.27 show examples of typical fabrics in quartz mylonites where differential stress can be estimated from dynamically recrystallised grain size. In some cases, even stress differences in a single aggregate can be determined, such as near rigid porphyroclasts that can cause a local increase in differential stress (Fig. 11.1).

Possible sources of error in the calculation of palaeostress are the presence of old grain relics that may be smaller or (usually) larger than the recrystallised ones. Old grain relics are recognisable by their irregular outline, deviant crystallographic orientation and well-developed intracrystalline deformation structures. Another possible source of error is the presence of a second mineral that inhibits growth of the mineral to be measured, e.g. mica in quartzite; therefore, only monomineralic aggregates should be used. Finally, static recrystallisation may have affected grain size. Static recrystallisation can be recognised by the presence of straight, polygonal grain boundaries and 'strain-free' recrystallised grains (Box p. 47 bottom; compare Fig. 3.24 with Figs. 3.29 and 11.2), and evidence for grain boundary adjustment to euhedral shape in strongly anisotropic crystals such as micas; they will show evidence for static recrystallisation before quartz and feldspar do. Static recrystallisation is commonly associated with hydration and retrograde transformation of mineral assemblages characteristic of higher grade metamorphic conditions.

8.6.2 Twins in Calcite and Dolomite

The number and volume of twins in calcite has been proposed as a microgauge for differential stress (Jamison and Spang 1976; Laurent et al. 1990) and has even been calibrated experimentally (Rowe and Rutter 1990). The idea is based on the fact that the critical resolved shear stress for twinning is between 2–12 MPa (Chap. 3.12.3); differential stress is twice the maximum shear stress at any point, and for a differential stress of 4–24 MPa, twins can only form in the direction parallel to the plane of maximum resolved shear stress. If differential stress is larger, twins can also form in other orientations. In this way, the size and sharpness of the principal shortening direction maximum determined for a population of twins is a function of the differential stress (Jamison and Spang 1976; Laurent et al. 1990). The method is also applicable to dolomite, where the critical resolved shear stress for twinning is expected to be higher than in calcite (Jamison and Spang 1976; Rowe and Rutter 1990; Newman 1994).

Unfortunately, the twin palaeopiezometer relies heavily on the assumption of homogenous stress distribution in a sample, which is probably never the case in nature. Inhomogeneous stress distribution can have a similar effect on the spread in the orientation of inferred principal stress directions as differential stress magnitude. Small crystals seems to have fewer twins than large grains (Schmid 1982; Newman 1994). The twin palaeopiezometer is therefore likely to give best results at very small strain values, at low temperature and in relatively even-grained and coarse-grained calcite and dolomite without an LPO (Burkhard 1993; Newman 1994). It should not be applied to strongly deformed rocks.

8.6.3 Microboudins

Flow of a ductile medium around an elongate rigid object can produce an internal stress field that can lead to tensile fracturing and boudinage. Microboudins can be used to calculate differential stress based on the *fibre-loading principle* (Lloyd and Ferguson 1981; Lloyd et al. 1982; Ji and Zhao 1994). A rigid fibre parallel to the extension direction in ductile coaxial flow is thought to experience a gradient in tensile stress that is maximum at the centre. Consequently, the fibre will break near the centre and this process will be repeated in the remaining fragments until some critical limit is reached that depends on mechanical properties of the fibre and on differential stress. The aspect ratio of microboudin fragments can therefore be used to estimate differential stress (Masuda and Kuriyama 1988; Masuda et al. 1989, 1990; Ji and Zhao 1993). The principle can be used in any rigid mineral, including feldspar at low-grade metamorphic conditions (White et al. 1980). The presence of tensional fractures (without a component of shear movement) is also useful because it restricts the possible magnitude of the differential stress to four times the tensile strength of the material under consideration (Etheridge 1983). The fibre-loading principle explains why some gaps between fragments are wider than others; the wider ones are thought to have formed earlier (Ferguson 1981,1987; Masuda and Kuriyama 1988).

8.6.4 Deformation Lamellae

Deformation lamellae have been proposed as palaeopiezometers (Drury and Humphreys 1987; Blenkinsop and Drury 1988). Subbasal deformation lamellae in quartz are thought to develop at differential stresses between 170–420 MPa. Spacing of deformation lamellae may also serve as a palaeopiezometer (Koch and Christie 1981).

8.7 Pressure Gauges

Lithostatic pressure is usually determined by classical petrological methods such as mineral composition of the rock and fluid inclusion density. However, geometries may help where older mineral assemblages or fluid inclusions have been destroyed. The presence of gas bubbles or amygdales (gas bubbles filled with crystalline material) in pseudotachylyte, for example, indicates that the fault rock formed at shallow crustal levels, the exact magnitude of which depends on the composition of the rock. Another promising development is the recognition of deformed pseudotachylyte in many ductile shear zones. Pseudotachylyte is a brittle fault rock that probably only forms in the upper crust, and whose geometry is not easily destroyed by later deformation (Chap. 5.2.3). Its presence can be used as an indication of low lithostatic pressure in the rock at some stage during its development (Passchier et al. 1990a).

8.8 Strain Rate Gauges

Geological strain rates are estimated to lie usually between 10^{-13} and 10^{-15} s^{-1} (Pfiffner and Ramsay 1982; Carter and Tsenn 1987) and could theoretically be estimated in rocks if differential stress and temperature of deformation are known, using known flow laws derived from experimental data (Chap. 3.14). Differential stress values can be obtained using a palaeopiezometer as discussed above. This method to estimate strain rates has been applied to peridotite using flow laws for olivine (Karato et al. 1986; Suhr 1993). The discrepancies between results of different experiments give 'error bars' of one, or even two orders of magnitude. Sources of error are in the flow laws and their extrapolation to geological strain rates, in the estimate of differential stress if grain growth is inhibited or if recrystallisation is important, and in temperature estimates. For olivine, an error of 50 °C in the temperature results in an error of one order of magnitude in the strain rates. Another possible method is the use of LPO fabrics; a relation exists between the slip systems that are active in a mineral and the strain rate (Lister et al. 1978); however, since other parameters (temperature, water activity) also influence the active slip systems and because it is not always possible to determine which slip systems were active in natural rocks, this method cannot (yet) be used. Therefore, estimates of strain rate are not yet accurate in practice, but promising progress is being made.

8.9 Temperature Gauges

Any experienced student of microtectonics is aware that there is a correlation between metamorphic grade during deformation and the presence and geometry of particular microstructures. Unfortunately, few of these structures have been calibrated to date; geometric temperature gauges could give independent data on temperature besides the classical petrological geothermometers and may be less easily modified by retrogression and later deformation than mineral composition.

The geometry of deformation twins (e-twins) in calcite has been proposed as a temperature gauge (Fig. 8.2; Ferrill 1991; Burkhard 1993). Narrow straight twins (less than 5 mm wide – Type I of Burkhard 1993) indicate temperatures below 200 °C, while wider twins (Type II, > 5 mm) indicate conditions up to 300 °C (Groshong et al. 1984; Rowe and Rutter 1990; Evans and Dunne 1991; Ferrill 1991). At temperatures over 200 °C, Type III intersecting twins and bent twins are present (Figs. 8.2, 8.3). Bending of twins is thought to be due to activity of dislocation glide on r and f planes (Burkhard 1993). At more elevated temperatures above 250 °C, twins obtain serrated boundaries due to grain boundary migration (Type IV twins of Vernon 1981; Burkhard 1993).

The width of exsolution symplectites (Chap. 7.8.3) formed by isochemical reactions of the type (A $\Rightarrow$ A'+B) can be used as a temperature gauge if properly calibrated (Joanny et al. 1991; van Roermund

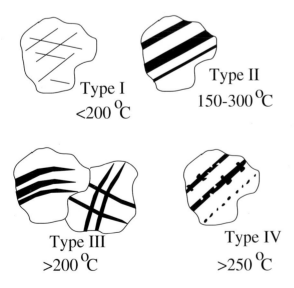

Fig. 8.2. Schematic diagram showing the geometry of deformation e-twins in calcite, developed at different temperature

Fig. 8.3. Two sets of intersecting deformation twins of type III in calcite. Orobic Alps, Italy. Width of view 1 mm CPL

1992). Such symplectites form by grain boundary diffusion mechanisms resulting in the nucleation of mineral B in the reacting interface as it migrates into the supersaturated adjacent parent mineral. Under such circumstances, grain boundary diffusion rates are fully temperature dependent, which is directly reflected by the spacing of the symplectite (Shewmon 1969). Since the exsolved volume percentage of mineral B depends on the original composition of mineral A, it is the combined width of a pair of lamellae of A′ and B that is critical, not their individual widths (Fig. 8.4; van Roermund 1992). Good examples of exsolution symplectites can be found in retrogressed eclogites in which the Na-bearing clinopyroxene becomes replaced by clinopyroxene-plagioclase symplectites (Boland and van Roermund 1983; van Roermund and Boland 1983).

Development of phase transformations such as exsolution structures can be shown in a *TTT diagram* (time – temperature – transformation) as pairs of curves, one for the time and temperature when a new phase is first detectable, the second for conditions when the reaction is completed (Putnis and McConnell 1980). At high temperature, approaching the critical temperature below which exsolution is possible,

diffusion rates are high but nucleation rates are low; at low temperature, the reverse is true. Consequently, the curves in a TTT diagram show a minimum time for nucleation at some intermediate temperature.

Figure 8.4 shows a TTT diagram with a scheme of possible geometries of exsolved plagioclase lamellae in clinopyroxene. At high temperature, lamellae form homogeneously distributed inside the clinopyroxene crystals, but at lower temperature exsolution symplectites are formed at grain boundaries. Curved paths in temperature-time space can give rise to unique microstructures (Fig. 8.4) which can help to reconstruct PTt paths. Obviously, such temperature gauges are most powerful when properly calibrated. If such calibrations are absent, traditional geothermometry and barometry methods have to be used in order to quantify the results.

The geometry of deformed grains of some minerals can be used as temperature microgauges. For example, the presence of ductilely deformed ribbon feldspar in a rock indicates high-grade metamorphic conditions (Chap. 3.12.4) and the presence of ribbon garnet very high grade (Ji and Martignole 1994). Greater accuracy can be attained using the geometry of biphase mineral aggregates (Chap. 3.13); if two

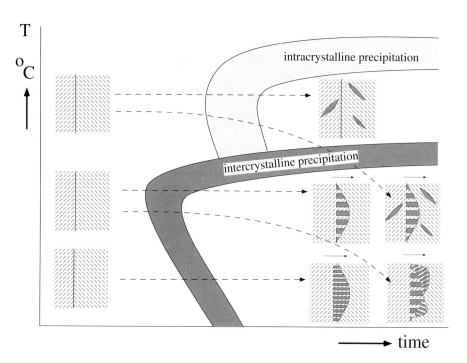

Fig. 8.4. Schematic TTT diagram showing the relative position of start and finish curves for inter- and intracrystalline exsolution of plagioclase from omphacite, after van Roermund (1992). *Straight dotted arrows* show isothermal trajectories of symplectite growth. *Insets* show schematic details of the developing microstructure along a grain boundary between two omphacite grains with identical chemistry but different orientation, indicated by *striping*. At high temperature, plagioclase nucleates inside the omphacite crystals. At lower temperature, exsolution symplectites are formed when the grain boundary migrates into one of the crystals. *Small arrows over insets* indicate movement direction of the grain boundary. The spacing of symplectite lamellae pairs decreases with decreasing temperature, as indicated. If temperature decreases significantly with time *(curved paths)*, complex internal structures are formed. Such microstructures can be used to reconstruct cooling paths

minerals deform together, both usually deform at different rates at a particular temperature. This leads, for example, to the development of porphyroclasts of feldspar in a quartz-feldspar aggregate, and of orthopyroxene in peridotite. With changing temperature conditions, this difference in behaviour may diminish or reverse (Chap. 3.13.2; Fig. 3.31), and this change in fabric may be a potential microgauge for temperature. As for all microgauges, these structures can only be calibrated if the effects of other parameters are also understood.

Other potential microgauges of temperature are LPO patterns, which can be used to determine the active slip systems in crystals (Chap. 8.8), the type of recrystallisation mechanism in quartz, feldspars and mica (Chap. 3.12), the presence of flame-perthite in K-feldspar and myrmekite in plagioclase (Chaps. 3.12.4, 7.8.3; Simpson and Wintsch 1989; Pryer 1993) and the geometry of foliations (Chap. 4.10.4).

8.10 Rheology Gauges

8.10.1 Introduction

Deformation experiments have taught us much about the rheology of rocks under a range of metamorphic conditions, but it would be useful to have more direct control from deformed rocks. There are indications that some fabric elements, which might be called rheology gauges, can be used to determine rheological constants (Chaps. 2.12, 3.14). Rheology gauges are a promising new subject in geology, but few structures have been tested in practice yet. We restrict ourselves here to outline the potential of the method with published examples. Rheology gauges can only be further developed with much theoretical work and experimental deformation of rocks and rock analogues.

8.10.2 Folding and Boudinage

The wavelength of buckle folds in isolated competent layers in a less competent matrix depends on layer thickness and *viscosity contrast* between the layer and the matrix. The wavelength measured along the surface of a layer can therefore be used to determine absolute viscosity contrasts (e.g. Ramsay and Huber 1983). Boudins can be used to the same purpose, but although buckle folding and boudinage in single layers both occur in response to a viscosity contrast, there is a difference; folding can occur in Newtonian and non-Newtonian materials, while boudinage is restricted to non-Newtonian materials (Chap. 2.12; Neurath and Smith 1982).

8.10.3 Mantled Objects

Mantled porphyroclasts can show wings with or without stair-stepping (Chap. 5.6.5). The absence of stair-stepping around these objects seems to be due to the activity of a special geometry of flow, known as an 'eye'-shaped flow pattern (Chap. 5.6.6). Experimental evidence and theoretical considerations (Passchier et al. 1993; ten Brink, pers. comm. 1994) now indicate that such a flow pattern only forms in Newtonian flow (Chaps. 2.12, 5.6.6). Further work is needed to determine which parameters influence the presence and shape of such flow patterns and of stair stepping. With proper calibration, it may be possible to distinguish Newtonian and non-Newtonian flow, and even to determine the stress exponent (Chap. 2.12).

9 Special Techniques

9.1 Introduction

The study of microstructures in thin sections under the petrographic microscope can give a lot of information for thematic and tectonic studies but has its limitations. In many cases, additional information has to be gathered by other techniques. In this chapter, we wish to give the reader an outline of some other analytical laboratory techniques that use *geometries* for the study of tectonics. We indicate what problems can be studied by these techniques, which type of materials can be studied and which type of samples are needed; and finally, what the limitations of the different techniques are. The aim is to allow the reader to assess whether other techniques can help him to solve his problem and, if so, what material has to be prepared. We do not treat microprobe analysis or field techniques since they are sufficiently covered in other textbooks.

9.2 Cathodoluminescence

Many minerals show luminescence when they are excited by a beam of electrons due to the presence of lattice defects or included trace elements (Richter and Zinkernagel 1981; ten Have and Heynen 1985; Solomon 1989). The pattern, colour and intensity of luminescence may be independent of optically visible microstructures and can give important information on the development of fabrics in the rock.

Cathodoluminescence is a well-established technique in sedimentology to study mineral growth processes and provenance of sediments (Marshall 1988) but is also useful in microtectonic studies since it can reveal material grown from solution, e.g. in microcracks (Narahara and Wiltschko 1986), in veins and along grain boundaries. In veins, it can reveal growth surfaces that are invisible in ordinary light (Dietrich and Grant 1985; Urai et al. 1991) and details of the microstructure of cataclasites (Stel 1981; Blenkinsop and Rutter 1986). Fracture patterns can be easily distinguished (Kanaori 1986). Overgrowth structures along grain boundaries which are invisible in normal transmitted light can be used for strain analysis (Onasch and Davis 1988). Dislocation networks can be made visible in some cases (Grant and White 1978). Original igneous quartz can be distinguished from quartz grown from solution, even after ductile deformation. Recrystallisation decreases the luminosity of quartz and therefore old, non-recrystallised grains can be distinguished from recrystallised aggregates. New grown quartz is commonly less luminescent (darker) than old quartz grains (Shimamoto et al. 1991). Although it is usually impossible to predict if a certain sample will show informative structures in cathodoluminescence, it is worth to use the technique for investigation of microstructures formed by solution transfer, including pressure fringes and shadows, veins and overgrowths (Dietrich and Grant 1985).

Cathodoluminescence can be carried out with a conventional 'luminoscope', in which a polished thin section is studied in vacuum under an ordinary microscope; however, small differences in luminosity will not be visible in this way. Better results can be obtained using a SEM with a detector for cathodoluminescence and an image processing device (Shimamoto et al. 1991; Lloyd 1994). Ordinary polished thin sections covered with a thin carbon layer can be used for cathodoluminescence studies. However, the samples should be dry and free of glues or resins which emit gasses that may cause difficulties in obtaining a good vacuum.

9.3 Fluid Inclusion Studies

Fluid inclusions are small pockets of fluid inside crystals. They are assumed to be samples of the fluid that was present in the rock during deformation and metamorphism, although the original composition and density may have been modified by leaking and preferential removal or addition of certain components (Roedder 1984; Crawford and Hollister 1986). Fluid inclusions of CO_2, H_2O, N_2 and CH_4 are relatively common. Frequently inclusions contain more then one phase; many contain gas bubbles and some contain also solid phases such as small salt cubes or graphite crystals.

Presently, it is possible to determine the composition and density of the fluid in inclusions without destroying the sample. To a first approximation, H_2O rich inclusions in quartz can be recognised by the presence of small salt cubes and gas bubbles, and by a small contrast in refractive index with quartz (Fig. 9.1). CO_2-rich inclusions may have gas bubbles but lack salt cubes, and have a stronger contrast in refractive index with quartz, leading to thick 'shades' along

the contacts (Fig. 9.1). Composition of the fluid can be determined with accuracy using a *Raman probe;* a laser beam is used to irradiate the phases in the inclusion to obtain Raman spectra from which the composition of the inclusion can be determined. Density is determined on a *heating-freezing stage* which fits under a normal microscope. A chip of rock less than 1 cm in diameter, 100 µm thick, and polished on both sides without attached glass plates is heated to 300 °C, or cooled down to –160 °C using liquid nitrogen. A single inclusion is observed during heating and cooling and the temperature at which a phase change occurs in the inclusion (homogenisation of a fluid with a gas bubble, freezing, or dissolution of a solid phase) is noted. If the composition of the inclusion is known by Raman probe analysis, the density can now be accurately determined. This density defines an *isochore,* a line of constant volume for the fluid in P–T space. If the inclusion did not leak, the metamorphic conditions at which the inclusion was sealed lie on this line; if either pressure or temperature during sealing is known, the other can be determined. In the case of fluid inclusions, fluid pressure was probably equal to lithostatic pressure since inclusions formed by sealing of open fluid filled surfaces (Chap. 2.11).

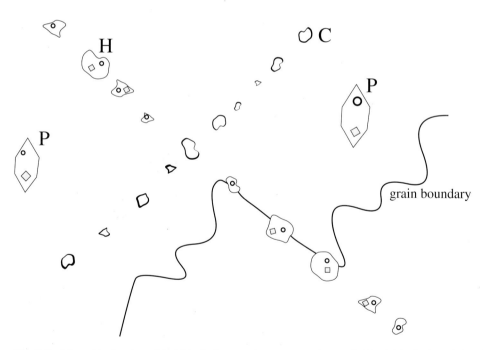

Fig. 9.1. Schematic drawing of fluid inclusions as they may appear in a thin section; large isolated inclusions with a negative crystal shape can be primary *(P).* Secondary inclusions occur in arrays that represent healed fluid-filled cracks, and have similar composition within a single array; two types are shown, H_2O-rich inclusions *(H)* with gas bubbles and small salt cubes, and CO_2-rich inclusions *(C),* with thick shades along the edge due to a difference in refraction with surrounding quartz. The H_2O inclusion array cuts a grain boundary, and the CO_2-rich array cuts the H_2O rich array, thus establishing the relative age of the structures

Fluid inclusions either occur isolated, or as swarms that commonly lie along a plane. Isolated inclusions, commonly with a negative crystal shape (Fig. 9.1), may represent inclusions that were captured when the grain in which they lie grew from a solution; they are therefore also known as *primary fluid inclusions*. Planes of inclusions commonly contain inclusions of similar composition and density, and are thought to represent healed fractures on which fluid has been present (Figs. 3.12, 9.1); they are also known as *secondary fluid inclusions*. Such fractures can normally be followed over considerable distances in a section, and may transect grain boundaries or even mineral boundaries (Fig. 9.1). Thus, the relative age of inclusions in the healed crack and structures or minerals in the rocks can be established; the composition and density of the inclusions can be related to deformation phases or metamorphic conditions. Where healed cracks transect grain boundaries, it is possible to determine whether they were tension fractures (without a shear component) or shear fractures. If their orientation is known, they can then be related to a stress tensor of a particular orientation and, in the case of tension fractures, an upper limit can be placed on the magnitude of the differential stress (Chap. 8.6). In many cases, several sets of healed cracks occur in a rock, and their relative age can be established at the intersection point, since inclusions of the older phase will have been destroyed by the younger fracture (Fig. 9.1). Thus, sequences of fracturing and associated fluid compositions and densities can be linked to phases of deformation and, in some cases, metamorphic conditions. Since fluids play a major role in deformation of rocks, such information is extremely valuable. However, there are also some disadvantages in the use of fluid inclusions: 1. inclusions are usually relatively young; the older inclusions are destroyed by deformation; 2. inclusions may have leaked or changed composition and density, and this is difficult to check; especially inclusions with strongly irregular shape, or with surrounding swarms of small inclusions may have leaked. In healed cracks the situation is probably relatively safe, since inclusions with strongly deviant composition and density can be regarded as suspect.

The relationship between healed cracks of fluid inclusions and other microstructures in a rock can be studied in ordinary thin sections or polished sections, although many inclusions will have leaked and are now empty; they appear as dark inclusions with unusually thick shades along the rims due to refraction of light through the empty inclusion. Intact inclusions can be recognised by a clear image and the presence of included bubbles or small crystals. The presence of fluid in an inclusion is proven by rapid Brownian movement of included gas bubbles. Fluid inclusions are mostly studied in quartz, but can be found in many minerals. Minerals with a strong mineral cleavage such as calcite and micas are less suitable for analytical purposes since they are likely to have leaked; similarly, minerals that are likely to have reacted with water or CO_2 are to be avoided.

9.4 Electron Microscopy

At magnifications exceeding 1000x, objects seen by the optical microscope become fuzzy; this is the direct consequence of the use of light as a medium to transport information; the wavelength of visible light varies from 400 to 750 nm and no objects smaller than 100 nm can be observed. Depending on their velocity, electrons have much smaller wavelengths and can therefore be used to carry information about smaller objects. Two types of electron microscope are commonly used in geology; the scanning electron microscope (SEM), and the transmission electron microscope (TEM).

9.5 Scanning Electron Microscope (SEM)

9.5.1 Introduction

Although this book deals with the interpretation of structures visible with the optical microscope, the scanning electron microscope (SEM) has proven to be an important aid in the study of microstructures; its accessibility in many labs and relatively easy use makes the SEM a powerful tool to complement the optical microscope. In a SEM, a sample is placed in a column under vacuum, and is then scanned line-by-line by an electron beam (Fig. 9.2). The electrons are either scattered back from the surface of the sample (Hall and Lloyd 1981) or cause the sample to emit secondary electrons, which are caught by a detector. The electrons which strike the detectors are used to build up an image of the sample on a monitor (Fig. 9.2). This technique allows magnifications of up to 50 000x, 50 times more than the optical microscope. This is an obvious advantage, but a disadvantage is that SEM images are always in black and white. The

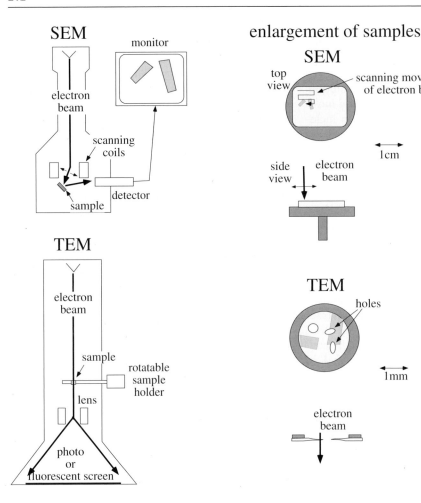

Fig. 9.2. Simplified diagram of the principles of SEM and TEM. In SEM the electron beam is focussed to a small area and scanned over the surface of the sample, while at the same time the electrons produced in the sample are detected and the result displayed on a monitor which is scanned at the same rate; in this way, an enlarged image of the sample is made. In the TEM, the electron beam passes through the sample and is then enlarged. SEM and TEM use different types of samples as illustrated

recognition of minerals by their interference colour, as in the optical microscope, is therefore not possible. However, recognition of minerals with the SEM is usually not problematic; the amount of electrons that are emitted or back scattered in a volume of material struck by the electron beam is directly proportional to the atomic number of the constituent elements in the minerals; heavy elements yield many electrons. It is therefore possible to identify individual minerals in a sample by their grey tone on the screen (the atomic number contrast). For example, in most cases the following sequence can be observed from dark to light; serpentine - quartz - feldspar - biotite - rutile - ilmenite - zircon. A more detailed list is given in Hall and Lloyd (1981). After some training, a SEM user can easily identify the common rock-forming minerals. It is even possible to see zoning in garnets and plagioclase and to compare the amount of Ti in two generations of biotite.

Most modern SEMs have linked energy dispersive X-ray analysis (EDAX) facilities available. This tool measures the energy of X-rays emitted by the irradiated sample, and can identify the elements that occur in the sample. With this tool, minerals can not only be easily identified, but their chemical compositions can be determined in a semi-quantitative way (for quantitative analysis a microprobe should be used). If a few grains in a sample have been analysed by EDAX, the rest can be recognised by their respective grey tones. Notice that EDAX cannot be used to analyse grains smaller than 5 μm since the X-rays are produced in a pear-shaped volume in the sample where the electron beam hits the surface. The diameter of this volume is much larger than the diameter of the electron beam.

9.5.2 Secondary and Backscatter Electrons

Two types of observation mode are available in the SEM. Secondary electron emission mode (Figs. 9.3,

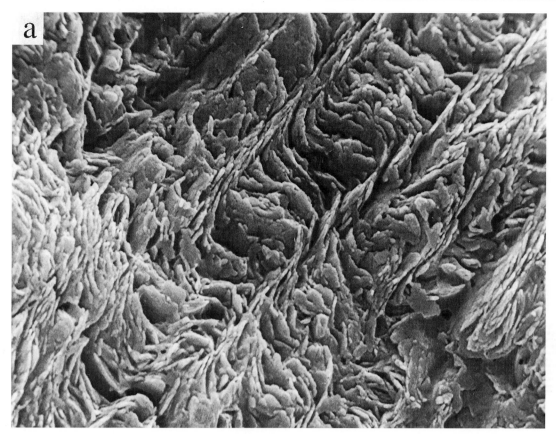

Fig. 9.3a–c. Secondary electron images of a series of fracture surfaces (see text) of a slate sample observed by SEM (continued on next page). Details of the structure can be seen, but grey tones cannot be used to distinguish mineral composition because of the rough surface. **a** A bedding parallel foliation is folded and fold limbs define a first slaty cleavage S$_1$. **b** Spaced slaty cleavage S$_1$. Microlithons contain micas that are truncated against micas in the cleavage lamellae. This slaty cleavage formed at slightly higher metamorphic grade than **a**. Massive grains in microlithons probably consist of quartz. **c** S$_2$ crenulation cleavage in slate overprinting an S$_1$ slaty cleavage. Rheinisches Schiefergebirge, Germany. Width of view **a** 20 μm; **b** and **c** 95 μm. (Photographs courtesy K. Weber. **a** and **b** Weber 1981, **c** Weber 1976)

9.4) is most commonly used; electrons which are detached from the sample are caught by a detector and used to build up a picture. This mode is useful to study topography in samples, and can also be used to get some information on the composition of minerals using grey-tones. Backscatter electron mode (Fig. 9.5) uses electrons from the primary beam which are reflected from the surface of the specimen. These electrons carry more information on the composition of the sample and grain orientation and this mode is therefore most useful if fine details of mineral composition or LPO are the subject of study.

9.5.3 Problems with Orientation

Although the large magnifications obtainable by SEM are an obvious advantage, it also means that it can be difficult to find a specific feature in a sample that was easily recognisable under the optical microscope. Turning the SEM to low magnification usually does not help, since very little detail will be visible. Therefore, if a specific feature in a sample such as a porphyroblast or a fault is to be studied, it is advisable to mark it under a reflected light microscope with a dot of silver glue, or to use a photograph or sketch of the sample; once the sample is in the SEM, it may be very difficult to find the object.

9.5.4 Sample Preparation

Samples used in the SEM are studied under vacuum, and should therefore be dry. This is no problem with most rock samples, but clay samples may have to be dried before use. One specific problem of the SEM is

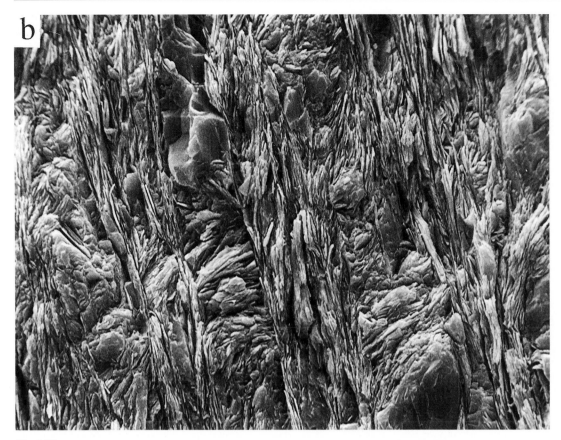

Fig. 9.3b

Fig. 9.3c

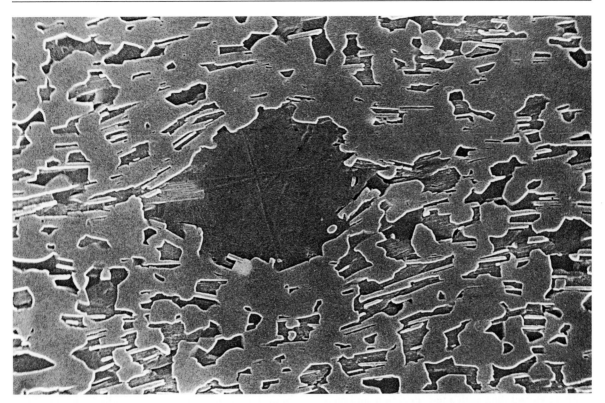

Fig. 9.4. Polished sample of ultramylonite, etched with HF vapour. Secondary electron mode. Gold cover. Fine detail is visible through the presence of etch pits and different grey-tones for the three minerals present. Quartz has not been etched much and forms the matrix *(light grey)*. Feldspar and biotite have been etched. Feldspar is *dark grey* and forms the central porphyroclast. The etched *medium grey* elongate grains with cleavage are biotite. Biotite seems to replace feldspar at the *left-hand side* of the porphyroclast. St Barthélemy Massif, Pyrenees, France. Width of view 40 μm

that the electron beam which hits the specimen tends to cause local electrostatic charging which can cause beam deflection, thereby distorting the image. It is therefore necessary that samples are conductive. This is a problem in most rock samples, which have to be coated with a thin conductive layer of a metal such as gold or carbon.

There are several methods of preparing samples for the SEM; since only the surface of the sample is studied, it is possible to use either polished thin sec-

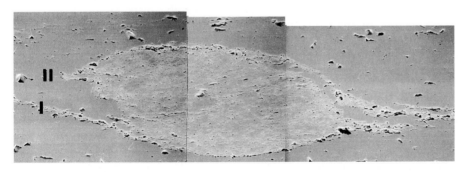

Fig. 9.5. SEM image of a complex mantled K-feldspar porphyroclast *(light grey)* in quartzite *(dark grey)*. Backscattered electron mode. Carbon cover. *I* Primary wing of recrystallised feldspar; *II* secondary wing. Sinistral shear sense. Although atomic number contrast allows distinction of K-feldspar and quartz, few details of the internal structure are visible. St Barthélemy Massif, Pyrenees, France. Width of view 0.5 mm

tions or small chips of rock (Fig. 9.2). Small chips can be polished or broken. The advantage of a broken surface is that it is free of contaminations and usually breaks along grain boundaries; it therefore shows a lot of information on grain shape, grain size and internal structure of grains (Fig. 9.3; Weber 1981). A disadvantage is that the surface is irregular and difficult to interpret by scientists familiar with the interpretation of planar sections through a material. This problem can be overcome by polishing a chip of rock (Hall and Lloyd 1981); this will give familiar geometries as in thin section, which is an advantage if one wishes to compare optical and SEM microstructures (Fig. 9.5). A disadvantage of such sample preparation is that polished samples will only show structures if sufficient atomic number contrast or difference in orientation exists between grains. Polishing also destroys the crystal lattice in a thin surface layer of the specimen, which may result in a blurred image of the grains. These problems can sometimes be solved by etching the specimen briefly in hydrofluoric acid (HF)[3]; this will remove the damaged top layer and may also etch some minerals more than others, generating a topography which outlines the fabric in the specimen (Fig. 9.4) The SEM may give better results with an etched than with a flat specimen, and etching combines the advantage of a relatively planar section with sufficient relief to see the fabric. However, after etching the chemical composition of grains may have changed and EDAX may give unreliable results.

Etching is most effective in biotite, less so in feldspars, and even less in quartz and white mica. In some quartz samples, grain boundaries will not etch by this method. After etching, the specimen should be treated in an ultrasonic water bath to remove dirt and loose fragments. The surface that is going to be studied should not be touched; this may spread grease over the sample and can decrease visible detail.

After the specimen has been prepared, it should be mounted on a special holder to fix it in the SEM. This should *not* be done with lakeside or common glues; these emit gasses under vacuum that soil the interior of the SEM, and are non-conductive; use a special conductive glue suitable for SEM samples.

---

[3] WARNING: Take great care when etching using HF; clean the polished surface with alcohol, then hold it for several seconds over the vapour of a small reservoir of HF using a pair of tweezers; use suitable gloves and work in a fume cupboard! It is useful to study the etched surface under a reflected light microscope; after a roughness becomes visible under the microscope, the sample is sufficiently etched. It is rarely necessary to submerge the specimen in the HF fluid.

After mounting, the specimen should be covered with a conductive layer. This is done by evaporation and precipitation of the conductive material in a special apparatus under vacuum. If the sample surface has high relief and chemical composition of minerals is of little interest, gold is a good cover material; it produces sharp contours and beautiful images in the SEM (Fig. 9.4). If the specimen is flat and atomic number contrast is important, carbon should be used; the disadvantage is that carbon does not give as sharp an image as gold (Fig. 9.5).

9.6 Transmission Electron Microscope (TEM)

9.6.1 Introduction

Transmission electron microscopy (TEM) allows observation of structures as small as a few nanometers at magnifications of up to 350 000x. Dislocations, deformation lamellae, subgrain and grain boundaries and twins can be studied with the TEM, since it allows interpretation of their nature and their orientation with respect to the crystal lattice. Although TEM analysis of intracrystalline structures is very powerful, considerable experience is needed before it can be applied, and a description of TEM techniques is outside the range of this text. However, a short outline is given to allow readers to assess whether TEM work can solve their problems.

In a TEM a beam of electrons with high velocity passes through a thin foil of sample material suspended in a high vacuum (Fig. 9.2). The electron beam is deflected by electronic lenses which enlarge the image, and the result is focused onto a fluorescent screen or a photographic plate. An intact crystal lattice is transparent for the beam, but a crystal defect such as a dislocation, either isolated or in a (sub)grain boundary is visible as a shadow on the image. A modern TEM has sample-holders in which a sample can be rotated in all directions (Fig. 9.2). In certain orientation and observation modes, a crystal will show diffraction patterns that can be interpreted in terms of crystal orientation. Dislocations will be visible in the TEM only if their Burgers vector has a particular orientation with respect to the electron beam; rotation of a crystal until the dislocation becomes invisible, together with determination of the diffraction pattern of the crystal in that orientation allows determination of the Burgers vector for the dislocation. Similarly, the orientation of other intra- and intercrystalline structures can be determined with great accuracy using diffraction or Kikuchi patterns (Gapais and White 1982; FitzGerald et al. 1983). TEMs usually also have equipment for energy dispersive X-ray analysis and scanning; therefore, the chemical composition of grains can also be determined, although not with great accuracy.

The TEM is most useful to identify and study microstructures on the grain scale, or to determine the mineral content and microstructure of very fine-grained rocks (<5 μm); such fine-grained rocks are difficult to treat by SEM. However, although the TEM is a very powerful devise for microstructural studies, it has its limitations. The volume of material which can be studied in a single session on the TEM is very small. Although it is possible to determine the orientation of single crystals, it is a rather tedious and time-consuming job and it is therefore advisable not to try and use the TEM as a devise to measure LPO patterns; electron channelling with the SEM (Chap. 9.8.7) is probably a better technique. Not all minerals can be studied by TEM; in general, minerals with a large water content such as clay minerals and muscovite are less suitable since they disintegrate in the electron beam; water-free minerals such as olivine and pyroxenes are most stable in the TEM.

9.6.2 Sample Preparation

TEM samples are small fragments of the rock slice of a thin section, attached to metal grids with a diameter of 3 mm (Fig. 9.2). The thin section should be prepared with a resin or glue such as 'lakeside' that is dissolvable in alcohol; metal grids are glued with araldite onto interesting parts of the sample as determined by optical microscope; a single grid is insufficient since many samples fracture, or are otherwise damaged during further preparation. The rock slice is then removed from the glass by submersion in alcohol, and broken into fragments to remove the metal grids and small attached rock chips. The chips must be thinned to a few nm before they are transparent for the electron beam, and since the sample should not be mechanically damaged during the process of thinning, the superfluous material is evaporated by bombardment with Ar-ions in a vacuum. This process of *ion thinning* continues till small holes are visible in the sample; observation in the TEM is only possible adjacent to these holes, where the sample is sufficiently thin (Fig. 9.2). Because of this sample preparation method and thinning procedure, it is difficult to

select just a single particular small grain or object in a thin section for observation by TEM; the chance that it will fall exactly on the edge of one of the 'observation holes' is rather small. SEM work is probably better if a particular isolated structure is to be studied.

9.7 Image Analysis

9.7.1 Introduction

Recently, several powerful computer programs have become available that allow 'automatic' analysis of certain microstructures (e.g. Masuda et al. 1991; Heilbronner and Pauli 1993). Microfabrics can be monitored with a video camera and the digitised image can be fed into a computer. The image can then be analysed in terms of the intensity and distribution of different colours. An image analysis program allows the calculation of percentages of particular colours visible in an image, and recognises sharp transitions in colour. Such transitions are commonly grain boundaries, and it is possible in some samples to identify individual minerals and mineral grains. With the use of filters, a single mineral may be selected, and the total percentage of this mineral in the image can be determined. In addition, the size and shape of the grains can be determined and plotted. This technique is obviously very useful if large numbers of grain shapes, grain sizes and volumetric fractions of minerals have to be determined, e.g. the percentage, shape, size and orientation of plagioclase grains in a basalt. Unfortunately, even the best presently available programs have difficulties with samples in which the contrast between minerals is small, or where grain boundaries are of variable sharpness and lattice misfit angle, as in dynamically recrystallised rocks. Best results are obtained in rocks that consist of few, clearly distinct phases, e.g. pyrite grains in quartz, or quartzite with pores. Another disadvantage of image analysis is that most commercially available software is expensive, sometimes difficult to operate, and not adapted for geological applications. However, *image analysis* programs are continuously being improved and promise to become an important addition to microtectonic analysis in the future. A single method is described below because it can be applied without access to expensive programs.

9.7.2 Heilbronner Method

A simple method to determine grain shape and orientation in a grain aggregate can be done without expensive software on a simple microcomputer (Panozzo 1983, 1984; Schmid et al. 1987). Drawings of grain boundaries are made from photographs or directly on a computer screen, and subdivided into segments of a fixed length, e.g. 2 mm on photographs. A projection line is then defined, all line segments are projected onto this projection line, and the total length of projections is added. This process is repeated after rotating the projection line over a small angle, e.g. 1°. In this way, 180 total projection lengths $A_{(\alpha)}$ are obtained for 180 angles of projection (α). This process can easily be automated with simple programming (Panozzo 1983, 1984; Schmid et al. 1987). When $A_{(\alpha)}$ is plotted against (α) in a diagram, the symmetry of the distribution can be assessed. If grains are elongate and define a simple shape fabric, the ratio of $A_{(\alpha)max}/A_{(\alpha)min}$ defines the elliptical ratio of the aggregate, which may be a measure of strain if grain boundaries were immobile (Chap. 8.2). The orientation (α) of $A_{(\alpha)max}$ is the orientation of the foliation defined by the longest axis of the grains.

9.8 Lattice-Preferred Orientation

9.8.1 Introduction

Several methods are used to measure lattice-preferred orientation in rocks (Chap. 4.14–4.16). The classical method is the use of a *U-stage,* which allows rotation of a thin section or sample in three directions to determine the orientation of fabric elements. Other methods are optical bulk analysis, texture goniometry, and electron microscope analyses. For goniometry, the term texture is commonly used instead of LPO in the literature and therefore maintained here (Box p. 1). All methods require rather expensive equipment and each has its advantages and disadvantages as listed in Fig. 9.6.

9.8.2 U-Stage Measurements

In a universal stage or U-stage a thin section is mounted between two glass hemispheres. The complete setting of hemispheres and thin section can be turned around several axes in such a way that a single crystal in the thin section at the centre of the half-spheres can be focussed in orientations up to 40° from the horizontal. In this way, crystals or microstructures such as twins, lamellae and inclusions can be rotated until they lie in a particular orientation with respect to the axes of the microscope. If the orientation of the U-stage axes are now read, these data can be used to calculate the orientation of the structure with respect to thin section axes, and eventually to geographic orientation. Modern versions of the U-stage have been modified to allow automatic storage of measurements in a computer.

Although the U-stage has a long history, it is still an important instrument to measure LPO patterns, especially for quartz. For those who do not have access to goniometers and electron microscopes it is the only means to assemble data on lattice-preferred orientation of minerals. A U-stage is also quite useful for study of microstructures such as twins, inclusions and cleavage planes which have been obliquely cut by a thin section. These will appear unsharp in a normal thin section, but in the U-stage they can be observed in a more suitable orientation, and their orientation can be measured with reasonable accuracy.

	U-S	PrM	CM	X-G	N-G	Ch	TEM
polymineralic rocks	●				●	●	●
small grains (< 20 µm)				●	●	●	●
large grains > 1 mm	●	·	●	·	●		
opaque grains				●	●	●	●
complete ODF wanted				●	●	●	●
AVA wanted	●		●			●	●
measurement of only some grains wanted	●		●			●	●
volumetric distribution of orientations wanted		●	●	●	●		
rapid results wanted (first impression)	●	●	●	·	·	●	·

Fig. 9.6. List of requirements for LPO analysis versus observation method. Suitability of each method for a certain purpose is indicated with ***increasing diameter of black dots***. *U–S* U-stage; *PrM* Price method; *CM* CIP-method; *X–G* X-ray goniometer; *N–G* neutron goniometer; *Ch* channelling mode on SEM; *TEM* transmission electron microscope

The U-stage can also be a useful tool to establish the relative orientation of subgrain boundaries and the crystal lattice of quartz on both sides. This method has been used to determine the orientation of slip systems in minerals like quartz; the orientation of a subgrain boundary depends on the orientation of the slip system of the dislocations which accumulate in it (Christie and Green 1964; Trepied et al. 1980; Mainprice et al. 1986). However, there is some doubt about the reliability of this method, and additional TEM analysis is always necessary.

U-stage measurements of LPO are inexpensive and can be done on a normal microscope. Notice, however, that some modern microscopes have insufficient working space to fit a U-stage. Full LPO can be determined for olivine, calcite and orthopyroxene, and with some difficulty also for minerals with lower symmetry like amphiboles and feldspars, provided that grains are large and that sufficient cleavage or twin planes can be measured. Full LPO of quartz cannot be measured with a U-stage, only the orientation of the c-axis. Nevertheless, U-stage measurements are very popular for quartz since they are relatively easy and fast to obtain, and normally the c-axis pattern is sufficient to determine shear sense.

Disadvantages of the U-stage are the laborious and time-consuming nature of the work and a lower limit of about 20 µm to grains that can be measured. Strong undulose extinction also hampers measurement. U-stage measurement of LPO patterns does not allow a statistically unbiased analysis of the fabric (Fig 9.6); the volume of minerals with a particular orientation is difficult to determine since normally only one measurement per grain is taken, and the relative size of the grains is not taken into account. AVA diagrams (Chap. 4.14) have been constructed for U-stage measurements but these tend to be inaccurate. A detailed account of sample selection for the U-stage and of the method to measure quartz/LPO is given in Chapter 9.10.

9.8.3 Sample Selection and Preparation for Measurement

The presence of an LPO in an aggregate can be checked for minerals with low birefringence by inserting a gypsum plate under crossed polarisers; if a preferential colour occurs in some orientations when the microscope table is turned, an LPO is probably present. It is important that a thin section used for LPO analysis does not contain too many minerals other than the one to be measured, and the other minerals should at least be clearly distinguishable. Grain size should not be less than 30 µm, otherwise it is better to use a texture goniometer (Fig. 9.6). The thin section should have a basal glass plate of less than 1 mm thick; presence of a thick basal glass plate makes focussing on single grains difficult. Make sure that the thin section is properly oriented. The range of measurements is usually restricted to 30% of the thin section in the centre; grains in the periphery cannot be measured. Interesting parts should therefore lie in the centre of the thin section. It is important to realise that several populations of grains with different LPO may be present in a rock. For example, course grains may represent an older generation, and fine grains a new, recrystallised phase. It is therefore usually advantageous to try and distinguish several groups of grains on the basis of size, shape and content of inclusions or intracrystalline deformation structures. In many cases it is useful to have enlarged photographs of a thin section before an attempt is made to measure the fabric. This will also allow construction of AVA diagrams.

9.8.4 Optical Bulk Analysis – Price Method

Price (1973, 1980) devised a method of LPO analysis of uniaxial minerals such as quartz that allows use of an ordinary thin section and an adapted microscope. All grains within the field of view are illuminated with monochromatic blue light, and the intensity of transmitted light is measured while the microscope stage and thin section are rotated. This allows reconstruction of the symmetry of the fabric, but does not give details on the orientation distribution over the sample. No other minerals than the one to be measured should be present in the thin section.

9.8.5 CIP Method

Another technique to measure LPO in an ordinary thin section, computer-integrated polarisation microscopy (CIP method), was devised by Heilbronner and Pauli (1993). They use an ordinary microscope with rotating polarising filters. A video camera monitors the brightness of all grains in the field of view while the polarising filters are rotated and the thin section is stationary. Video images for each rotation increment are stored in a computer and the results used to calculate the LPO orientation of each grain segment represented by a single pixel in the image on the computer screen. A colour code is devised to allow marking of the plunge and plunge direction of each grain segment by a single colour, and the image is translated into a colour 'map' where each coloured *pixel* indicates a particular orientation; this image is an ideal AVA diagram which can be used for accurate analysis of fabric on the grain scale using image analysis techniques. Statistically balanced analysis of the fabric can also be carried out on the orientation, as in goniometer data. A disadvantage is that the method only applies to uniaxial minerals such as quartz, calcite and ice, and can only determine and plot the orientation of c-axes.

9.8.6 Texture Goniometers

Two types of goniometers are commonly used to study fabrics in rocks; the X-ray and neutron texture goniometers. The X-ray goniometer is most accessible and is most easily operated on monomineralic rocks, although bimineralic rocks can be studied in some cases (Braun 1994). Samples should be relatively fine-grained (<200 µm) and homogeneous, preferably with a high crystal and lattice symmetry. Neutron texture goniometry can only be carried out with a neutron diffractometer and suitable neutron source, few of which are presently available, and is rather time-consuming. The method has great advantages, however, since large and therefore coarse-grained samples can be used (Brokmeier 1994); samples can be up to 4 cm in diameter and need not be polished, although spherical or cylindrical samples are preferred. Neutron goniometry is suitable for polymineralic aggregates containing minerals with low symmetry such as amphiboles and plagioclase, and for measurement of weak fabrics (Wenk et al. 1986b; Brokmeier 1994; Siegesmund et al. 1994; Ullemeyer et al. 1994). Both types of goniometers can give full LPO patterns which are statistically balanced for the volume of each of the present directions. Goniometers have been used to study the LPO of micas in foliated rocks for finite strain analysis (Chap. 8.2; Tullis and Wood 1975; Wood and Oertel 1980; van der Pluijm et al. 1994) and even sense of shear from the skewness of the fabric (O'Brien et al. 1987). For minerals like quartz and calcite goniometry has been used to determine full ODFs (Chap. 4.14; Casey 1981; Schmid and Casey 1986). A disadvantage of goniometers is that they cannot show how the different orientation peaks are distributed over the sample. This implies that no AVA diagram can be constructed and that no link can be made to microstructures which could give information on the mechanisms by which the LPO originated. For this reason, additional U-stage observa-

tions are commonly made on thin sections prepared from a sample that was analysed by goniometry.

9.8.7 Channelling

Electron channelling is a technique that allows study of grain orientation in an adapted SEM (Lloyd and Hall 1981; Lloyd et al. 1981; Joy et al. 1982; Lloyd 1987; Lloyd and Freeman 1991, 1994; Mainprice et al. 1993). If the electron beam in the SEM is directed at a fixed point in a crystal in the sample and rocked around this point, channelling patterns can be observed; these patterns consist of a complex arrangement of lines that are typical for the crystal symmetry and orientation. Comparison of the channelling pattern of a crystal with standard patterns allows reconstruction of the orientation of the crystal. At present, the technique can be used for quartz and some other minerals, especially cubic minerals such as garnet. The method is a very useful addition to optical means of determining preferred orientation of grains since it allows determination of the LPO with an accuracy up to 1° in tiny grains and subgrains down to 1 µm in diameter (Lloyd and Freeman 1991; Lloyd 1994). Any type of rock sample can in principle be studied.

For electron channelling, 'superpolished' specimens are used. Normal polishing damages the surface layer of a specimen slightly, and this means that no good channelling patterns can be made. Therefore, ordinary polished rock chips, mounted in epoxy, are repolished using a silica solution in a special polishing rig. Such superpolished sections are also useful to do careful work on small-scale structures in a normal SEM, since they give much better resolution than ordinary polished sections.

9.9 Analogue Modelling

9.9.1 Introduction

Our understanding of the way in which microstructures develop is mainly based on careful observation of microstructures from simple tectonic settings in various stages of development in thin section, on data from metallurgy and on experimental deformation of rocks. Recently, an interesting additional method has been developed; the deformation of *rock analogues*. Rock analogues are crystalline materials such as camphor, paraffin wax and ice which can be deformed in

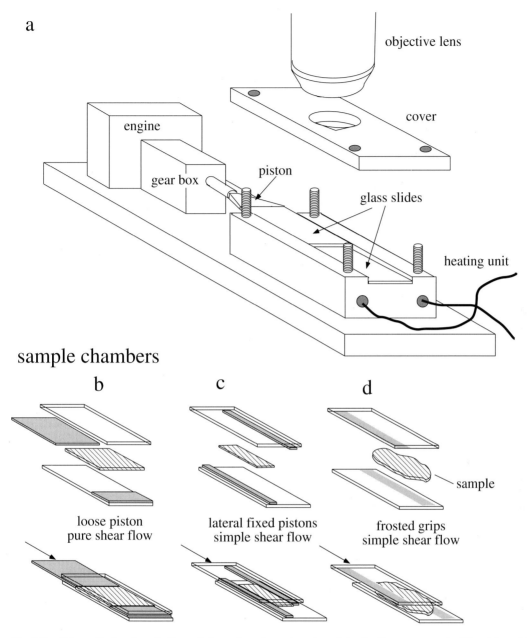

Fig. 9.7. a Schematic drawing of a linear deformation rig used to deform analogue material. **b–d** Three setups of specimen chambers for the rig. The analogue material is deformed in experiments by movement of a piston **b** or of one of the two glass plates **(c, d)**; arrangement of the pistons determines how the material is deformed, either in bulk pure shear or simple shear flow

a ductile way by dislocation- or diffusion creep at atmospheric pressure and temperatures between –10 and 300 °C, usually at strain rates between 10^{-2} and 10^{-6} s^{-1}. Such materials can be pressed or ground into thin slabs which can be placed between glass slides, and deformed under the microscope. In this way, the development of microstructures can be directly observed. Rock analogue experiments are therefore an important new tool in research and teaching. Three main types of apparatus have been developed for rock analogue experiments: a linear deformation rig, a torsion rig, and a triaxial press.

9.9.2 Linear Rig

In the linear rig (Fig. 9.7a), a thin sample of analogue material is mounted between two glass slides, usually normal slides used for thin section preparation (Fig. 9.7b–d; Means and Xia 1981; Wilson 1984; Burg et al. 1986; Means 1989). The sample can be deformed in coaxial or non-coaxial flow by the geometric arrangement of pistons. Pure shear deformation can be initiated by pressing a thin sheet of metal (at least 70 μm thick, otherwise the piston will buckle) between the glass slides against the sample (Fig. 9.7a), or by 'frosting' both glass slides at front or back with silicon carbide powder; the sample will remain attached to the frosted part of the glass, and will slide past the untreated glass, especially if the latter is lubricated with silicone grease (Fig. 9.7d). With this setup, sam-

ples as thin as 30 μm can be deformed. Simple shear can be initiated by the use of indented piston grips glued onto the glass plates (Fig. 9.7c), or frosted grips (Fig. 9.7d). General non-coaxial flow can be generated with obliquely mounted grips or pistons. The choice of thickness for the sample depends on the amount of detail that is required, and the birefringence of the mineral; minerals like ice and camphor have low birefringence and can be studied in relatively thick samples that are easy to prepare and can be deformed with separate pistons between glass slides. In such thick samples, it may be difficult to resolve small grains, grain boundaries and other small details. Materials with higher birefringence can be studied in thin sections with frosted grips; this has the advantage that a similar view as a thin section is obtained and that small details can be studied. Disadvantages are difficult sample preparation and the possibility

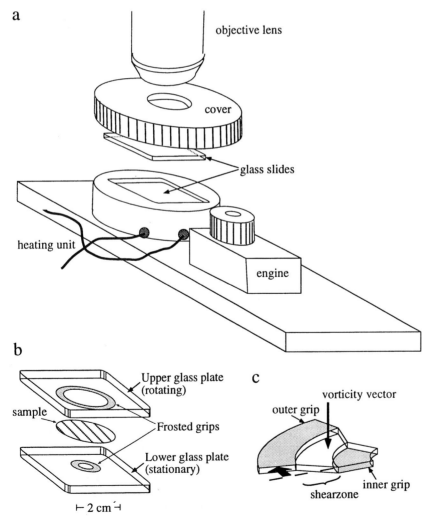

Fig. 9.8. a Schematic drawing of a torsion deformation rig used to deform analogue material. **a** Setup of the specimen chamber for this rig; analogue material is deformed in torsion between two glass plates that rotate with respect to each other. Presence of frosted grips on the glass causes a small ring-shaped part of the sample to deform in non-coaxial flow. **c** Detail of the ring-shaped deforming part of the sample. (**b** and **c** courtesy C. ten Brink)

that friction of the sample against the glass plates causes deviations or distortions. The sample and glass slides are contained in a metal frame which can be heated and kept within a certain temperature range with a thermocouple and a temperature control unit. The sample is deformed by movement of a piston or one of the glass slides which is driven by a motor that moves at a constant rate (Fig. 9.7a); different strain rates are realised by use of engines with different rotation rates. The deforming sample is observed through a microscope and can be monitored with a camera or video equipment.

9.9.3 Torsion Rig

The torsion rig (Fig. 9.8a) deforms a sample between two glass slides (Fig. 9.8b). Each glass slide has a ring-shaped frosted grip, one of small and one of large diameter. When one of the glass slides rotates, a ring-shaped part of the sample is deformed between the two frosted grips (Fig. 9.8b,c). The rotating glass slide is fixed in part of the metal frame of the rig, and both are driven by an engine as described above (Fig. 9.8).

The advantage of the torsion rig is that very high finite shear strain (exceeding 100) can be reached; in the linear rig, shear strains are limited to values of 5–10. In mylonites, shear strain values exceeding 10 are common, and may be required for the development of some structures. A disadvantage of the torsion rig is that the deforming sample is circular and therefore does not deform in simple shear; in fact, there is a strain rate and stress gradient from inside to outside in the ring-shaped part of the deforming sample (Passchier and Sokoutis 1993; Masuda et al. 1995b). However, the gradient is accurately known and such gradients may also occur in natural shear zones.

9.9.4 Triaxial Rig

A triaxial deformation rig (Bons 1993) can be used to determine the rheology of analogue materials. Small columns of analogue material are compressed by a weight and the shortening rate is monitored. Normally, a confining pressure is applied using compressed air. The data are used to determine stress-strain rate curves. Such experiments are done at different temperatures and loads and the results can be used to determine the rheology of the material. Pure materials, or mixtures can all be measured. It is not possible, however, to observe the deforming sample in the triaxial rigs that are presently available.

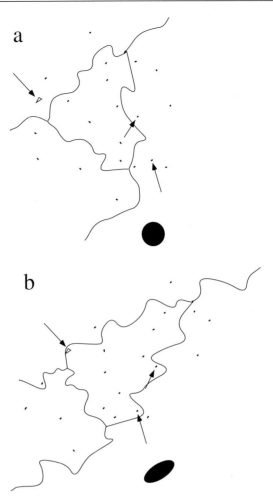

Fig. 9.9a,b. Schematic drawing of marker particles in an analogue material that shows grain boundary migration during deformation. In **b** the marker particles have an arrangement other than in **a** because of deformation of the aggregate. Grain boundaries do not show the same deformation because they have migrated. Marker particles indicated by *arrows* have passed from one grain to another. The position of marker particles before and after this deformation step can be used to reconstruct maps of deformation and deformation gradient in the sample as shown in Fig. 9.12

9.9.5 Marker Particles

During development of structures in analogue experiments, deformation is usually inhomogeneous. Besides observation of developing structures, the analogue experimental setup also allows detailed monitoring of gradients of inhomogeneous deformation over the sample. This is realised by insertion of fine silicon carbide powder in the sample (1000-grid powder, normally used for preparation of thin sections). This powder does not react with the sample material and does not seem to interfere with the deformation process on the scale of observation. The particles act therefore as passive material points (Chap. 2.2; Figs. 2.1, 2.3); structures like grain boundaries cannot be used as markers since they may migrate through the material (Fig. 9.9). If photographs or video images of a deforming sample at various stages of development are combined, the positions of individual particles can be compared and used to reconstruct local deformation (Fig. 9.9, 9.10). If the position of at least three particles is known in two subsequent stages of the experiment, finite strain, vorticity and area change can all be determined (Figs. 9.11, 9.12; Chap. 2.6; Box p. 82). The position of particles must be digitised and can be processed with a computer. Bons et al. (1993) presented a computer program that can process data on positions of particles into contours of strain, vorticity and area change.

9.9.6 Analogue Experiments

In the past 10 years, a large number of experiments has been carried out with analogue materials (Fig. 9.10). The materials that have been mostly used are octachloropropane (OCP - Fig. 9.10; Jessell 1986; Ree 1990, 1991; ten Brink and Passchier 1995), biphenyl, paradichlorobenzene (Means 1980), camphor (Urai et al. 1980; Urai and Humphreys 1981), norbornene, naphthalene (Blumenfeld and Wilson 1991), sodium nitrate (Tungatt and Humphreys 1981a,b), paraffin wax (Abbassi and Mancktelow 1992; Mancktelow and Abbassi 1992; Chatterjee 1994) and ice (Wilson 1982,1994; Burg et al. 1986; Wilson et al. 1986; Wilson and Zhang 1994). Effects that have been studied include the development of steady state fabrics (Ree 1990, 1991), lattice-preferred orientation and dynamic recrystallisation mechanisms (Jessell 1986), the influence of temperature and finite strain on these processes (Jessell 1986), the development of low and high angle grain boundaries and their classification (Means and Ree 1988), grain boundary migration (Means and Jessell 1986), grain boundary sliding and void development (Ree 1994), the development of shear band cleavage (Passier 1991; Chatterjee 1994), deformation twinning (Blumenfeld and Wilson 1991), the development of mantled porphyroclasts and the effect of a second phase on deformation patterns (Figs. 9.11, 9.12; Bons 1993; ten Brink and Passchier 1995). A review of analogue modelling and a list of the most commonly used analogue experimental materials is given by Means (1989). Some examples of results of analogue experiments are shown in Figs. 9.10-9.12.

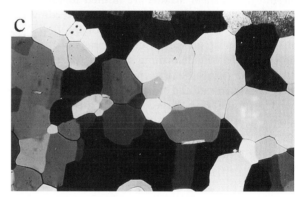

Fig. 9.10a–c. Examples of a deformation experiment using a sample of octachloropropane (OCP) which is deforming in simple shear in a linear deformation rig (dextral sense of shear). The sample has already undergone a shear strain of 1.7 at stage **a**. Between **a** and **b** a shear strain of approximately 0.1 has accumulated, as shown by the displacement of two marker points indicated by *circles at top and bottom right.* Due to this extra shear stain, the shape of the grains has changed and grain boundaries have migrated in **b**. After step **b** the experiment was stopped. **c** Shows the same area as **b**, but after 16 h of static recrystallisation. A polygonal fabric has developed in response to grain boundary area reduction (GBAR); grain boundaries have become relatively straight and there is evidence for grain growth. Subgrain boundaries developed in some grains. Unpublished experiment by J.-H. Ree. Part of this experiment was published in Means (1989). Width of view 2.1 mm. CPL. (Photographs courtesy J.-H. Ree)

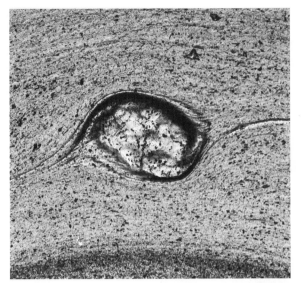

Fig. 9.11. Example of a δ-type mantled porphyroclast developed in a rock analogue experiment in a torsion rig (ten Brink and Passchier 1995). A square polycrystalline aggregate of camphor was embedded in a matrix of octachloropropane (OCP), and both were deformed together at 60 °C and a shear strain rate of 2.6×10^{-3} s^{-1}. Camphor is stronger than OCP at these conditions, and the camphor object rotated in response to non-coaxial flow in the OCP matrix. In the rim of the camphor object, fine-grained material is produced, probably by recrystallisation. This caused development of a fine-grained camphor mantle that deformed into δ-type wings. The entire evolution of this mantled porphyroclast could be studied under the microscope. **Black dots** in the matrix are grains of silicon carbide that act as marker particles. Figure 9.12 shows some results of the analysis of displacement of these marker particles. The **dark rim at the bottom** of the photograph is the inner grip of the rig (Fig. 9.8). Shear strain in the matrix γ = 94. Width of view 2.5 mm. PPL. (Photograph courtesy C. ten Brink)

9.10 Use of the U-Stage

9.10.1 Introduction

The U-stage consists of a number of rings which can turn independently of each other, and allow rotation of a thin section over a large range of orientations. Such rotations would normally lead to refraction and reflection on the glass-surfaces of the section, but in a U-stage the thin section is contained between two glass hemispheres with approximately the same refractive index as the mineral to be studied; hemispheres with a refractive index of 1.56 are used for quartz, feldspar and calcite; 1.65 for olivine, biotite, hornblende and pyroxenes. Moreover, immersion oil of the right refractive index is used between the thin section and the hemispheres, in order to reduce reflection to a minimum. The rotation axes of the U-stage are numbered as follows (Fig. 9.13):

A1 for the inner vertical axis,
A2 for the N-S axis,
A3 for the outer, vertical axis,
A4 for the horizontal E-W axis, usually handled with a large knob,
A5 for the microscope table (vertical axis).

9.10.2 Preparation of the Stage for Measurement

This section describes the sequence of action necessary to prepare a U-stage for measurement of quartz or calcite c-axes, or for observation of obliquely transected structures in thin section. The following procedure should be followed *in the sequence given.*

1. The U-stage has a ring to adjust the elevation of the thin section with respect to A2 and A4 axes on the inside of the A1 bearing (Fig. 9.13). Check if this ring rotates smoothly. If not, try to loosen it gently or have the stage repaired.
2. Build the U-stage on the microscope table and replace condensor and objective lenses by the lenses which are to be used with the stage
3. Mount the glass disc of the U-stage in the inner ring, and attach the lower hemisphere to the glass plate with a drop of immersion oil. Glycerine can also be used if quartz is to be measured. Make sure that no air bubbles are left between the glass surfaces.
4. Assemble the upper parts of the U-stage; place a drop of immersion oil on the glass disc, mount the thin section, place another drop of oil on the thin section, then mount the upper hemisphere and tighten the screws of the upper hemisphere gently. Use very little oil, just enough to enable the thin section to move freely over the U-stage table; too much oil will swamp the U-stage table and make a sticky mess, but too little will cause the thin section to become jammed, and may cause great difficulty if it occurs during the measurement; the thin section and upper hemisphere will have to be taken out of the stage, cleaned, and reassembled with new oil. Make sure no air bubbles occur between the glass surfaces since this will hamper measurement.

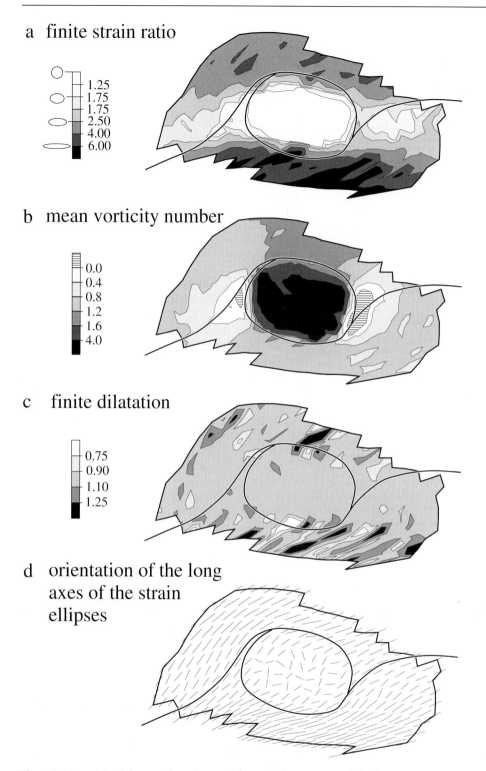

a finite strain ratio

1.25
1.75
1.75
2.50
4.00
6.00

b mean vorticity number

0.0
0.4
0.8
1.2
1.6
4.0

c finite dilatation

0.75
0.90
1.10
1.25

d orientation of the long
   axes of the strain
   ellipses

Fig. 9.12. Example of the use of marker particles to analyse the deformation pattern in an experiment in the torsion rig. The experiment was on development of δ-type mantled porphyroclasts using a core object of camphor in a matrix of octachloropropane, as shown in Fig. 9.11. The drawings are maps of the four components of finite deformation, determined from displacement of marker particles. The contour of a developed camphor δ-shaped mantled porphyroclast is shown in each diagram. (After ten Brink and Passchier 1995)

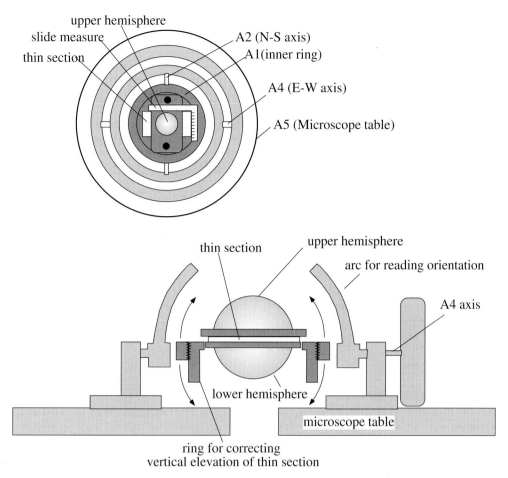

Fig. 9.13. Schematic top view and cross section of a U-stage, showing the various parts

5. Make a sketch of the orientation of the thin section and any markings on the section (number, arrows) as positioned between the hemispheres, including a mark indicating where the 0-position of the inner ring (A1) is. This may help if problems appear later with the orientation of the crystallographic axes.

6. Use a key to centre each of the objective lenses with respect to A5 (turn the microscope stage when centering the lenses; not the inner ring A1 of the U-stage).

7. Centre the U-stage itself. Place A2 and A4 axes in the neutral position (stage horizontal). Choose an objective lens with large magnification, and focus on a grain in the thin section. Now centre the stage while the A5 axis (microscope table) is fixed. This is done with centering screws at the base of the U-stage while turning the A1 ring (or by shifting the stage by hand for older U-stages).

8. Check if the A2 and A4 axes are orthogonal; this need not be the case if the A3 axis has been loosened.

Correct the orthogonal position of both axes if needed and fix the A3 axis tightly; this axis is not used for measurement of quartz or calcite c-axes.

9. Bring the A2 and A4 axes in a position parallel to microscope symmetry axes. Make sure that a hair ocular is present in the microscope with cross hairs vertical and horizontal. Bring the microscope table down until it is possible to focus on the top of the upper hemisphere (it may be necessary to loosen the microscope table from the frame by a screw on the side of the microscope. Rotate the U-stage centre around the A4 axis. Small scratches or dust particles will be seen to move in a straight line; they should move exactly from top to bottom of the field of view parallel to the cross hairs. If this is not the case, unlock the A5 axis and rotate the microscope stage while moving A4; when the particles move parallel to the cross hairs, fix the A5 axis again and mark the position of the microscope table on the nonius of the

table. This can be done with a piece of tape or a felt-tip pen. Since the A4 and A2 are orthogonal, A2 will now be automatically in the right position.

10. Adjust the elevation of the thin section in the U-stage such that the rotation centre of A4 and A2 axes lies in the sample. This is done by rotation of the adjustment ring in which the glass disc is resting. The ring can be rotated with four corners at the lower side of the U-stage table. Focus on a grain in the thin section and turn A4 or A2; usually, the grain will rotate out of the field of view or at least loose sharpness. Try turning the adjustment ring and determine in which direction the movement of the grain becomes less (or try to argue from the movement of the grain whether the thin section is too low or too high). With trial and error a position can be reached where the grain in the section shows minimal defocusing and movement on rotation of A4 or A2. Depending on the quality of the U-stage, there can still be a lot of movement and the effect can be disappointing. If the section is too thick, there will be trouble now since it will be impossible to bring the adjustment ring low enough to focus the grains. Another common problem is that the thin section has been mounted with the cover glass below. In that case, start again.

11. Mount the L-shaped metal slide-measure (Fig. 9.13); make sure that the thin section is always tight against this slide-measure and that it is shifted parallel to its long axis; any deviation will make the measurements useless, since it will add an extra, unknown angle of rotation (cf. Fig. 2.4). Place the measurement arcs on both sides of the table into the vertical position.

12. Move the thin section to the position where measurement is started.

13. Check the position of the indicatrix in the gypsum plate; this can be done with a mineral in a thin section for which the orientation of the indicatrix is known, or with a second gypsum plate.

9.10.3 Measurement of c-Axes of Quartz

Measurement of quartz c-axes is possible in aggregates with a grain size exceeding 20 μm. Strong internal deformation such as undulose extinction inhibits accurate measurement. The sequence of measurement given below must be carried out exactly in the given order to obtain correct measurements (Fig. 9.14).

a) Turn the U-stage table and the thin section parallel to the microscope table by turning A2 and A4 axes to their zero position. Make sure that the A5 axis is at its standard position as marked in step (9) above. Fix the A5 axis.

b) Choose a quartz grain and shift its centre to the centre of the cross hairs in the image. Use crossed polarisers. If the grain is in extinction, rotate around A1 until its goes out of extinction; if it still remains dark, rotate A2 slightly till it goes out of extinction.

c) Insert the gypsum plate and check the position of the indicatrix of the grain – take the gypsum plate out again.

d) Rotate around A1 such that the long axis of the indicatrix is exactly EW. The rotation angle around A1 can never be more than 90° for this purpose. The rotation direction depends on the orientation of the quartz indicatrix as indicated by the blue or yellow colour of the grain (blue – long axis of the indicatrices of the quartz grain and the gypsum plate are in the same quadrant; yellow – in opposite quadrants). Rotate A2 back to its zero position in case it was tilted.

e) Tilt the U-stage table over at least 30° by rotation of the A4 axis. The grain usually becomes lighter; leave the A4 axis in this position.

f) Tilt the U-stage table around the A2 axis, with A4 inclined, until the grain goes into a maximum extinction position. The indicatrix is now either steep or horizontal; this will be determined in the next steps (Fig. 9.14).

g) Rotate A4: the grain should now remain dark; if it goes out of its extinction position, one of the following possibilities applies: there is an error in the measurement sequence; the steps (e) and (g) were insufficiently accurate; the grain has strong undulose extinction; or it is not quartz. In any case, the sequence has to be started again.

h) Bring the A4 axis into its zero position and rotate around A5. There are two possibilities (Fig. 9.14):
1. The grain lights up; the c-axis is E-W horizontal
2. The grain remains dark; the c-axis is vertical parallel to the microscope tube.

i) Return the A5 axis to its standard position and fix it.

j) Read the measurement. If the U-stage has automatic data storage facilities, this may be a push of the button; if not, a procedure for reading and notation of measurements is described below. After some exercise, the measurement procedure given above should take less than a minute per grain.

k) Find the next grain and continue measuring. Follow a distinct path through the section in order to avoid measuring the same grain twice. It may also be useful to measure recrystallised and old grains separately. A photograph of the thin section with numbered grains may be useful in such a case.

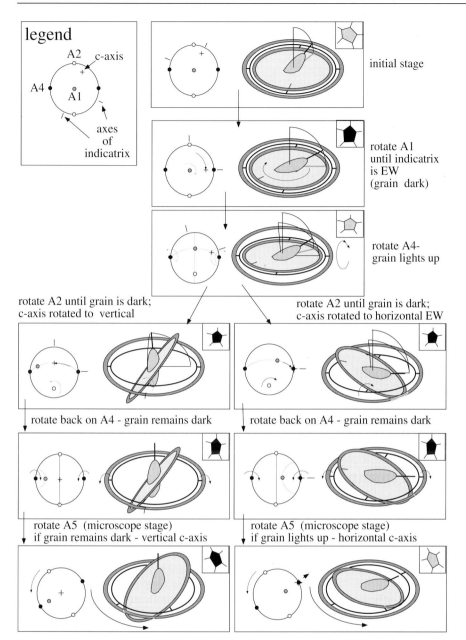

legend

A2 c-axis

A4 A1

axes
of
indicatrix

initial stage

rotate A1
until indicatrix
is EW
(grain dark)

rotate A4-
grain lights up

rotate A2 until grain is dark;
c-axis rotated to vertical

rotate A2 until grain is dark;
c-axis rotated to horizontal EW

rotate back on A4 - grain remains dark

rotate back on A4 - grain remains dark

rotate A5 (microscope stage)
if grain remains dark - vertical c-axis

rotate A5 (microscope stage)
if grain lights up - horizontal c-axis

Fig. 9.14. Procedure for measuring c-axes of quartz with a U-stage, illustrated by a sequence of windows. *At left* in each window, stereograms with the position and rotation angles of a c-axis and of U-stage axes are indicated. *Lines on the outside of the stereogram* indicate the extinction positions of the indicatrix for each case. At the *centre of each window* the U-stage and an indicatrix are shown; *arcs* indicate the indicatrix orientation in each case. *Black bold line* is the c-axis; *bold grey* line is the projection of the c-axis in the horizontal plane. The aspect of the grain to be measured as seen through the microscope is shown at *top right* in each window. Further explanation in text

Before or after measuring the required grains, determine the orientation of fabric elements in the thin section with the U-stage, notably poles to a reference foliation and lineation S_r and L_r (Chap. 4.14). This should be done by imagining the orientation of these structures as lines (i.e. use the pole to a folia-

tion) and measuring them in a similar way as an imaginary c-axis. Only in this way can the orientation of the c-axes be correctly represented in a reference frame of S_r and L_r.

The number of measurements necessary to obtain a representative image of the c-axis fabric

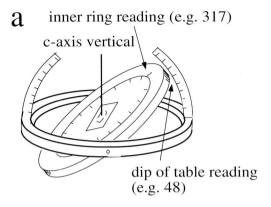

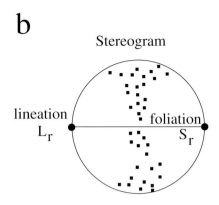

Fig. 9.15. a Orientation of U-stage table after measurement with c-axis vertical. The measurement is read from the arc at right and from the inner ring (A1) and can be written

317 ← 48V. (V = vertical); see text for explanation. **b** Method of plotting c-axis measurements in a stereogram. S_r and L_r reference foliation and lineation

depends on the nature of the sample. In coarse-grained samples, all grains should be measured, but in fine-grained samples, a limited number is normally adopted. In quartzite, measurement of 200 grains usually gives a clear impression of the c-axis pattern. It is rarely necessary to measure more than 400 grains in a thin section, since the c-axis pattern does not improve further when a critical limit is reached.

9.10.4 Notation of Measurements

Notation of measurements from a non-automatic U-stage is done as follows:

At the end of the measurement sequence, the orientation of the c-axis should be determined from the orientation of the axes of the U-stage. Four data are required to do this (Fig. 9.15):
1. The arc on which the dip of the U-stages is to be read, either on the left or on the right as seen when sitting behind the microscope (Fig. 9.15). This can be noted R or L or indicated with arrows as shown below.
2. The dip of the U-stage table, to be read from one of the arcs, in degrees.
3. The position of the inner ring A1 in degrees.
4. The horizontal or vertical orientation of the c-axis as determined with the A5 axis [step (h) above], noted as H or V.

If the U-stage table is oriented as shown in Fig. 9.15, the measurement can be written as:

R:317–48V

or 317←48V.

The arrow indicates the dip direction of the U-stage table.

When sufficient measurements have been made, the results can be plotted. First the orientation of reference fabric elements in the thin section, notably poles to S_r and L_r (Chap. 4.14) should be plotted (Fig. 9.15). Ideally, these should be fabric elements which are associated with deformation that caused the preferred orientation of the c-axes. Next, all data should be recalculated to a plunge direction and plunge and plotted as linear data in the stereogram (Fig. 9.15). If necessary, all data should next be rotated in such a way that the lineation is E–W on the edge of the diagram, and the foliation indicated by a vertical great circle. If the diagram is to be used for sense of shear determination, its orientation with respect to geographical coordinates should be carefully checked. This can be done by plotting three of the measured c-axes that are approximately orthogonal on a stereogram, together with geographic poles such as compass directions. Most reliable results are obtained when the original oriented sample and the thin section are fitted together and a three-dimensional sketch of the whole assemblage is made.

10 From Sample to Section

10.1 Introduction

A sound analysis of microstructures relies on correct sampling and on the right choice of the direction in which thin sections are cut from samples. This chapter discusses the steps of sample collection; choice of sectioning plane, and problems involved in the interpretation of three-dimensional structures from two-dimensional sections.

10.2 Sampling

The choice of samples for thin sections depends on the topic of interest and methods that are going to be used. In any case, it is important that the main structure in the area is understood in broad lines before samples are taken; thin sections usually contain a lot of information which is useless if no good field record exists. For example, if a foliation is found in thin section that has not been recognised in the field, it cannot be fitted in a tectonic model and is useless unless a new field trip can be made to identify it. Thin section studies usually give best results if they are undertaken to solve a specific problem that has been defined before the sections were cut (cf. Passchier et al. 1990b). Thin sections cut at random to 'see what it looks like' will be less useful than those collected with a specific aim.

10.3 Orientation of Hand Specimens

Hand specimens for structural studies should be oriented in the field. This is best done by marking dip and strike of a planar surface of the specimen on that surface (Fig. 10.1). Notice, however, that this still leaves two possible orientations, since the mark could be made on the top surface or on the lower side of a sample. An extra mark is therefore needed; for example, a cross on the top surface or an arrow indicating top (Fig. 10.1b).

Mistakes can easily be made in orienting samples and for the most important samples (e.g. those needed to determine shear sense) it is therefore useful to make a photograph or simple sketch of the sample, its orientation in outcrop and of the marking. Also, samples should be wrapped in paper or plastic bags to avoid breakage and erosion of markings and numbers.

10.4 Where to Sample in Outcrop

If a PTt path is to be reconstructed for a specific area (Chaps. 1.3, 7.9), the most informative lithologies to sample are pelites and metabasites. Pelitic rocks generally develop foliations which are not easily destroyed

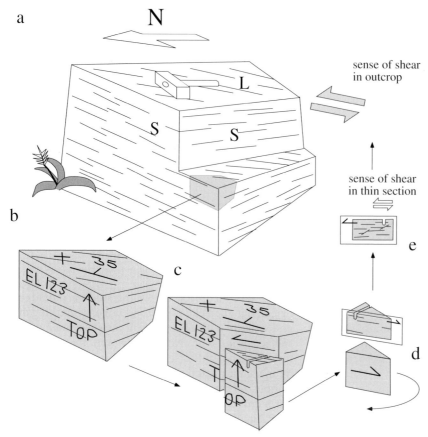

Fig. 10.1a–e. Method to obtain an oriented sample from an outcrop and an oriented thin section from a sample. A sample for structural studies must be oriented, for example as shown in **a, b.** A *strike-dip symbol* (here 160–35) on the planar top surface of the sample and a *cross* (marking the top) fix the orientation of the sample in space. When a thin section is to be cut parallel to the lineation (here 200–15), a chip is cut from the sample with a diamond saw. In order to orient the chip, an *arrow* with a single barb pointing in the direction of the top surface can be used and is drawn on both the sample and the chip **c.** Care should be taken that this arrow is copied correctly onto the thin section **d.** Alternatively, a small sawcut scar can be made in the top surface of the chip, which can be found back in the thin section **e.** Shear sense determined in the thin section, e.g. by shear bands **e** can now be directly related to the sample, and through the sample to the original outcrop. Here, the outcome is thrusting to the NE

by subsequent deformation phases. Metabasites have a weaker memory for a sequence of deformation phases but, as for pelites, their mineral content is sensitive to changes in PT conditions. Psammites usually develop relatively coarse structures which are difficult to study in thin section, and limestones have a weak memory for a sequence of deformation phases because calcite recrystallises readily, even at low temperature.

Samples should preferably be taken in association with major structures which are understood and of which the relative age is known. If three phases of deformation have been recognised, it is useful to have samples from foliations belonging to each of the phases. If porphyroblasts are visible, these should also be sampled in order to determine their relative age with respect to the structure. Samples in which overprinting relations are visible are particularly important. Small fold closures or shear zones of each of the phases, if possible from several lithotypes, should also be sampled. The mineral assemblage in such structures may allow an estimation of metamorphic conditions during each deformation phase. If a sample is taken

in a major fold, it is useful to know from which limb it was taken. Shear zones should be sampled in the high strain core, in the rim and in the wall rock; in many cases, it is useful to compare mineral assemblages in the undeformed wall rock with those in a shear zone, in order to determine which metamorphic conditions accompanied deformation in the zone, and which ones are older.

If shear sense in a shear zone is to be determined, care should be taken that samples are correctly oriented and that suitable small-scale structures such as porphyroclasts are present in the sample. In many ductile shear zones, fine-grained mylonites and samples representing highly strained parts of the shear zone give better results than samples of coarse-grained or low strain domains.

Different shear sense markers are preferentially found in different lithologies; C′- shear bands in strongly foliated mica-rich mylonite; C/S fabric mainly in granite mylonite; mantled porphyroclasts in deformed granites or pegmatites, and mica fish in quartzite-mylonites. Deformed quartzite should be sampled where possible to determine LPO of quartz;

in many shear zones, this is the only suitable shear sense indicator.

If gradients in the style of a structure exist over an area it is useful to take a series of samples of this gradient in a single lithology. In all cases, it is useful to write down in the field for what purpose a sample was taken. Photographs of important sampling sites are also useful and should ideally be taken before the sample is removed.

Structures like large folds and boudins are spectacular in the field and are consequently often sampled. However, they may be difficult to interpret on the scale of a thin section where only a small fragment of the structure is seen[4]. In many cases it is more advantageous to sample also directly adjacent to such structures where the rock deformed more homogeneously. Care should also be taken to sample the more fine-grained parts of a structure; in coarse-grained rocks only a small (and possibly non-representative) part of the structure can be studied in thin section. For example, if a sample is taken of a mylonite with large feldspar porphyroclasts in a shear zone, and a thin section is made of the matrix between two large feldspar grains, this matrix may give a shear sense opposite to that of the main zone (cf. Bell and Johnson 1992).

One should also not forget to take samples of the 'ordinary matrix rock'; some geologists realise afterwards that they took samples only of the curious and exceptional. If a metamorphic gradient is present or suspected, it is useful to take samples at a regular distance across this gradient for possible later microprobe work.

10.5 Cutting Samples

When oriented samples are cut to make thin sections, it is crucial to avoid loss of orientation data. Although several methods can be used, we suggest the following procedure. After a saw cut is made, the orientation of the sample should be copied on both sides of the saw cut in mirror image (Fig 10.1); we propose a

system in which an arrow with a single barb is drawn parallel to the lineation, with the barb indicating the top of the sample. The arrow should be copied from the rock chip that is used to make the thin section onto the glass as shown in Fig. 10.1. Be careful when preparing the rock chips for thin sections that the orientation is not lost or confused. Alternatively, a small saw-cut scar can be made in the top surface of the rock chip used to make the thin section. This scar can be found back in the thin section and reduces the chances of confusion in its orientation.

10.6 Types of Thin Sections

Standard thin sections consist of a basal glass plate of 0.8 to 1.9 mm thick, a slice of sample material, and a cover glass with a thickness of 0.2 mm. The parts of the thin section are assembled with glues with a fixed refractive index, usually between 1.5 and 1.6. The standard thickness of the sample material is 30 μm. The presence of a cover glass is important because the objective lenses of most microscopes have been constructed to give best results when a cover glass is present. Sections should therefore be studied with the cover glass towards the objective lens. Besides standard thin sections, a number of other sections are used for various purposes:

Large thin sections, up to 20 cm long can be made for unusually coarse-grained rocks and large structures; they can be made in the same way as standard sections.

Polished sections and thin sections without cover glass are used for microprobe work and for observation of opaque minerals in reflected light. They usually have a standard thickness of 30 μm and can also be used for normal microtectonic observations. If small scale, delicate structures are to be studied, it can be advantageous to use a polished rather than a standard thin section. Even better results are obtained with sections polished at both sides. Polished thin sections can also be used in the SEM which has the advantage that the same feature can be observed by optical and electron microscope.

TEM sections are prepared with a dissolvable resin such as lakeside, and without a cover glass. After a reconnaissance study of the structure by optical microscope, small rings are glued on the surface with araldite, and subsequently the thin section is emerged in ethanol which dissolves the lakeside and leaves the rock chip floating in the fluid; the metal rings remain

---

[4] It is our opinion that sampling of prominent large folds, boudins and shear zones destroys field evidence and potential teaching material, and should therefore only be undertaken if samples cannot be taken from other parts of an outcrop. The same applies to drill cores which should also preferably be taken in parts of the outcrop where they do not destroy the geometry of beautiful structures.

attached to the chip since araldite does not dissolve in ethanol. The chip can now be broken into fragments to free the metal sample rings with the attached fragment of the rock chip. This fragment can be mounted with the metal ring in an ion-thinning device and subsequently be studied in the TEM (Chap. 9.6).

Ultrathin sections with a thickness of 5 μm or even less are used to study minerals with a high birefringence such as calcite. Polishing of the surface is important in this case. Production of ultrathin sections is relatively difficult and requires some experience.

Ultrathick sections are 100 μm thick and are polished on both sides. They are not mounted on a glass slide since they are thick enough to be handled without breaking. Because of their thickness, these sections show high order interference colours and are difficult to use for normal tectonic studies. However, they are suitable for microthermometry of fluid inclusions, since these remain intact in thick sections, but commonly fracture and leak in normal thin sections. Ultrathick sections are also useful to determine the orientation of planar and linear microstructures such as fluid inclusion walls, solid inclusions, grain and subgrain boundaries and axes of microfolds.

Thin sections of unconsolidated material can be made in some cases. Samples can be taken using a small container that is pressed into the outcrop face, peeled of and closed with tape. The samples can even be oriented by measuring the orientation of the container. The sample should be impregnated with a raisin such as araldite before sectioning. Penetration of the impregnation fluid can be improved by applying a vacuum-technique (Stoffel 1976). If water-swelling clay minerals are present, samples can be cut with a diamond saw using isopropyl alcohol and should be impregnated with epoxy between cuts. Dehydrated kerosene can be used as a lubricant during polishing (Chester and Logan 1987).

10.7 Geometries in Thin Section – a Problem of Dimensions

Thin sections are cross sections through complex three-dimensional structures and are therefore not always easily translated into their three-dimensional equivalents. There is a general tendency to simplify things in the sense that angles, sizes and shapes in thin section are directly assumed to be 'maximum values' in the three-dimensional shape, often with

erroneous results. We therefore list some three-dimensional features and the limits within which the geometry of their two-dimensional sections will lie. Figure 10.2 demonstrates the importance of the preparation of several thin sections of different orientation in the case of complex or irregular geometries.

Grain diameter. The presence of grains of variable diameter in thin section does not mean that grains have variable diameter in three dimensions; even if small grains in an aggregate are equidimensional and have equal radius, the grain diameter in thin section will show both small and large grains, and all grain diameters are smaller than or equal to the true diameter (Fig. 10.2a). If the three-dimensional diameter is variable, the distribution of grain size in thin section will be even more irregular. If three-dimensional grain size has to be determined, e.g. the size of recrystallised grains in order to determine the differential stress (Chap. 8.6.1), a correction factor has to be used.

Grain shape. If grains are elliptical in thin section, the ellipticity will lie between the maximum and minimum elliptical ratios of the ellipsoidal shape in three dimensions. Even if all ellipses in the thin section have equal size and orientation, this does not necessarily mean that they represent the maximum ellipticity. An equidimensional shape of grains in thin section may occur if elongate grains are cut normal to their maximum elongation axis. The presence of a shape fabric in thin section may result from a planar or linear fabric in three dimensions. Planar structures are seen as lines in thin section and are therefore indistinguishable from linear structures. An interesting phenomenon that results from this relation may be observed in inclusions of porphyroblasts (Fig. 10.2b). If inclusions have a prolate ellipsoidal shape, as seems to be common in nature, some sections may show elongate aligned inclusions, and others equidimensional ones. The former porphyroblasts may be classified as inter- or syntectonic ones, and the latter erroneously as pretectonic (Fig. 7.9). This illustrates the need to investigate thin sections in at least two orthogonal sections if complex inclusion patterns are studied.

Ellipticity of tubes. Sections through elliptical tubes such as burrows or vermicular intergrowth in symplectites will have an ellipticity that is equal to or exceeding the ellipticity in a section normal to the tube (Fig. 10.2c). In sections parallel to the tube, the structure may resemble layering. Sheath folds (Chap. 5.3.2) can be considered as a special category of tubu-

three dimensional shape | thin section

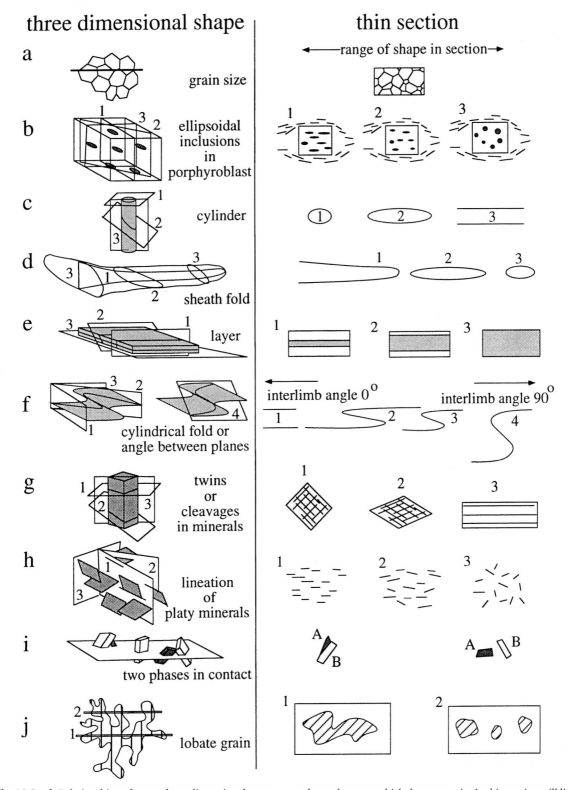

Fig 10.2a–j. Relationships of some three-dimensional geometries and the corresponding two-dimensional geometries visible in thin section. Two end-member geometries are shown in each case between which the geometries in thin section will lie. The *numbers* in the drawings refer to section planes. Further explanation in text

lar structures (Fig. 10.2d); in sections parallel to the tube they resemble tight to isoclinal folds, while in other sections they appear as elliptical shapes.

Thickness of layering. Thickness of layering in thin section corresponds only to true thickness if the section is cut perpendicular to the layering (Fig. 10.2e); in other sections it exceeds true thickness.

Angle between planes and tightness of cylindrical folds. The angle between two planar elements in thin section can be greater or smaller than the true angle (Fig. 10.2f). This principle applies to the angle between a quartz grain shape fabric and layering in a mylonite, but also to cleavage planes in minerals (Fig. 10.2g). By analogy, cylindrical folds in sections oblique to the fold axis may appear tighter than, or less tight, than in sections perpendicular to the axis (Fig. 10.2f).

In sections parallel to an intersection lineation or fold axis, intersecting planes cannot be distinguished and seem to be parallel. Folds are not visible and the structure may resemble undisturbed layering. Polyphase deformation may be missed in this way; a crenulation cleavage may not be recognised if sections are cut parallel to the intersection lineation (the crenulation axis). Microkinks in large single crystals may be confused with undulose extinction or faults if cut parallel to the kink axis.

A special case exists where platy minerals or fractures are oriented in such a way that they share a common axis (Fig. 10.2h). In this situation, thin sections parallel to the joint axis may give the impression that a foliation is present, while those normal to the axis show no preferred orientation whatsoever.

Contact between minerals. In many cases it is critical to determine whether minerals are in contact or not. When minerals A and B are in contact in a thin section, they must be in contact in three dimensions (Fig. 10.2i); however, if A and B are not in contact in the section, they may or may not be in contact in three dimensions. This principle is important for the reconstruction of metamorphic reactions between minerals in rocks (Chap. 7.8).

Lobate grains. Large grains with a lobate shape may appear as such in thin section, but may also occur as isolated small sections through the grain that may resemble separate grains (Fig. 10.2j); the latter can lead to misinterpretation of grainsize in a rock. However, isolated sections through lobate grains can usually be recognised since they all have the same crystallographic orientation. Lobate grains are common in high-grade gneisses and quartzites, and in dunites.

Complex arrangement of inclusions in porphyroblasts. Some porphyroblasts such as garnets can have a complex three-dimensional arrangement of inclusions that show completely different geometries in different sections (Figs. 7.36, 7.38). These complex patterns and their interpretation are discussed in Chapter 7.4–7.7.

Structures indicative of area change. Some structures such as those due to pressure solution (Figs. 3.3, 4.3, 4.19) can be interpreted in terms of an area increase or decrease in the plane of observation. Commonly such structures are erroneously interpreted to imply volume change; however, the presence or absence of volume change cannot be assessed in a single thin section, since information on the third dimension is lacking (Box p. 82).

10.8 Choosing the Orientation of Thin Sections

Thin sections should be cut in such an orientation as to obtain a maximum amount of information from a structure. From the examples given above, it may be clear that it is important to take the three-dimensional geometry of structures into consideration, before a choice of sectioning plane is made.

Non-coaxial deformation histories (Chap. 2.7, 5.3) give rise to planar and linear fabrics with a monoclinic shape symmetry; sections normal to the symmetry axis, i.e. normal to the main foliation and parallel to a stretching or mineral lineation will give a maximum amount of information; they will show the true angle between foliation planes, the most asymmetric shape of porphyroclasts and sheath folds, and spiral structures in garnets. In principle, at least some thin sections should be cut normal to the lineation to check the nature of the fabric in this section; in rocks with a truly monoclinic shape symmetry in three dimensions, the fabric should have an orthorhombic symmetry in this section.

If folds are present with a fold axis parallel to the stretching lineation (oblique folds; Chap. 5.3.2), another section should be cut perpendicular to the fold axis if the folds are to be studied. Crenulation cleavages are best cut at right angles to the crenulation axis. If two intersecting foliations are present, sections should be cut perpendicular to the intersection lineation.

Porphyroblasts with inclusion patterns are best cut in several directions, e.g. parallel and normal to a stretching lineation of the same age as the blasts. If the internal structure of porphyroblasts is not clear, or if no lineations are visible in the rock, it may be useful to make a section parallel to the foliation in order to determine which section normal to the foliation is most advantageous. It is important to check whether a lineation is a stretching lineation or an intersection lineation, and also whether it belongs to the same phase of deformation as the other fabric elements in the rock. If several lineations are present, if the internal structure of porphyroblasts is not clear, or if no lineations are visible in the rock, it may be useful to cut the sample in several directions and slightly polish the surfaces. If this does not help to decide which plane to choose for thin section preparation, thin sections should be cut from a single sample in several directions. Especially sections parallel to the foliation may help in such cases.

11 Exercises

11.1 Introduction

This chapter presents photographs of microstructures similar to those discussed in the previous chapters. The photographs are meant as exercises, to be studied and interpreted by the reader. We have given only the essential information in the figure captions, and our interpretations of the structures are given at the end of the section. The subjects of the problems follow the sequence of treatment in the book. The reader may not always agree with our interpretations, but the main purpose of this chapter is to provide some examples of how information can be obtained from thin sections and which arguments can be used for their interpretation.

11.2 Problem Section

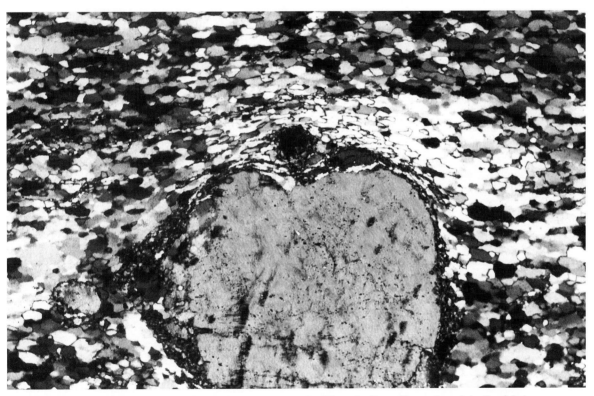

Fig. 11.1. Quartz-feldspar mylonite. Southern Qin Ling Mountains, China. Width of view 1.8 mm. CPL

Problem 1 – Describe and explain the fabric.

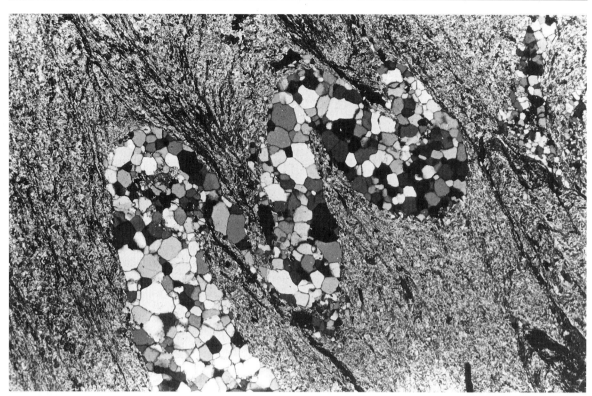

Fig. 11.2. Micaschist with a folded quartz vein. Southern Minas Gerais, Brazil. Width of view 4 mm. CPL. (Thin section courtesy André Ribeiro)

Problem 2 – Describe and explain the fabric.

Fig. 11.3. Micaschist from Seridó, NE Brazil. Width of view 16 mm. Polarisers at 45°

Problem 3 – Name the foliations and describe their origin

Fig. 11.4. Fine-grained phyllite, Smith Island, South Shetland Islands, West Antarctica. Width of view 10 mm. Polarisers at 30°

Problem 4 – Name the foliations and describe their origin

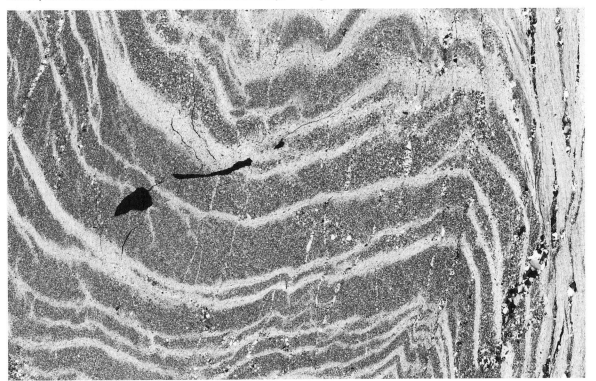

Fig. 11.5. Fine-grained quartz-mica phyllite. The light-coloured bands are mica-rich. Small quartz veins are common, especially at the *right hand side* of the picture. *Black parts at left of the centre* are holes in the thin section. Pyrenees, Spain. Width of view 21 mm. CPL

Problem 5 – Name the foliations and describe their origin

Fig. 11.6. Fine-grained layered mylonite in a section normal to the foliation and parallel to the stretching lineation. St. Bar-thélemy massif, Pyrenees, France. Width of view 4 mm. PPL

Problem 6 – Describe the structure and determine the sense of shear

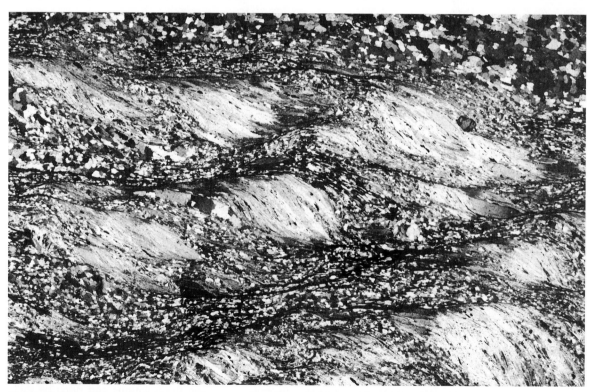

Fig. 11.7. Mylonitic micaschist in a section normal to the foliation and parallel to the stretching lineation. Southern Minas Gerais, Brazil. Width of view 13 mm. CPL

Problem 7 – Describe the structure and determine the sense of shear

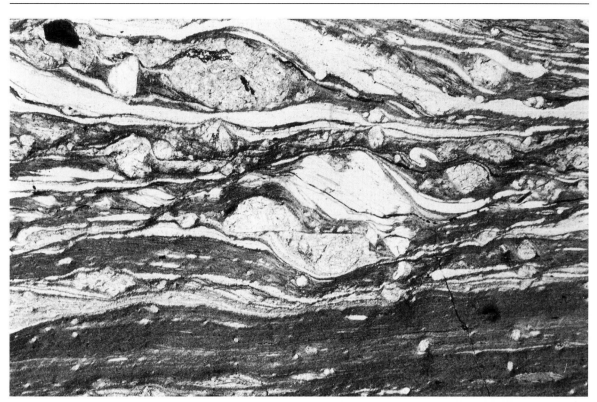

Fig. 11.8. Granodiorite-mylonite in a section normal to the foliation and parallel to the stretching lineation. St Barthélemy Massif, Pyrenees, France. Width of view 4 mm. PPL

Problem 8 – Describe the structures, determine sense of shear and mention the criteria that are used.

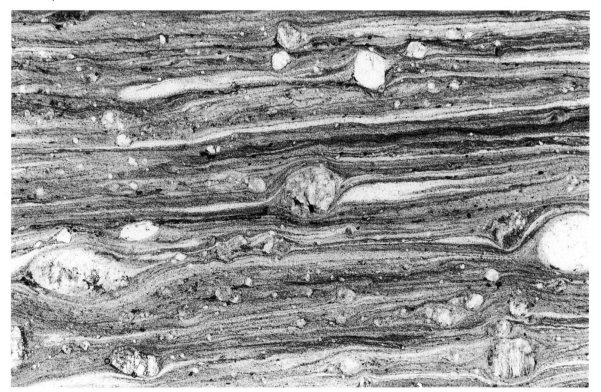

Fig. 11.9. Mylonite derived from a narrow shear zone in weakly deformed granodiorite, shown in a section normal to the foliation and parallel to the stretching lineation. Saint Bar-thélemy Massif, Pyrenees, France. Width of view 4 mm. PPL

Problem 9 – Define the sense of shear and mention the criteria that are used.

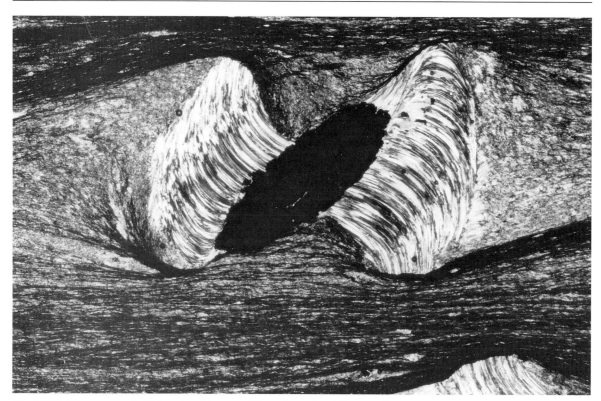

Fig. 11.10. Elongate framboidal pyrite with quartz fringes in a carbonaceous slate in a section normal to the foliation and parallel to a stretching lineation. Fibres show little undulose extinction. Lourdes, Pyrenees, France. Width of view 7 mm. CPL. (Photograph courtesy Domingo Aerden)

Problem 10 – Explain the development of the quartz fringes and the relationship with the fabric in the slate.

Fig. 11.11. Biotite schist, Orós, NE Brazil. Width of view 2.5 mm. PPL

Problem 11 – Discuss the relation between foliation formation and biotite growth.

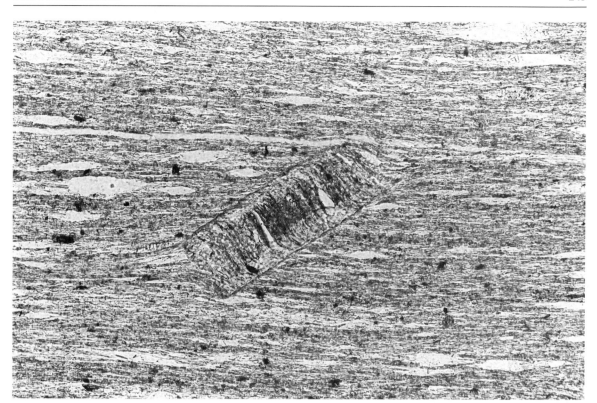

Fig. 11.12. Chloritoid porphyroblast in slate. Curaglia, Switzerland. Width of view 2 mm. PPL

Problem 12 – Describe the development of the microstructure and the relative age of the foliation and porphyroblast.

Fig. 11.13. Garnet mica schist from southern Minas Gerais, Brazil. Width of view 4 mm. Polarisers at 45°
Problem 13 – Comment on the structural and meta-

morphic evolution of the specimen based on comparison of the inclusion pattern in the garnet and the surrounding schistosity.

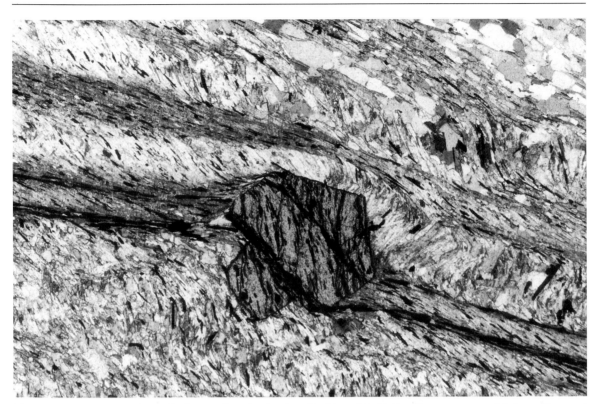

Fig. 11.14. Garnet micaschist with elongate ilmenite, Cavalcante, Goiás, Brazil. Width of view 4 mm. Polarisers at 45°. (Sample courtesy Reinhardt Fuck)

Problem 14 – Define the sequence of deformation and growth of metamorphic minerals.

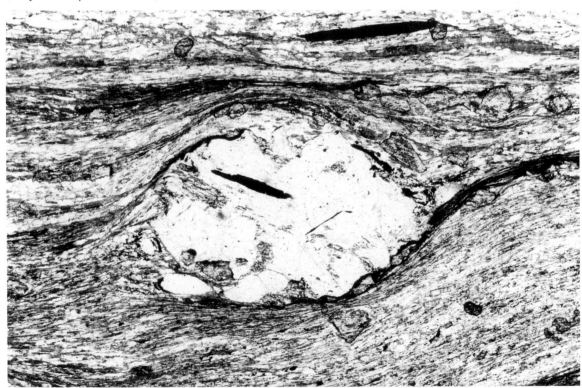

Fig. 11.15. Graphite micaschist with a central porphyroblast of andalusite. Grains with high relief in the matrix and in the andalusite are staurolite. The sample was taken in micaschist less than 100 m from the contact of a major granite intrusion. Both granite and micaschist are mylonitised. Andalusite and staurolite have only been found adjacent to the granite in this area. Menderes Massif, Turkey. Width of view 2.5 mm. PPL. (Photograph courtesy Ralph Hetzel)

Problem 15 – Reconstruct the sequence of events in this area.

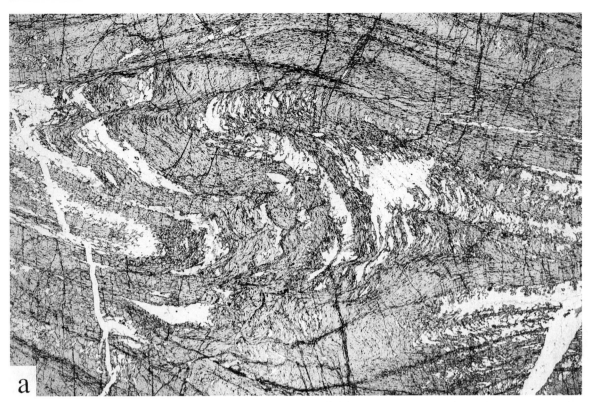

a

Fig. 11.16. a Partial view of a large garnet crystal from garnet mica schist, Vermont, USA. Width of view 15 mm. PPL. **b** Detail of the *upper left part* of **a**, slightly rotated in a clockwise sense.

Width of view 2 mm. PPL. (Sample courtesy Chris Schoneveld)
Problem 16 – Explain the inclusion pattern.

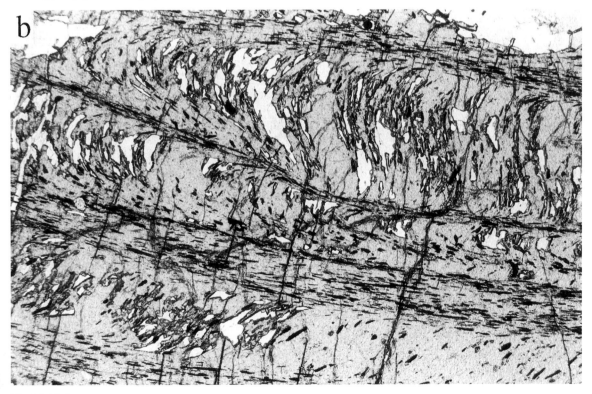

b

Fig. 11.16. b

Fig. 11.17. Garnet albite schist. The *large white* and *grey* porphyroblasts are albite and the *small black* ones are garnet. The matrix is principally composed of white mica and quartz. Elephant Island, West Antarctica. Width of view 18 mm. CPL

Problem 17 – Establish the growth sequence of garnet and albite and relate this sequence with the deformation phases.

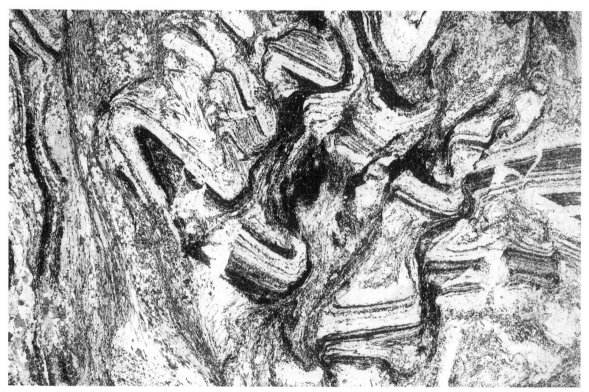

Fig. 11.18. Garnet-albite schist with large albite porphyro-blasts. Dark layers are metachert, mainly composed of tiny garnet and quartz; the matrix is predominantly composed of mica and quartz. Elephant Island, West Antarctica. Width of view 18 mm. Polarisers at 30°

Problem 18 – Define successive deformation phases and establish the relative growth period of albite.

Fig. 11.19a,b. Garnet-staurolite micaschist; **a** shows a large garnet crystal in the centre and two staurolite crystals at *left.* Width of view 13 mm. Polarisers at 25°; **b** shows a detail of **a** with one of the staurolite porphyroblasts and a small garnet at *left.* Width of view 4 mm. PPL. Notice that, because of space restrictions, **b** has been rotated over 90° clockwise with respect to **a.** Cristallina, Alps, Switzerland

Problem 19 – Define deformation phases and determine the growth periods of garnet and staurolite.

Fig. 11.19. b

11.3 Interpretations

Problem 1. The picture shows a porphyroclast of K-feldspar in a matrix of fine-grained quartz. The irregular grain boundaries and the uniform grain size of the small quartz grains away from the porphyroclast suggest that they formed by dynamic recrystallisation. Fine-grained, probably recrystallised feldspar occurs to the *right* and *left* of the porphyroclast. *Above* the porphyroclast, the quartz grains are smaller, have a more elongate shape and more irregular boundaries than those further away. A weak shape fabric is present in quartz, defined by the elongate shape of the grains. This foliation is deflected around the porphyroclast. The structure in quartz can be attributed to vertical shortening and horizontal extension. Relatively high differential stress atop the porphyroclast would cause enhanced intracrystalline deformation and dynamic recrystallisation (probably mainly grain boundary migration recrystallisation), and a relatively small grain size (Chap. 8.6.1). Further away, smaller differential stress and strain rates cause a larger grain size. Grain-boundary area reduction (Chap. 3.10) may also have affected grains in these domains.

Problem 2. The micaschist has a dominant spaced foliation trending *upper left – lower right;* in the fold closures of the quartz vein, cleavage lamellae of this foliation (S_{n+1}) are most clearly developed, and relics of an earlier continuous foliation (S_n) are visible within the microlithons. On the right, the quartz vein is truncated against an S_{n+1} cleavage lamella; pressure solution was probably important during development of S_{n+1}. In the vein, quartz grains have a polygonal shape and are strain-free, both in the limbs and the hinges of the folds. This indicates that static recrystallisation was important in the vein after folding. Hence, the temperature during and/or after D_{n+1} must have been sufficiently high for recrystallisation to proceed.

Problem 3. The subvertical compositional layering can be interpreted as bedding (S_0) because of its asymmetric internal nature (note the gradational transition in the micaceous layer, *left*). It is subparallel to a well-defined, mica preferred orientation (S_1). The superposed inclined compositional layering deforms S_1 and must therefore have formed later. It is a differentiated crenulation cleavage (S_2), selectively developed in mica-rich layers.

Problem 4. Two foliations are visible: a folded one and a straight, vertical one. The variation in composition and thickness of layering in the former indicate that it is bedding (S_0). However, the strong preferred orientation of platy minerals parallel to this surface justifies the suggestion that there is also a foliation S_1 parallel to S_0. From the photograph it is impossible to determine whether S_1 results from diagenetic compaction or from a tectonic phase. Later deformation caused folding of S_0 parallel to S_1 and started the development of a vertical crenulation cleavage (S_2) in the dark (pelitic) layers.

Problem 5. The anastomosing and bimodal character of the folded, mainly horizontal compositional layering is suggestive of a secondary origin, in which case it can be classified as S_n. S_n can be defined as a disjunctive foliation (or secondary compositional layering). Differentiation, probably mainly by solution transfer, caused a new compositional layering (S_{n+1}) in a vertical position, just visible at the *right-hand side* of the photograph. Note that quartz veins are boudinaged at this site.

Problem 6. The rock can be classified as an ultramylonite and shows a regular mylonitic layering at the *bottom* of the photograph. In the *upper part* of the photograph, the layering is disturbed by tight to isoclinal asymmetric folds and shear bands dipping towards the right. Both are indicative of a dextral sense of shear.

Problem 7. The section consists of alternating quartz rich layers, and polycrystalline foliation fish. The sense of shear is sinistral as defined by foliation fish and shear bands. The well-recrystallised quartz along the shear bands indicates that metamorphic conditions during and/or after the shear movements were probably in the greenschist facies or higher.

Problem 8. The mylonite has a foliation defined by quartz ribbons and ribbons of biotite-feldspar-white mica. The *lower part* of the photograph is an ultramylonite. Several shear sense indicators are present; a fragmented feldspar crystal (*centre;* synthetic), white mica fish (*top right* and *left* of the broken feldspar), an asymmetric fold (*top right* of the mica fish), several sigma objects (*top*) and a weak C'-type shear band cleavage in the ultramylonite. All indicators show sinistral sense of shear.

Problem 9. This sample is an ultramylonite with a well-developed mylonitic foliation and numerous mantled porphyroclasts produced by intense deformation of an originally more coarse-grained rock; the sample stems from an ultramylonite band that transects a granodiorite pluton, and the feldspars are the modified original igneous crystals from the intrusion. A dextral sense of shear is indicated by the δ- and σ-type mantled porphyroclasts of feldspar, and by weak shear bands at *top left*. Note the stair-stepping of the δ-type porphyroclast in the centre.

Problem 10. The fact that the curved quartz fringes show little undulose extinction indicates that the curvature must be mostly due to growth. The fringes are partly dissolved by pressure solution at their tips, indicating that they must be antitaxial. The older, external parts of the fringes are gently curved and probably developed in dextral non-coaxial flow as shown in Fig. 6.17. The abrupt change in orientation of the fibres at the *top* and *bottom* of the fringe could be interpreted to mean that the fibres developed by face-controlled growth and that two groups which developed at different faces of the pyrite are separated by a suture, as shown in Fig. 6.17. However, close observation shows that another interpretation is also possible. The fibres at the *top right of the right-hand fringe* seem to be continuous and curved over 90° to 170°, rather than interrupted by a suture. This high angle is not due to an oblique transection effect (Fig. 10.2f) since the fibres are continuous around the bend, and must therefore lie in the plane of the thin section. An important difference between the pyrite in Fig. 11.10 and the model core objects in Fig. 6.17 is that the former is strongly elongate. This implies that its rotation rate in a non-coaxial flow will be pulsating, with the fastest rotation rate when the pyrite long axis is normal to the fabric attractor. Therefore, active fibre growth switches rapidly from a position along the long faces of the pyrite to the short faces and this may cause the abrupt change in curvature. The structure can therefore be explained by a single phase of dextral non-coaxial flow.

Problem 11. The main foliation (S_n) in the matrix can be traced as S_i in the biotite crystals, demonstrating that biotite grew relatively late with respect to the foliation formation. However, the presence of clear strain shadows in the direction of the foliation shows that the last part of D_n deformation must have postdated biotite growth. Note that strain shadow formation is, in this case, accompanied by very restricted foliation deflection, indicating area increase in the plane of observation. Note also that the strain shadows are free of opaque inclusions and have sharp boundaries with the matrix in which opaque inclusions are plentiful. This probably indicates that the matrix was detached from the biotite crystals.

Problem 12. The inclusion pattern of S_i is straight in the centre of the chloritoid porphyroblast, curved along the rim and in continuation with S_e. Towards the tips of the porphyroblast, the angle between S_i and S_e decreases. This can be interpreted as growth of the core of the porphyroblast (probably the dark interior) over an existing slaty cleavage, followed by noncoaxial progressive deformation and further attenuation of the cleavage accompanied by continuous growth of the porphyroblast. The structure cannot have formed by continuous coaxial progressive deformation with shortening direction normal to S_e, since in that case the porphyroblast would also have remained normal to S_e. The contrast between the straight central S_i and the curved outer S_i can be explained in either of two ways; the porphyroblast is intertectonic between two deformation phases, the second of which was non-coaxial flow, or the chloritoid is syntectonic with respect to a single deformation phase during which the kinematics changed from coaxial to non-coaxial progressive deformation (see also Zwart and Calon 1977).

Problem 13. At least two scenarios are possible in this case. **a** The structure was generated during a single deformation phase. In that case, the garnet is syntectonic and rotated about 150° in an anticlockwise sense with respect to S_e. There may have been an interruption in garnet growth between the growth of the core, rich in quartz inclusions, and the rim that apparently overgrew mica caps and contains only fine-grained opaque inclusions. A truncation plane (Chap. 7.6.8; Bell and Johnson 1989; Passchier et al. 1992) between core and rim may result from this interval. The matrix became coarser in response to increasing metamorphic grade after garnet growth and fine-grained opaques present as inclusions in the garnet rims were apparently concentrated in a few large crystals, or diffused/reacted away. **b** The inclusion pattern is an overgrown crenulation cleavage. According to this interpretation, the S-shaped foliation in the core, rich in quartz inclusions, represents S_n, and the foliation in the garnet rim S_{n+1}. In this case, the garnet would be syntectonic with respect to D_{n+1} (case F1 in Fig. 7.9). The observation with respect to the coarsening of the matrix would be equally valid.

Note that in both cases no sense of shear is mentioned and only relative rotation with respect to S_e is reported. In fact, this structure does not give a clue as to whether or not the garnet rotated in space (cf. Bell and Johnson 1989; Passchier et al. 1992).

Problem 14. The photograph shows a subhorizontal differentiated crenulation cleavage (S_{n+1}) deforming an older continuous schistosity (S_n). The garnet overgrew S_{n+1} at a stage of deformation when crenulations were slightly less tight than at present; this can be deduced from the separation of the two dark-coloured cleavage lamellae that lie in the garnet crystal. The garnet must have grown relatively rapidly during D_{n+1} (syn-D_{n+1}). The garnet and S_{n+1} rotated with respect to each other over about 30°, as indicated by the angle between S_i and S_e. The garnet did not grow within a single microlithon domain as in Fig. 7.25b, but over a mica-rich cleavage domain. The micas and most ilmenite grains follow S_n and are therefore interpreted to have grown before or during D_n. Some ilmenite grains along the dark lamellae that traverse the garnet follow S_{n+1}, probably because of recrystallisation during D_{n+1}.

Problem 15. Since andalusite and staurolite only occur near the granite, they probably grew as a consequence of contact metamorphism. Inclusion patterns in the andalusite and staurolite are straight, indicating that they overgrew a straight foliation. The thin, elongate grain *right of the centre* of the andalusite may be a growth inclusion (Chap. 7.7). At present, the foliation S_e is deflected around andalusite and most of the staurolite grains, indicating that they predate at least part of the deformation. The andalusite has an asymmetric shape similar to that of a δ-object in mylonites. This asymmetry probably arose in non-coaxial flow when the schist and granite were mylonitised together. The concentration of graphite in the 'wings' of the andalusite is possibly a relict of cleavage domes (Chap. 7.7). The orientation of graphite inclusions in the andalusite suggests that the crystal and S_e underwent relative rotation. Corroded crystal faces on the andalusite may be due to a breakdown reaction. The inclusion of staurolite in the rim of the andalusite crystal does not give reliable information about the relative age of these minerals (Fig. 7.30). This andalusite crystal is an example of a porphyroblast which is deformed into a porphyroclast. Concluding, the sequence of events can be resumed as follows: first foliation formation, then intrusion of the granite, followed by static growth of andalusite and staurolite. Later deformation caused mylonitisation, deflection of the foliation, and clockwise rotation of the andalusite porphyroblast with respect to the foliation in the matrix, transforming it into a δ-type object indicative of dextral shear sense.

Problem 16. Although at first sight this inclusion pattern resembles that of a spiral-S_i garnet (Chap. 7.6.8),

the structure is quite different; it can be explained as a progressively overgrown tightening crenulation cleavage. The detail **b** shows that in the upper part of **a** the horizontal foliation is a differentiated crenulation cleavage in which the mica-rich cleavage domains are substituted by a continuous garnet lattice with inclusions of opaque minerals, whereas the fold hinges appear as areas with a considerable amount of quartz inclusions (cf. Fig. 7.5b). Similar crenulations can be seen in the (older) core of the garnet crystal at **a** but here they are more open. The crenulations become progressively tighter from the core outward in all directions. This tightening is more pronounced in the *central upper part,* probably reflecting the overgrowth of a mica-rich strain cap. Relatively quartz-rich areas on the sides of the core may reflect strain shadows.

Problem 17. The albite crystals mostly include a straight horizontal S_i, interpreted as an S_n foliation. Tight D_n-folds with a horizontal axial plane can be seen in albite crystals at the *lower right,* indicating that S_n formed by transposition of an older foliation, possibly S_0. S_n is crenulated in the matrix in open to gentle crenulations with vertical axial plane (D_{n+1}). Albite crystals are therefore intertectonic between D_n and D_{n+1}. Small garnets are included in the centre of albite porphyroblasts and are therefore probably older (however, see Chap. 7.6.6). This idea is reinforced by garnets included in the *top-right* albite crystal that show a slight deviation of S_n and are therefore interpreted to be late syn – D_n and hence older than the post-D_n albites.

Problem 18. A tightly folded layering is visible in most of the photograph. Layers have a strongly variable thickness and probably represent bedding. The layering is tightly folded by D_1 folds with hinges that are included in albite porphyroblasts *(left of centre).* Later transposition generated a vertical S_2 that deviates around the albite crystals. Albite grew intertectonically between D_1 and D_2 but continued to grow during D_2 as shown by the *lowermost* crystal with included D_2 folds in the rim. This crystal shows in fact a millipede geometry (cf. Fig. 7.23 from the same thin section).

Problem 19. The *upper left corner* of **a** shows crenulations that demonstrate that the vertical foliation is a partly transposed crenulation cleavage (S_{n+1}), deforming an older foliation (S_n). At the *right-hand side* S_{n+1} cleavage is folded by D_{n+2}. Open folds of this last deformation phase are included in the large garnet porphyroblast. This porphyroblast has a quartz-rich strain shadow at its *right-hand side;* it must therefore have grown rapidly during D_{n+2}, after the open folds had formed and before the deformation responsible for the strain shadow occurred. The staurolite crystal in the enlargement **b** shows tight D_{n+1} folds as inclusions and some deflection of S_{n+1} at the *right-hand side.* From the detail in **b** only, the staurolite could be interpreted as late syn-D_{n+1} with the deflection explained as the result of late D_{n+1} deformation. However, in the context of **a** it seems more probable that the staurolite grew approximately contemporaneously with the garnet and that the deflection was caused by late D_{n+2} deformation as can also be observed at the upper side of the garnet in **a.** Note the euhedral small garnet at the *left* of the staurolite in **b** that shows a post-tectonic relation with the S_{n+1} cleavage.

Glossary

This glossary provides definitions of the main terms used in this book. The definitions do not always cover the significance of all aspects of the term completely, but are meant as a short reference. Additional information on the complete meaning and application of each term can be found in the main text using the index.

acicular – needle-shaped (from the Latin diminutive of 'acus' – needle).

active foliation – foliation that consists of microshear zones or other 'active' planes. It is normally not parallel to the XY plane of finite strain. Examples are shear band cleavage and some compressional crenulation cleavages.

A_k – kinematic dilatancy number.

amoeboid fabric – fabric composed of crystals with strongly curved and lobate, interlocking grain boundaries, like an amoeba.

anastomosing – term used to describe the shape of some foliations: braided, dividing the rock into lenses (Fig. 4.6).

anhedral crystal – crystal with irregular shape and lack of planar crystal faces.

anisotropic – term indicating that a material property is not of equal magnitude in all directions; this may refer to birefringence of light, to growth rate, grain boundary energy, elastic strength, etc. (opposite of isotropic).

annealing – term from metallurgy used to indicate processes of recovery and static recrystallisation induced by passive heating of a previously deformed material. The term is also sometimes used for the interpretation of microstructures in rocks.

anti-perthite – plagioclase with inclusions of K-feldspar, formed by exsolution of the K-feldspar solid solution in plagioclase.

antitaxial fringe – fringe in which the growth surface lies between the fringe and the core object.

antitaxial vein – vein with fibres growing along their contacts with the wall rock, i.e. along both outer surfaces of the vein (see also syntaxial and ataxial vein).

antithetic – term used for minor faults or shear bands with the opposite sense of shear or dip direction as the major structure in which they develop.

ataxial vein – vein containing fibres that lack a localised growth surface.

atoll structure – ring-shaped crystal in thin section surrounding a mineral aggregate similar to the matrix. Atoll structures of garnet are common in some micaschists and probably form as corona structures, followed by breakdown of the crystal around which they originally formed.

augen – (German: eye) – lens-shaped crystal or crystal aggregate. The term is usually applied to feldspar augen (augengneiss). Most feldspar augen are probably porphyroclasts that developed from feldspar megacrysts in intrusive or high-grade metamorphic rocks by partial recrystallisation along the rim in response to deformation.

AVA diagram – diagram showing the distribution of lattice preferred orientation over a volume of rock (from German 'Achsenverteilungsanalyse').

axial planar foliation – foliation which is approximately parallel to the axial plane of folds. This term is used as an alternative term for *secondary foliation*.

blast – crystal in a metamorphic rock that has grown during metamorphism (see also porphyroblast).

blastomylonite – mylonite which underwent static recrystallisation of part of the fabric after deformation ceased. The term is also used for high-grade mylonite with a relatively coarse recrystallised matrix. Because of the genetic character of the term, its use in not recommended.

bulging – process of local migration of a grain boundary into a neighbouring grain with a higher dislocation density, eventually producing new crystals. Bulging is important in GBM recrystallisation.

Burgers vector – vector indicating the displacement of a crystal lattice associated with a dislocation.

C'-type shear band cleavage – specific type of shear band cleavage commonly developed in strongly foliated and mica-rich mylonites. C'-type shear bands are curved and anastomosing and inclined to the shear zone boundary; a synonym is extensional crenulation cleavage.

C-type shear band cleavage – specific type of shear band cleavage, particularly common in mylonitised granitoid rocks. C-type shear bands or C-planes are relatively straight and thought to lie parallel to the shear zone boundary. (C from French 'cisaillement' – shear).

C/S fabric – fabric consisting of C-type shear band cleavage and S-planes. S-planes define a shape or mineral foliation that is cut by C-type shear band cleavage or C-planes. See also Type I and II S-C mylonite.

cataclasite – a rock composed of angular rock and mineral fragments, thought to have formed principally by brittle fracturing without melting.

cathodoluminescence – luminescence shown by minerals when excited by a beam of electrons.

chlorite stack – aggregate of chlorite, commonly lens shaped, occurring in microlithons of many slates. Chlorite may be alternating with white mica. (001) planes of chlorite are commonly oblique to slaty cleavage. Chlorite stacks are probably pre- or early syntectonic porphyroblasts.

clast – see porphyroclast.

cleavage – secondary foliation defined by a preferred orientation of inequant fabric elements. The name is usually restricted to fine-grained rocks such as slates and phyllites, but is also used by some authors as a general name for any secondary foliation except coarse layering.

cleavage bundle – local area of concentrated cleavage development, probably related with local high strain.

cleavage domain – layer or lens with a relatively high content of elongate grains (such as micas or amphiboles) and low content of equidimensional grains (such as quartz, feldspar or carbonate). Together with microlithons they make up a spaced foliation. Micas in cleavage domains commonly have a preferred orientation parallel or at a small angle to the domain.

cleavage dome – dome-shaped structure, usually a graphite aggregate, attached to the crystal face of a porphyroblast. The structure is probably formed by porphyroblast growth .

cleavage lamella – synonym for cleavage domain (plural: lamellae).

coaxial – term used for flow or progressive deformation with principal finite strain axes remaining parallel to ISA.

Coble creep – solid state diffusion along grain boundaries.

competent – descriptive but imprecise, interpretative term for highly viscous or relatively strong.

complex object – mantled porphyroclast with more than one set of wings.

compositional layering – non-genetic term for an alternation of layers with different lithological composition. This may be bedding, igneous layering or a layering induced by secondary differentiation processes. See also differentiated layering.

constrictional strain – type of three-dimensional strain for which X/Y > Y/Z. Constrictional strain produces a prolate strain ellipsoid.

core object – rigid object in the centre of a strain shadow or strain fringe. Commonly a pyrite or magnetite crystal.

core-and-mantle structure – deformed crystalline core, usually a single crystal, surrounded by a mantle of fine-grained material of the same mineral. The structure is thought to develop by preferential dynamic recrystallisation in the outer shell of a deforming large single crystal in response to intracrystalline deformation. Feldspar core-and-mantle structures are common in rocks subject to low to medium-grade deformation.

corona – shell of a single or several minerals around a crystal of another composition. Usually formed by metamorphic reaction.

CPL – abbreviation used in this book for crossed polarised light.

crack-seal growth – growth of minerals along a fracture, thought to result from periodic fracturing and sealing by growth from a fluid.

crenulation – other word for folds with a wavelength of 1 cm or less, usually developed in an earlier continuous foliation.

crenulation cleavage – secondary spaced foliation with microhinges of an older crenulated foliation in the microlithons recognisable with the optical microscope.

crinoid type – synonym for syntaxial fringe; these commonly form around crinoid stem fragments.

critical resolved shear stress (CRSS) – property of a slip system in a crystal. The CRSS defines at which shear stress, resolved on the slip plane, a dislocation will start to move.

crystalloblastic – synonym for granoblastic.

crystallographic preferred orientation – other term for lattice preferred orientation.

crystalplastic flow – permanent deformation by intracrystalline deformation mechanisms.

δ-type object – mantled porphyroclast with thin asymmetric wings of mantle material fixed to opposite sides of the porphyroclast and stretching into the matrix. The shape resembles the Greek letter δ.

decussate fabric – an arrangement of randomly oriented elongate grains (such as mica) in a metamorphic rock.

deflection fold structure – structure around a porphyroblast in which S_e is deflected through isoclinal folding at both sides of the porphyroblast (Fig. 7.22b).

deflection plane – surface inside a porphyroblast where the inclusion pattern abruptly changes orientation without a break in continuity.

deformation – change in shape and orientation of objects or volumes of rock from an initial to a final state. We use the term deformation in this general sense, while the word *strain* has a more restricted significance, that is, the change in shape of an object or part of the rock.

deformation lamella (plural lamellae) – intracrystalline lamella of slightly different optical relief than the host grain, consisting of damaged crystal lattice or arrays of sub-microscopic inclusions.

deformation mechanism map – a diagram, usually showing the conditions of stress and homologous temperature for which specific deformation mechanisms are dominantly active; each map is only valid for a specific mineral and grain size.

deformation partitioning – local subdivision of the deformation pattern into domains with different deformation parameters such as strain and volume change, or with different dominant active deformation mechanisms.

deformation path – path of a volume of rock from the undeformed to the deformed state, as seen in an external reference frame. Also, sum of the displacement paths for a volume of rock.

deformation phase – period of deformation during which a group of structures has formed, separated from other structures by overprinting criteria. Successive deformation phases may merge into each other or may be separated by time intervals with little or no deformation, during which metamorphic conditions and the stress field may have changed.

deformation tensor – tensor describing finite deformation, including strain and rotation.

deformation twin – twin formed by deformation, common in deformed carbonates and plagioclase feldspar.

diagenetic foliation – foliation, usually parallel to bedding, thought to have formed by diagenetic compaction and dewatering.

diagenetic strain – strain due to diagenetic compaction, usually resulting in a shortening normal to bedding and volume loss.

differential stress – non-hydrostatic or lithostatic component of stress, usually defined as $(\sigma_1 - \sigma_3)$.

deviatoric stress – non-hydrostatic or lithostatic component of stress defined as $(\sigma_n - \sigma_{mean})$, where σ_n is normal stress on a surface and σ_{mean} is the mean stress.

differentiated layering – secondary, spaced foliation in which cleavage domains and microlithons are recognisable with the naked eye. Differentiated layering is inferred to have formed by differentiation in an originally more weakly layered or even homogeneous material. In fabric descriptions the non-genetic term *compositional layering* should be used if the origin is not known.

diffusion creep – deformation due to migration of vacancies through the crystal lattice.

dilatancy – here: area increase during deformation of a plane (two dimensions). Sometimes (erroneously) used as a synonym for volume increase.

displacement path – path traced by a particle in a deforming rock from the undeformed to the deformed state, as seen in an external reference frame.

disjunctive foliation – secondary spaced foliation without fold hinges in the microlithons. If microlithons are wide and continuous, the term compositional layering is used as a synonym.

dislocation – linear defect in a crystal.

dislocation climb – movement of a dislocation out of its slip plane, normally by migration of vacancies to the dislocation site .

dislocation creep – movement of dislocations in a crystal lattice accommodated by climb.

dislocation glide – movement of dislocations in a crystal lattice without dislocation climb.

domainal slaty cleavage – secondary disjunctive foliation with lens-shaped microlithons in fine-grained rocks.

dragging microstructure – strong curvature of a boundary between two grains of mineral A where it joins the contact with a mineral B (Fig. 3.18). This structure is interpreted to have formed when the grain boundary migrated and was pinned to some extend at the contact with mineral B.

dynamic recrystallisation – recrystallisation during intracrystalline deformation. It occurs by nucleation, grain boundary migration and/or subgrain rotation.

ecc – abbreviation used for extensional crenulation cleavage.

EDAX – energy dispersive X-ray analysis. Facility to measure the chemical composition of minerals in an electron microscope.

en-echelon – French term meaning a parallel but obliquely dislocated disposition of planar elements, like tiles on a roof (from French 'échelon' – rung of a ladder).

epitaxy – preferential nucleation of a mineral on the lattice of another, with a fixed orientation relationship between the two crystal lattices.

equigranular fabric – fabric in which all grains have roughly equal size.

euhedral crystal – crystal with well-developed crystal shape and crystal faces.

extensional crenulation cleavage – synonym for C'-type shear band cleavage.

external foliation – foliation outside and immediately adjacent to a porphyroblast. It is commonly referred to by the abbreviation S_e (e for external), and used in comparisons with the internal foliation (S_i).

φ-type object – mantled porphyroclast with symmetric wings (no stair stepping is developed).

fabric – the complete spatial and geometrical configuration of all those components that are contained in a rock (Hobbs et al. 1976) and that are penetratively and repeatedly developed throughout the volume of rock under consideration. This includes features such as foliation, lineation, lattice-preferred orientation and grain size. The term can also be defined as: the relative orientation of parts of a rock mass.

fabric attractor (FA) – line or plane in space towards which material lines and some fabric elements rotate.

fabric element – part of a fabric such as a foliation, lineation etc.

fabric gradient – a gradual change in the geometry of a fabric in the field or in thin section.

fabric skeleton – crest lines on a contoured plot of crystallographic axes in a stereogram, used to describe lattice-preferred orientation patterns.

feather-edge structure – pattern of crystallographically determined inclusions resembling a feather edge.

fibre – strongly elongate crystal grown in dilatation sites.

fibre trajectory analysis – reconstruction of the deformation path in a volume of rock from the shape of fibres in veins or fringes.

finite deformation – deformation accumulated over a finite period of time.

finite displacement vector – vector connecting particles in the undeformed and deformed state for finite deformation.

finite strain – strain accumulated over a finite period of time.

flame-perthite – perthite with flame-shaped lamellae.

flattening strain – type of three-dimensional strain for which Y/Z>X/Y. Flattening strain produces an oblate strain ellipsoid.

flow – instantaneous movement of material particles making up a deforming volume of rock. If flow is *homogeneous*, the pattern of particle displacements can be described by a simple *velocity field*, or *flow pattern*. A velocity field describes the motion of a population of material particles at a given instant in time. A sequence of velocity fields, describing the accumulation of finite displacements of material particles with time, is a *deformation path* or *progressive deformation history*. Here we must clearly distinguish between the notions of ongoing progressive deformation and the end product of the progressive deformation (finite deformation, finite strain).

flow law – equation describing the dependence of strain rate on parameters such as stress, temperature and grain size.

flow partitioning – local subdivision of a bulk flow pattern into domains with different flow parameters such as vorticity and volume change rate.

flow pattern – pattern of velocity vectors defining distribution of flow over a volume of rock.

flow tensor – tensor describing the velocity of particles at specific points in space.

foam-structure – fabric of grain boundaries resembling a foam; it forms by GBAR.

foliation – planar fabric element that occurs penetratively on a mesoscopic scale in a rock. Primary foliation includes bedding and igneous layering; secondary foliations are formed by deformation induced processes. Joints are not normally considered as foliations since they are not penetrative on a mesoscopic scale.

fracture cleavage – alternative and slightly outdated term for disjunctive cleavage. The use of this term is discouraged because of its (commonly erroneous) genetic implication.

fringe – body of fibrous crystalline material formed adjacent to a relatively rigid core object during progressive deformation.

garben – (German for 'stack') – sheafs of elongate minerals such as hornblende, usually arranged along the foliation plane.

gauge – (or gage) instrument capable of providing quantitative data. In this book the term 'natural microgauge' refers to a microstructure that can be used to obtain quantitative data from a rock.

GBAR – grain boundary area reduction.

GBM recrystallisation – grain boundary migration recrystallisation; recrystallisation by migrating grain boundaries in response to differences in dislocation density between two grains.

generation surface – approximately planar vein filled with pseudotachylyte and thought to be the site of a fault where pseudotachylyte was generated by frictional heating.

geometric softening – softening of a mineral aggregate by development of a lattice-preferred orientation.

ghost structure – outline of an overgrown mineral in a porphyroblast visible as a local relative scarceness of inclusions.

gneissic layering – compositional layering in a gneiss.

gneissosity – general term for foliation in a gneiss. Use of this term is discouraged because of its vague connotation; several types of foliation (layering, schistosity) may occur in the same gneiss.

gouge – non-consolidated fractured rock, commonly very fine-grained, formed by brittle deformation at a shallow crustal level along a fault.

grain – crystal.

grain boundary – planar domain of distorted crystalline material between two crystal lattices of different orientation and/or nature.

grain boundary area reduction – grain boundary migration leading to reduction in the total surface area of grain boundaries in an aggregate. The process operates spontaneously in response to the decrease in internal free energy that a grain aggregate gains by decreasing the area of (high-energy) grain boundaries; it leads to straight grain boundaries and large grains.

grain boundary sliding – deformation mechanism where grains slide along grain boundaries. This mechanism is limited to fine-grained rocks and/or relatively high temperature.

granoblastic fabric – fabric dominantly formed by equidimensional crystals. An example is a foam structure, formed by GBAR in which platy or acicular mineral shapes are absent, and most grains have equant shape.

growth inclusion – small mineral grain included in a porphyroblast, usually parallel or orthogonal to crystal faces. Such inclusions are thought to have formed during growth of the porphyroblast and do not represent part of the matrix that was overgrown by the porphyroblast, as for passive inclusions.

growth twin – twin formed during growth of the crystal in which it is contained; this in contrast to a deformation twin, which forms during deformation of the crystal.

habit – crystal shape, specifically referring to the relative development of individual crystal faces (e.g. prismatic habit; tabular habit).

hardening – increasing resistance to deformation, expressed as increasing differential stress at constant strain rate, or decreasing strain rate at constant differential stress.

helicitic fold – pattern of inclusions in a porphyroblast resembling a fold and thought to have formed by overgrowth of a pre-existing fold in the matrix.

homologous temperature – fraction of the melting temperature for a mineral phase in Kelvin. A homologous temperature of 0.7 indicates 7/10th of the melting temperature. This is an example of a dimensionless number.

hydrolithic weakening – softening of a material due to the presence or introduction of water.

hydrostatic pressure – pressure due to the weight of a column of water acting equally in all directions.

hypidiomorphic – synonym for subhedral, mainly used in igneous rocks.

idiomorphic – synonym for euhedral, mainly used in igneous rocks.

inclusion – small crystal included in a larger one of another composition. Inclusions can be subdivided into passive, growth and exsolution inclusions.

incremental deformation – imaginary, infinitely small deformation.

incremental displacement vector – vector connecting particles in the undeformed and deformed state for incremental deformation.

inequigranular fabric – a fabric showing inhomogeneous distribution of grain size, e.g. bimodal with large grains of approximately equal size in a fine-grained equigranular matrix.

injection vein – wedge-shaped or branching vein filled with pseudotachylyte and usually connected to one or more generation surfaces.

instantaneous stretching axes (ISA) – three imaginary orthogonal axes in space, along two of which stretching rates are minimal and maximal (known as the shortening and extensional ISA respectively). The third axis is called the intermediate instantaneous stretching axis. ISA exist for any homogeneous flow.

interlobate fabric – fabric composed of crystals with irregular, lobate grain boundaries.

internal foliation – foliation defined by the preferred orientation of passive inclusions in a porphyroblast, thought to mimic the orientation and geometry of a foliation that was overgrown by the porphyroblast. The abbreviation S_i (i for internal) is commonly used for internal foliation. S_i is often used in comparison with the external foliation S_e.

interstitial – point defect in a crystal lattice; an additional lattice element in between regular lattice units.

intracrystalline deformation – deformation by movement of vacancies or dislocations in the crystal lattice.

ISA – instantaneous stretching axes.

isochore – a line on a PT diagram showing the variation of the pressure of a fluid with temperature, when the volume of the fluid is kept constant.

isotropic – term indicating that a material property is of equal magnitude in all directions; this may refer to birefringence of light, to growth rate, grain boundary energy, elastic strength, etc. (opposite of anisotropic).

kelyphitic structure – a type of symplectititic reaction rim bordering olivine; also used for symplectitic amphibole-plagioclase coronas (from Greek 'κελυφος' – pod).

kinematic dilatancy number – (A_k) measure of the dilation rate of flow, normalised against strain rate; dimensionless number.

kinematic vorticity number – (W_k) measure of the vorticity of flow, normalised against strain rate; dimensionless number.

L-tectonite – deformed rock with a linear fabric; no foliation is present.

lattice-preferred orientation (LPO) – statistical preferred orientation of the crystal lattices of a population of crystals in a rock. In older texts also referred to as texture, crystallographic fabric or crystallographic preferred orientation.

left-over grain – one of a group of small grains with identical orientation that lie within or at the edges of another large grain (Fig. 3.18). They are interpreted as relics of a large single old grain that is incompletely overgrown by a neighbour.

lepidoblastic fabric – planar fabric defined by the preferred orientation of tabular or platy crystals (from Greek 'λεπις' – scale).

line defect – dislocation.

linear shape fabric – fabric defined by the linear shape of deformed constricted grains or grain aggregates.

lineation – linear fabric element that occurs penetratively on the mesoscopic scale in a rock. Striations and fibres are not normally considered to be lineations since they do not occur penetratively on the mesoscopic scale.

lithostatic pressure – pressure at a point in the earth due to the weight of the overlying column of rock. Lithostatic pressure at a point is uniform in all directions by definition.

LPO – lattice-preferred orientation.

LS tectonite – deformed rock containing both planar and linear fabric elements.

M-domain – alternative term for cleavage lamella in a micaschist (M stands for mica-rich, in contrast to Q(uartz)-domain.

mantled porphyroclast – porphyroclast with an elongated mantle of the same mineral composition as the porphyroblast, stretched in the direction of the foliation. It is inferred to have formed at the expense of the porphyroclast by recrystallisation in its rim. Mantled porphyroclasts are common in mylonites and are used to determine sense of shear. See also δ-object, σ-object and strain shadow.

material line – line that consists of material particles: as opposed to (imaginary) space lines such as coordinate axes.

matrix – 1. method of notation for components of a tensor; 2. fine-grained ground mass in a rock.

mean stress – hydrostatic or lithostatic component of stress, of equal magnitude in any direction.

median line/surface – line (surface) dividing a vein into parts that grew in opposite directions.

metamorphic cycle – cycle of changing pressure and temperature experienced by a volume of rock.

metamorphic event – episode of metamorphism, characterised by changes in mineral assemblage in a volume of rock.

mica-fish – lensoid mica grain common in mylonites. Their asymmetry can be used to determine sense of shear.

microgauge – see gauge.

microlithon – layer or lens with a relatively small degree of preferred orientation as compared to cleavage domains. A crenulated older foliation may be present in microlithons. Together with cleavage domains, microlithons make up a spaced foliation.

millipede structure – inclusion pattern in a porphyroblast resembling an Australian millipede.

mimetic growth – growth of minerals controlled by pre-existing grain arrangements (Vernon 1976).

moat – monomineralic corona.

mortar structure – Porphyroclast surrounded by a fine-grained aggregate of the same mineral. Mortar structure is similar to core-and-mantle structure but the new grains are smaller. A mortar structure is not necessarily formed by recrystallisation, but possibly by cataclasis or a combination of both. The use of this term is discouraged because of its (commonly erroneous) genetic implication of "mechanically crushed rock".

mylonite – strongly deformed rock from a ductile shear zone, commonly with a planar foliation and usually with a stretching lineation. Evidence for high strain such as quartz ribbons are common. Mylonite was originally (Lapworth 1885) defined as a brittle fault rock, but mylonites are now thought to have formed predominantly by crystalplastic flow of the matrix, although some minerals suspended in the matrix may show brittle fracturing. The word derives from the Greek 'μυλον', a mill.

mylonitic foliation – type of secondary foliation developed in mylonites.

myrmekite – symplectite of quartz and plagioclase, commonly adjacent to K-feldspar, indicating replacement.

Nabarro-Herring creep – solid state diffusion through the crystal lattice.

nematoblastic fabric – linear fabric defined by preferred orientation of acicular or prismatic crystals (from Greek 'νημα' – thread).

new grain – recrystallised grain or grain of a new mineral formed by metamorphic reaction.

Newtonian flow – flow in which strain rate depends linearly on differential stress.

non-coaxial – term used for flow or progressive deformation in which material lines that were initially parallel to ISA rotate to another orientation.

non-Newtonian flow – flow in which strain rate depends on differential stress through a non-linear relation (e.g. stress to the power of a constant n).

normal stress – component of stress acting on a plane (a vector), normal to that plane.

oblique fabric or oblique foliation – shape- or lattice-preferred orientation oblique to mylonitic or other foliation. Oblique fabrics commonly develop in response to non-coaxial flow.

oblique fold – type of approximately cylindrical fold common in mylonites with its fold axis subparallel to the stretching lineation. Oblique folds lack the closed tubular shape of sheath folds.

oblique-S_i porphyroblast – porphyroblast with a straight inclusion pattern at an angle with the foliation in the matrix.

ODF – orientation distribution function. Function describing the three-dimensional orientation of crystals in a rock.

palaeopiezometer – a microgauge used to measure differential stress.

palaeostress – stress value reached in a rock at some time in geological history.

partitioning – see flow partitioning, deformation partitioning.

passive foliation – foliation that is rotating passively towards the fabric attractor. Passive foliations are subparallel to the XY plane of finite strain. Examples are most types of continuous foliations. See also active foliation.

passive inclusion – mineral grain included in a porphyroblast or larger grain in the rock matrix. Such inclusions are thought to represent a fragment of the matrix which was overgrown by the porphyroblast and passively included in its crystal lattice without significant displacement or rotation.

pencil cleavage – term used for a structure where two intersecting foliations are of equal grade of development, causing the rock to fracture into pencil-shaped fragments upon weathering. The term is mostly used for diagenetic cleavage intersected at a high angle by tectonic cleavage (Fig. 4.28).

penetrative fabric element – a fabric element that occurs penetratively throughout a rock. A foliation is an example of a penetrative fabric element. We use the word penetrative to mean: at the scale of observation. In thin section this means: down to the scale of individual mineral grains.

perthite – K-feldspar with inclusions of plagioclase, formed by exsolution of the albite solid solution in alkali-feldspar.

phenocryst – large, commonly euhedral single crystal in an igneous rock or pseudotachylyte, thought to have formed by growth from a melt.

phyllonite – micaceous mylonite, sometimes (erroneously) used for ultramylonite (from Greek 'φυλλον' – leaf).

pinning microstructure – strongly indented boundary between two grains of a mineral A where it is attached to a small grain of mineral B (Fig. 3.18). The structure is thought to be caused by pinning of a migrating grain boundary on the grain of B.

pixel – small element of an image on a computer screen.

planar shape fabric – planar fabric defined by the shape of deformed flattened grains or grain aggregates (see also linear shape fabric).

plane strain – type of three-dimensional strain for which $Y/Z = X/Y$. In the absence of volume change this means that $Y = 1$.

platy quartz – monocrystalline quartz ribbon with few or no intracrystalline deformation structures, common in high-grade gneisses.

poikiloblast – poikiloblastic crystal.

poikiloblastic crystal – crystal containing a large volume fraction of passive inclusions; such crystals have a 'spongy' aspect (from Greek 'ποικιλος' – various).

polygonal arc – arc-shaped distribution of non-deformed mica grains, probably formed by static recrystallisation of a folded mica foliation.

polygonal fabric – fabric composed of crystals with straight grain boundaries, commonly with anhedral or subhedral crystals.

porphyroblast – (with *b*, sometimes abbreviated as 'blast') single crystal of a diameter exceeding the surrounding matrix and inferred to have grown in a solidified rock in response to changes in metamorphic conditions. The word derives from Greek: Porphyro- refers to the large crystals of feldspar in a porphyry, from Greek 'πορφυριτες λιθος'-purple stone; blast comes from Greek 'βλαστος' – bud.

porphyroclast – (with *c*, sometimes abbreviated as 'clast') single crystal of a size exceeding the mean grain size in the surrounding matrix and inferred to represent a remnant of an originally coarse grained rock. Porphyroclasts are common in mylonites. The word derives from Greek porphyry (see porphyroblast) and 'κλαστος', shattered, from 'κλαν' – to break.

power-law flow – special type of non-Newtonian flow.

PPL – abbreviation used in this book for plain polarised light.

pressure fringe – alternative, but genetic term for strain fringe.

pressure shadow – alternative, but genetic term for strain shadow.

pressure solution – localised dissolution of material induced by enhanced solubility of solids in response to the presence of a differential stress field.

primary foliation – foliation that was present in a sedimentary or igneous rock before deformation. Primary foliation includes bedding and igneous layering.

principal strain axes – orthogonal axes along which shear strain is zero. Along two of these axes, stretch values are maximal and minimal. The third axis is called the intermediate principal strain axis.

principal strain values – values of stretch along the principal strain axes.

principal stress axes – orthogonal axes normal to planes on which shear stress is zero. Along two of these axes normal stress is maximal and minimal. The third axis is called the intermediate principal stress axis.

principal stress values – values of normal stress along principal stress axes.

principal stretches – values of stretch along principal strain axes. Also known as principal strain values.

progressive deformation – process of the accumulation of deformation with time.

protomylonite – weakly to moderately deformed rock in a shear zone, transitional between the undeformed wall rock and a mylonite. Also a mylonite with 10–50% matrix.

pseudomorph – shape of a crystal aggregate or crystal, inherited from an older crystal or object which has been replaced.

pseudotachylyte – (or pseudotachilyte) dark brittle fault rock occurring in veins and fractures in host rocks with low porosity. Pseudotachylyte is thought to form by local melting of a host rock along a fault in response to seismic activity on the fault and associated local generation of frictional heat. The name was derived from 'tachylyte' (basalt glass) occurring in settings that could not be explained by igneous activity.

pure shear flow – a special type of coaxial flow, usually defined as having no stretch along the intermediate principal ISA.

pyrite-type fringe – synonym for antitaxial fringe. Such fringes commonly develop around pyrite grains.

Q-domain – alternative term for quartz-rich microlithon. See also M-domain.

quarter structure – asymmetric microstructure around a porphyroclast with similar geometry in opposite quadrants. These structures can be used as a shear sense indicator.

quartz ribbon – highly elongated disc- or lens-shaped crystal or aggregate of quartz, common in mylonites and high-grade rocks. In thin section the crystals are ribbon-shaped, hence the name. Quartz ribbons form by flattening of originally equidimensional quartz grains, or possibly by migration of grain boundaries to form single large grains from more fine-grained parent aggregates. They may exhibit undulose extinction, or be recrystallised into polycrystalline ribbons.

re-entrant zone – zone of passive inclusions along the ribs of a euhedral porphyroblast. An example are the cross-shaped re-entrant zones in chiastolite.

reaction softening – softening induced by the growth of new minerals which are more easily deformable than minerals of the host rock.

recovery – general name for the processes in a crystal or crystal aggregate that lead to a decrease in the combined length of included dislocations, and rearrangement of dislocations into subgrain walls. The process of recovery is driven by a decrease in the internal free energy of a crystal or crystal aggregate. Processes of dynamic recrystallisation and GBAR are not included in recovery as described in this text. Recovery is also active during the process of static recrystallisation.

recrystallisation – rearrangement of crystalline matter to a modified set of crystals by migration and modification of grain boundaries. Recrystallisation does not necessarily involve chemical changes. It usually involves a decrease or increase in the crystal size.

rheology – study of the deformation and flow of matter, more specifically the mechanics of flow.

ribbon – highly elongated lens-shaped single crystal or monomineralic aggregate.

rock analogues – crystalline materials used in deformation experiments as analogue for rocks.

S-C fabric – other way to write C/S fabric, which is the original nomenclature.

S-tectonite – deformed rock characterised by a planar fabric (no lineation is present).

σ-type object – mantled porphyroclast with a geometry resembling the Greek letter σ.

schistosity – secondary foliation defined by preferred orientation of inequant fabric elements in a medium to coarse-grained rock. Individual foliation-defining elements (e.g. micas) are visible with the naked eye. Sometimes used as a general term for any secondary foliation.

screw dislocation – dislocation with a Burgers vector parallel to the dislocation line.

secondary foliation – foliation developed in response to deformation and/or metamorphic processes in a rock in the solid state.

sector zoning – preferential incorporation of passive inclusions in specific zones of a crystal.

SEM – scanning electron microscope.

separatrix – imaginary surface in inhomogeneous flow, separating different flow patterns.

seriate fabric – a fabric showing complete grain size gradation of fine to coarse.

shear band – minor shear zone.

shear band cleavage – structure with shear bands, with a similar aspect as crenulation cleavage. The older foliation is apparently extended and not shortened as in crenulation cleavage. Shear band cleavages are common in mylonites and can be divided into two types; C-type and C′-type (the latter also known as extensional crenulation cleavage).

shear sense indicator – structure with a monoclinic symmetry that can be used to find the sense of shear in a rock.

shear stress – component of stress acting on a plane (a vector), parallel to that plane.

shear zone – planar zone of relatively intense deformation in which progressive deformation is non-coaxial.

sheath fold – strongly non-cylindrical fold in the form of a sheath, usually oriented parallel to a stretching lineation. Sheath folds are common in shear zones and especially in mylonites.

simple shear flow – a type of non-coaxial plane strain flow in which a plane exists (the flow plane) that does not deform. This plane lies at 45° to the shortening and extensional ISA, and contains the intermediate ISA.

slaty cleavage – secondary foliation, either continuous or spaced in fine-grained rocks (slates and phyllites). Spacing up to 50 μm is included in the definition of slaty cleavage.

slickenfibres – fibrous grains along a fault surface, subparallel to the fault and usually parallel to the direction of latest movement along the fault.

slickenside – smoothed or polished fault surface.

slip system – combination of crystallographic plane and direction in which a dislocation can move, defined by the dislocation and its Burgers vector.

softening – decreasing resistance to deformation, expressed as decreasing differential stress at constant strain rate, or increasing strain rate at constant differential stress.

solution transfer – displacement of matter through an aqueous solution in a rock. This process is usually associated with pressure solution and precipitation.

spaced foliation – secondary foliation containing microlithons and cleavage lamellae.

spin – rotational component of flow, more specifically the angular velocity of instantaneous stretching axes in an external reference frame.

spiral S_i-garnet – garnet with a spiral-shaped inclusion pattern (S_i) in thin section. The three-dimensional shape may be more complex.

SR recrystallisation – subgrain rotation recrystallisation.

stacking fault – strip of misfitted crystal lattice between two partial dislocations in a crystal.

stair-stepping – two planes show stair-stepping if they are parallel to each other but offset across a porphyroclast. Stair-stepping is common in recrystallised trails around porphyroclasts and can be used to determine sense of shear.

static recrystallisation – general term for recovery and grain boundary migration processes, driven by remaining dislocations and a large surface of grain boundaries, mainly after deformation. It involves GBAR and minor SR- and GBM recrystallisation and recovery, and leads to removal of undulose extinction, straightening of grain boundaries and grain growth.

steady state fabric – fabric in a deforming rock that does not change essentially with further deformation. Oblique preferred orientation of elongate dynamically recrystallised quartz is an example of a steady state fabric.

strain – tensorial quantity describing change in shape; a strained situation is commonly represented as an ellipsoid, comparing with an unstrained situation represented by a sphere.

Three principal stretches along the axes of the strain ellipsoid define the magnitude of three-dimensional strain. Strain is a more restricted term than deformation, which also includes rotational and translational components.

strain cap – strongly foliated domain adjacent to a rigid object, usually enriched in mica or insoluble minerals. Strain caps generally occur together with strain shadows; the former lie in the shortening direction and the latter in the extension direction around the object.

strain ellipse – representation of strain in a plane. A circle with radius 1 deforms into a strain ellipse.

strain ellipsoid – representation of strain in three dimensions. A sphere with radius 1 deforms into a strain ellipsoid. The symmetry axes of the ellipsoid are the principal strain axes.

strain-free – descriptive term for an optically undeformed-looking crystal lattice, i.e. without undulose extinction and subgrains. A strain free grain may be undeformed, or have lost intracrystalline deformation features by recovery or recrystallisation.

strain fringe – type of strain shadow containing fibrous material precipitated adjacent to a stiff or rigid object. The fringe is usually composed of another mineral than the rigid object (see also strain shadow).

strain hardening – hardening of a rock with increasing strain; see hardening.

strain rate – strain per time unit.

strain shadow – approximately cone-shaped domain adjacent to a porphyroclast or -blast in the direction of the foliation and usually composed of another mineral than the porphyroclast or -blast. It forms by rearrangement of material in response to inhomogeneous deformation of the matrix adjacent to the porphyroclast or -blast. Strain shadows are usually massive or contain equidimensional crystals; if they contain fibres, the term strain fringe is used instead. A mantled porphyroclast differs from a strain shadow in that the mantle has the same mineral composition as the porphyroclast and is inferred to have formed at the expense of the porphyroclast by recrystallisation.

strain softening – softening of a rock with increasing strain; see softening.

stress – tensorial quantity with six independent variables describing the orientation and magnitude of force vectors acting on planes of any orientation at a specific point in a volume of rock.

stretch – change in length of a line: new length, divided by original length.

stretching rate – stretch per time unit.

striation – linear stripes or scratches on a fault plane, formed by movement on the fault.

striped gneiss – gneiss with planar compositional layering interpreted as a mylonite, formed at high metamorphic grade.

structure – geometrically distinct feature in a rock; if penetratively developed, it is known as a fabric element.

stylolite – irregular, commonly jagged surface in a rock formed by local removal of material by pressure solution (from Greek 'στυλος' – pillar).

subgrain – volume of crystalline material surrounded by subgrain boundaries.

subgrain boundary – planar array of dislocations separating two volumes of crystalline material with the same composition but with slightly misoriented crystal lattices (usually less than 5°).

subgrain wall – subgrain boundary.

subhedral crystal – crystal with irregular crystal form but with some well developed crystal faces (see also anhedral, euhedral and hypidiomorphic).

superplastic deformation – deformation in which very high strains are reached without development of elongated grains or a lattice-preferred orientation.

suture – surface separating two parts of a strain fringe with different orientation of fibres.

symplectite – lamellar or vermicular intergrowth of at least two minerals, usually produced by metamorphic replacement.

syntaxial fringe – fringe in which the growth surface lies between the fringe and the matrix (see also crinoid type fringe).

syntaxial vein – vein with fibre growth from the walls towards the median line.

syntaxy – type of epitaxy where the crystal lattices of the overgrown phase and the new phase are parallel.

synthetic – term used for minor faults or shear bands with the same sense of displacement or dip direction as the major structure in which they develop.

Θ-type object – mantled porphyroclast without wings.

tectonic event – period of deformation recognisable over a large area, distinct and separable from earlier and later events. Tectonic events may correspond to one or more deformation phases (cf. Fig. 7.57).

tectonic strain – finite strain of a volume of rock accumulated after diagenesis.

TEM – transmission electron microscope.

tension gash – vein formed by dilatation.

textural sector zoning – pattern of inclusions in a porphyroblast controlled by crystallographic directions.

texture – synonym for microfabric or microstructure in most geological literature. In the non-geological literature on metals and ceramics the term is used for lattice-preferred orientation. Because of this conflicting use, this term has been largely avoided in the text (see Box p. 1).

tiling – structure of imbricate large grains, arranged as tiles on a roof; this structure may occur in igneous rocks with phenocrysts and in mylonites with porphyroclasts, and can be used to determine sense of shear.

tiltwall – type of subgrain boundary that consists of an array of edge dislocations with the same Burgers vector.

total strain – complete finite strain undergone by a volume of rock from its origin as a sediment or igneous rock, including diagenetic strain.

transposition – erasure of older fabric elements by strong deformation and/or metamorphic processes.

truncation plane – surface inside a porphyroblast where an inclusion pattern is interrupted and truncated against an inclusion pattern with another orientation.

twistwall – type of subgrain boundary that consists of two intersecting sets of screw dislocations with different Burgers vectors.

Type I crossed girdle – preferred orientation pattern of crystallographic axes in a stereogram defined by two small circles connected by a central girdle (Fig. 4.40b).

Type I S-C mylonite – other term for C/S fabric as found in granites (Lister and Snoke 1984).

Type II crossed girdle – preferred orientation pattern of crystallographic axes in a stereogram resembling the letter X (Fig. 4.40b).

Type II S-C mylonite – term mainly used for stair stepping wings around mica fish in quartzite mylonite, and interpreted as a type of C/S fabric (Lister and Snoke 1984).

ultramylonite – extremely fine-grained mylonite or mylonite with 90-100%vol matrix and 0-10%vol porphyroclasts.

undulose extinction – irregular extinction of a single crystal under crossed polars due to a distorted crystal lattice with a high concentration of defects. Undulose extinction should not be confused with zoning.

vacancy – point defect in a crystal lattice; a missing lattice element in between regular lattice units.

vermicular – worm-shaped.

vorticity – rotational component of flow, measured as the mean angular velocity of material lines with respect to instantaneous stretching axes.

window structure – type of grain boundary microstructure in which a grain boundary between two grains of a mineral A bulges between two grains of a mineral B (Fig. 3.18). The structure is inferred to form by grain boundary migration.

winged object – 1. bird; 2. plane; 3. mantled porphyroclast in which the mantle has been deformed into wings.

wings – term used for the appendages present on both sides of porphyroclasts trending parallel to the foliation.

W_k – kinematic vorticity number.

X, Y and Z axes – principal strain axes. X is the maximum, Y the intermediate and Z the minimum stretch.

yield stress – differential stress value, above which a material starts to deform permanently. Below the yield stress deformation is elastic. Since stress and elasticity are tensors, the yield stress is not a single number in most materials.

References

Abbassi MR, Mancktelow NS (1992) Single layer buckle folding in non-linear materials I. Experimental study of fold development from an isolated initial perturbation. J Struct Geol 14:85–104

Allen AR (1979) Mechanism of frictional fusion in fault zones. J Struct Geol 1:231–243

Allison I, La Tour TE (1977) Brittle deformation of hornblende in a mylonite: a direct geometrical analogue of ductile deformation by translation gliding. Can J Earth Sci 14:1953–1958

Allison I, Barnett RL, Kerrich R (1979) Superplastic flow and changes in crystal chemistry of feldspars. Tectonophysics 53:41–46

Alvarez W, Engelder T, Lowrie W (1976) Formation of spaced cleavage and folds in brittle limestone by dissolution. Geology 4:698–701

Augustithis SS (1973) Atlas of the textural patterns of granites, gneisses and associated rock types. Elsevier, Amsterdam

Avé Lallemant HG, Carter NL (1970) Syntectonic recrystallization of olivine and modes of flow in the upper mantle. Bull Geol Soc Am 81:2203–2220

Bak J, Korstgard J, Sorensen K (1975) A major shear zone within the Nagssugtoquidian of West Greenland. Tectonophysics 27:191–209

Bard JP (1986) Microtextures of igneous and metamorphic rocks. Reidel, Dordrecht

Barker AJ (1990) Metamorphic textures and microstructures. Blackie, Glasgow

Barker AJ (1994) Interpretation of porphyroblast inclusion trails: limitations imposed by growth kinetics and strain rates. J Metam Geol 12:681–694

Beach A (1975) The geometry of en-echelon vein arrays. Tectonophysics 28:245–263

Beach A (1979) Pressure solution as a metamorphic process in deformed terrigenous sedimentary rocks. Lithos 12:51–58

Behr HJ (1965) Zur Methodik tektonischer Forschung im kristallinen Grundgebirge. Ber Geol Ges DDR Gesamtgeb Geol Wiss 10:163–179

Behrmann JH (1983) Microstructure and fabric transition in calcite tectonites from the Sierra Alhamilla (Spain). Geol Rdsch 72:605–618

Behrmann JH (1987) A precautionary note on shear bands as kinematic indicators. J Struct Geol 9:659–666

Behrmann JH, Mainprice D (1987) Deformation mechanisms in a high-temperature quartz-feldspar mylonite: evidence for super plastic flow in the lower continental crust. Tectonics 140:297–305

Behrmann JH, Platt JP (1982) Sense of nappe emplacement from quartz c-axis fabrics. Earth Plan Sci Lett 59:208–215

Bell IA, Wilson CJL, McLaren AC, Etheridge MA (1986) Kinks in mica: role of dislocations and (001) cleavage. Tectonophysics 127:49–65

Bell TH (1981) Foliation development – the contribution, geometry and significance of progressive bulk inhomogeneous shortening. Tectonophysics 75:273–296

Bell TH (1985) Deformation partitioning and porphyroblast rotation in metamorphic rocks: a radical reinterpretation. J Metam Geol 3:109–118

Bell TH (1986) Foliation development and refraction in metamorphic rocks: reactivation of earlier foliations and decrenulation due to shifting patterns of deformation partitioning. J Metam Geol 4:421–444

Bell TH, Cuff C (1989) Dissolution, solution transfer, diffusion versus fluid flow and volume loss during deformation/metamorphism. J Metam Geol 7:425–447

Bell TH, Etheridge MA (1973) Microstructure of mylonites and their descriptive terminology. Lithos 6:337–348

Bell TH, Etheridge MA (1976) The deformation and recrystallization of quartz in a mylonite zone, Central Australia. Tectonophysics 32:235–267

Bell TH, Hayward N (1991) Episodic metamorphic reactions during orogenesis: the control of deformation partitioning on reaction sites and duration. J Metam Geol 9:619–640

Bell TH, Johnson SE (1989) Porphyroblast inclusion trails: the key to orogenesis. J Metam Geol 3:109–118

Bell TH, Johnson SE (1992) Shear sense: a new approach that resolves conflicts between criteria in metamorphic rocks. J Metam Geol 10:99–124

Bell TH, Rubenach MJ (1980) Crenulation cleavage development – evidence for progressive bulk inhomogeneous shortening from "millipede" microstructures in the Robertson River Metamorphics. Tectonophysics 68:T9–T15

Bell TH, Rubenach MJ (1983) Sequential porphyroblast growth and crenulation cleavage development during progressive deformation. Tectonophysics 92:171–194

Bell TH, Rubenach MJ, Fleming PD (1986) Porphyroblast nucleation, growth and dissolution in regional metamorphic rocks as a function of deformation partitioning during foliation development. J Metam Geol 4:37–67

Bell TH, Johnson SE, Davis B, Forde A, Hayward N, Wilkins C (1992) Porphyroblast inclusion-trail orientation data: eppure non son girate. J Metam Geol 10:295–307

Berlenbach JW, Roering C (1992) Sheath-fold-like structures in pseudotachylytes. J Struct Geol 14:847–856

Berthé D, Choukroune P, Jegouzo P (1979a) Orthogneiss, mylonite and non-coaxial deformation of granites: the example of the South Armorican shear zone. J Struct Geol 1:31–42

Berthé D, Choukroune P, Gapais D (1979b) Orientations préférentielles du quartz et orthogneissification progressive en régime cisaillant: l'exemple du cisaillement sud-armoricain. Bull Minéral 102:265–272

Best MG (1982) Igneous and metamorphic petrology. Freeman, New York

Beutner EC (1978) Slaty cleavage and related strain in Martinsburg slate, Delaware Water Gap, New Jersey. Am J Sci 278:1–23

Beutner EC (1980) Slaty cleavage unrelated to tectonic dewatering: the Siamo and Michigamme slates revisited. Bull Geol Soc Am 91:171–178

Beutner EC, Charles EG (1985) Large volume loss during cleavage formation, Habburg sequence, Pennsylvania. Geology 13:803–805

Beutner EC, Diegel FA (1985) Determination of fold kinematics from syntectonic fibres in pressure shadows, Martinsburg Slate, New Jersey. Am J Sci 285:16–50

Beutner EC, Fisher DM, Kirkpatrick JL (1988) Kinematics of deformation at a thrust fault ramp (?) from syntectonic fibers in pressure shadows. Sep Pap Geol Soc Am 222:77–88

Bhagat SS, Marshak S (1990) Microlithon alteration associated with development of solution cleavage in argillaceous limestone: textural, trace-elemental and stable-isotopic observations. J Struct Geol 12:165–176

Biermann C (1979) Investigations into the development of microstructures in amphibole-bearing rocks from the Seve Köli nappe complex. PhD Thesis, Leiden State Univ

Biermann C (1981) (100) deformation twins in naturally deformed amphiboles. Nature 292:821–823

Biermann C, van Roermund HLM (1983) Defect structures in naturally deformed clinoamphiboles – a TEM study. Tectonophysics 95:267–278

Blacic JD, Christie JM (1984) Plasticity and hydrolytic weakening of quartz single crystals. J Geophys Res 89: 4223–4239

Blenkinsop TG, Drury MR (1988) Stress estimates and fault history from quartz microstructures. J Struct Geol 10:673–684

Blenkinsop TG, Rutter EH (1986) Cataclastic deformation of quartzite in the Moine thrust zone. J Struct Geol 8:669–682

Blenkinsop TG, Treloar P J (1995) Geometry, classification and kinematics of S-C fabrics. J Struct Geol 17:397–408

Blumenfeld P (1983) Le "tuilage des mégacristaux" – un critère d'écoulement rotationnel pour les fluidalités des roches magmatiques – application au granite de Barbey. Bull Soc Geol Fr 25:309–318

Blumenfeld P, Bouchez JL (1988) Shear criteria in granite and migmatite deformed in the magmatic and solid states. J Struct Geol 10:361–372

Blumenfeld PR, Wilson CJL (1991) Boundary migration and kinking in sheared naphthalene. J Struct Geol 13:471–484

Blumenfeld P, Mainprice D, Bouchez JL (1985) Glissement de direction dominant dans le quartz de filons de granite, cisaillés en conditions sub-solidus (Vosges, France). CR Acad Sci, Sér II 301:1303–1308

Boland JN, van Roermund HLM (1983) Mechanisms of exsolution in omphacites from high temperature, type B, eclogites. Phys Chem Miner 9:30–37

Bons PD (1993) Experimental deformation of polyphase rock analogues. Geol Ultraject 110:1–112

Bons PD, Urai JL (1992) Syndeformational grain growth: microstructures and kinetics. J Struct Geol 14: 1101–1109

Bons PD, Jessell MW, Passchier CW (1993) The analysis of progressive deformation in rock analogues. J Struct Geol 15:403–411

Borg IY, Heard HC (1969) Mechanical twinning and slip in experimentally deformed plagioclase. Contrib Mineral Petrol 23:128–135

Borg IY, Heard HC (1970) Experimental deformation of plagioclase. In: Paulitsch P (ed) Experimental and natural rock deformation. Springer, Berlin Heidelberg New York, pp 375–403

Borges FS, White SH (1980) Microstructural and chemical studies of sheared anorthosites, Roneval, South Harris. J Struct Geol 2:273–280

Borradaile GJ, McArthur J (1990) Experimental calcite fabrics in a synthetic weaker aggregate by coaxial and non-coaxial deformation. J Struct Geol 12:351–364

Borradaile GJ, Bayly MB, Powell CMA (1982) Atlas of deformational and metamorphic rock fabrics. Springer, Berlin Heidelberg New York

Bouchez JL (1977) Plastic deformation of quartzites at low temperatures in an area of natural strain gradient. Tectonophysics 39:25–50

Bouchez JL (1978) Preferred orientations of quartz <a> axes in some tectonites: kinematic inferences. Tectonophysics 49:25–30

Bouchez JL, Lister GS, Nicolas A (1983) Fabric asymmetry and shear sense in movement zones. Geol Rdsch 72:401–419

Boullier AM, Bouchez JL (1978) Le quartz en rubant dans les mylonites. Bull Soc Geol Fr 20:253–262

Boullier AM, Gueguen Y (1975) SP-mylonites: origin of some mylonites by superplastic flow. Contrib Mineral Petrol 50:93–104

Brandon MT, Cowan DS, Feehan JG (1994) Fault-zone structures and solution-mass-transfer cleavage in Late Cretaceous nappes, San Juan Islands, Washington. In: Swanson DA, Haugerud RA (eds) Geologic field trips in the Pacific Northwest. Geol Soc Am Ann Mtg Seattle, Washington

Braun G (1994) A statistical geometric method for quantitative texture analysis. In: Bunge H J, Siegesmund S, Skrotzki W, Weber K (eds) Textures of geological materials. DGM Informationsges, Oberursel, pp 29–60

Brokmeier HG (1994) Application of neutron diffraction to measure preferred orientations of geological materials. In: Bunge H J, Siegesmund S, Skrotzki W, Weber K (eds) Textures of geological materials. DGM Informationsges, Oberursel, pp 327–344

Brunel M (1986) Ductile thrusting in the Himalayas: shear sense criteria and stretching lineations. Tectonics 5:247–265

Buatier M, van Roermund HLM, Drury M, Lardeaux JM (1991) Deformation and recrystallization mechanisms in naturally deformed omphacites from the Sesia-Lanzo zone; geophysical consequences. Tectonophysics 195:11–27

Bucher K, Frey M (1994) Petrogenesis of metamorphic rocks. Springer, Berlin Heidelberg New York

Burg JP, Laurent P (1978) Strain analysis of a shear zone in a granodiorite. Tectonophysics 47:15–42

Burg JP, Wilson CJL, Mitchell JC (1986) Dynamic recrystallization and fabric development during the simple shear deformation of ice. J Struct Geol 8:857–870

Burkhard M (1993) Calcite-twins, their geometry, appearance and significance as stress-strain markers and indicators of tectonic regime: a review. J Struct Geol 15:351–368

Burton KV, O'Nions RK (1991) High resolution garnet chronometry and the rates of metamorphic processes. Earth Planet Sci Lett 107:649–671

Busa MD, Gray NH (1992) Rotated staurolite porphyroblasts in the Littleton Schist at Bolton, Connecticut, USA. J Metam Geol 10:627–636

Carmichael DM (1969) On the mechanism of prograde metamorphic reactions in quartz-bearing pelitic rocks. Contrib Mineral Petrol 20:244–267

Carter NL, Avé Lallement HG (1970) High temperature flow of dunite and peridotite. Bull Geol Soc Am 81:2181–2202

Carter NL, Raleigh CB (1969) Principal stress directions from plastic flow in crystals. Bull Geol Soc Am 80: 1213–1264

Carter NL, Tsenn MC (1987) Flow properties of continental lithosphere. Tectonophysics 136:27–63

Casey M (1981) Numerical analysis of x-ray texture data: an implementation in Fortran allowing triclinic or axial specimen symmetry and most crystal symmetries. Tectonophysics 78:51–64

Casey M, Dietrich D, Ramsay JG (1983) Methods for determining deformation history for chocolate tablet boudinage with fibrous crystals. Tectonophysics 92:211–239

Cashman KV, Ferry JM (1988) Crystal size distribution (CSD) in rocks and the kinetics and dynamics of crystallization: III Metamorphic crystallization. Contrib Mineral Petrol 99:401–415

Chatterjee K K (1994) Micro- and meso-scale deformation structures in experimental fault zones. J Struct Geol 16:1463–1476

Chester FM, Logan JM (1987) Composite planar fabric of gouge from the Punchbowl fault, California. J Struct Geol 9:621–634

Chester FM, Friedman M, Logan JM (1985) Foliated cataclasites. Tectonophysics 111:139–146

Choukroune P (1971) Contribution à l'étude des mécanismes de la déformation avec schistosité grace aux cristallisations syncinématiques dans les "zones abritées" ("pressure shadows"). Bull Soc Geol Fr 13:257–271

Choukroune P, Lagarde JL (1977) Plans de schistosité et déformation rotationelle: l'exemple du gneiss de Champtoceaux (Massif Armoricain). CR Acad Sci Paris 284:2331–2334

Choukroune P, Seguret M (1968) Exemple de relations entre joints de cisaillement, fentes de tension, plis et schistosité (autochtone de la nappe de Gavarnie – Pyrenées Centrales). Rev Géogr Phys Géol Dyn 10:239–247

Christensen JN, Rosenfeld JL, De Paulo DJ (1989) Rates of tectonometamorphic processes from rubidium and strontium isotopes in garnet. Science 244:1465–1468

Christie JM (1958) Dynamic interpretation of the fabric of a dolomite from the Moine thrust-zone in north-west Scotland. Am J Sci 256:159–170

Christie JM, Green HW (1964) Several new slip mechanisms in quartz. EOS 45:103

Christie JM, Ord A (1980) Flow stress from microstructures of mylonites: example and current assessment. J Geophys Res 85 (B11):6253–6262

Clark MB, Fisher DM (1995) Strain partitioning and crack-seal growth of chlorite-muscovite aggregates during progressive noncoaxial strain – an example from the slate belt of Taiwan. J Struct Geol 17:461–474

Clark MB, Fisher DM, Chia-Yu L (1993) Kinematic analysis of the Hfuehshan Range: a large-scale pop-up structure. Tectonics 12:205–217

Clarke GL (1990) Pyroxene microlites and contact metamorphism in pseudotachylyte veinlets from MacRobertson Land, East Antarctica. Aust J Earth Sci 37:1–8

Clarke GL, Collins WJ, Vernon RH (1990) Successive overprinting granulite facies metamorphic events in the Anmatjira Ranges, central Australia. J Metam Geol 8:65–88

Cobbold P (1976) Mechanical effects of anisotropy during large finite deformations. Bull Soc Geol Fr 18:1497–1510

Cobbold PR, Quinquis H (1980) Development of sheath folds in shear regimes. J Struct Geol 2:119–126

Cobbold PR, Cosgrove JW, Summers JM (1971) Development of internal structures in deformed anisotropic rocks. Tectonophysics 12:23–53

Coe RS, Kirby SH (1975) The orthoenstatite to clinoenstatite transformation by shearing and reversion by annealing: mechanism and potential applications. Contrib Mineral Petrol 52:29–55

Cosgrove JW (1976) The formation of slaty cleavage. J Geol Soc Lond 262:153–176

Cox FC (1969) Inclusions in garnet: discussion and suggested mechanisms of growth for syntectonic garnets. Geol Mag 106:57–62

Cox SF (1987) Antitaxial crack-seal vein microstructures and their relationship to displacement paths. J Struct Geol 9:779–787

Cox SF, Etheridge MA (1983) Crack-seal fibre growth mechanisms and their significance in the development of oriented layer silicate microstructures. Tectonophysics 92:147–170

Craig J, Fitches WR, Maltman AJ (1982) Chlorite-mica stacks in low-strain rocks from Central Wales. Geol Mag 119:243–256

Crawford ML, Hollister LS (1986) Metamorphic fluids: the evidence from fluid inclusions. Adv Phys Geochem 5:1–35

Cumbest RJ, van Roermund HLM, Drury MR, Simpson C (1989) Burgers vector determination in clinoamphibole by computer simulation. Am Mineral 74:586–592

Daly JS, Cliff RA, Yardley BWD (1989) Evolution of metamorphic belts. Geol Soc Lond Spec Publ 43:566

Darwin C (1846) Geological observations in South America. Smith-Elder

Davis GH (1984) Structural geology of rocks and regions. Wiley, New York

Davis GH, Gardulski AF, Lister GS (1987) Shear zone origin of quartzite mylonite and mylonitic pegmatite in the Coyote Mountains metamorphic core complex, Arizona. J Struct Geol 9:289–297

Dayan H (1981) Deformation studies of the folded mylonites of the Moine Thrust, Eriboll District, Northwest Scotland. PhD Thesis, Univ Leeds

Debat P, Sirieys P, Deramont J, Soula JC (1975) Paléodeformations d'un massif orthogneissique. Tectonophysics 28:159–183

Debat P, Soula JC, Kubin L, Vidal JL (1978) Optical studies of natural deformation microstructures in feldspars (gneiss and pegmatites from Occitania, Southern France. Lithos 11:133–145

De Bresser JHP (1989) Calcite c-axis textures along the Gavarnie thrust zone, central Pyrenees. Geol Mijnb 68:367–376

De Bresser JHP (1991) Intracrystalline deformation of calcite. Geol Ultraject 79:1–191

De Bresser JHP, Spiers CJ (1993) Slip systems in calcite single crystals deformed at 300–800 C. J Geophys Res 98: 6397–6409

De Hoff RT, Rhines FN (1968) Quantitative microscopy. McGraw Hill, New York

De Paor DC (1983) Orthographic analysis of geological structures – 1 Deformation theory. J Struct Geol 5:255–277

Dell'Angelo LN, Tullis J (1989) Fabric development in experimentally sheared quartzites. Tectonophysics 169:1–21

Den Brok B (1992) An experimental investigation into the effect of water on the flow of quartzite. Geol Ultraject 95:1–178

Dennis AJ, Secor DT (1987) A model for the development of crenulations in shear zones with applications from the Southern Appalachian Piedmont. J Struct Geol 9:809–817

Dietrich D, Grant PR (1985) Cathodoluminescence petrography of syntectonic quartz fibres. J Struct Geol 7:541–554

Dietrich D, Song H (1984) Calcite fabrics in a natural shear environment, the Helvetic nappes of western Switzerland. J Struct Geol 6:19–32

Dornbush HJ, Weber K, Skrotzki W (1994) Development of microstructure and texture in high-temperature mylonites from the Ivrea Zone. In: Bunge H J, Siegesmund S, Skrotzki W, Weber K (eds) Textures of geological materials. DGM Informationsges, Obersursel, pp 187–201

Drury MR, Humphreys FJ (1987) Deformation lamellae as indicators of stress level. Abstr Trans Am Geophys Un (EOS) 68:1471

Drury MR, Humphreys FJ (1988) Microstructural shear criteria associated with grain boundary sliding during ductile deformation. J Struct Geol 10:83–90

Drury MR, Urai JL (1990) Deformation-related recrystallisation processes. Tectonophysics 172:235–253

Dunne WM, Hancock PL (1994) Palaeostress analysis of small-scale brittle structures. In: Hancock P (ed) Continental deformation. Pergamon Press, Oxford, pp 101–120

Durney DW (1972) Solution transfer, an important geological deformation mechanism. Nature 235:315–317

Durney DW, Ramsay JG (1973) Incremental strains measured by syntectonic crystal growths. In: De Jong KA, Scholten R (eds) Gravity and tectonics. Wiley, New York, pp 67–96

Eggleton RA, Buseck PR (1980) The orthoclase-microcline inversion: a high-resolution transmission electron microscope study and strain analysis. Contrib Miner Petrol 74:123–133

Eisbacher GH (1970) Deformation mechanics of mylonitic rocks and fractured granites in Cobequid Mountains, Nova Scotia. Can Bull Geol Soc Am 81:2009–2020

Elliott D (1973) Diffusion flow laws in metamorphic rocks. Bull Geol Soc Am 84:2645–2664

Ellis MA (1986) The determination of progressive deformation histories from antitaxial syntectonic crystal fibres. J Struct Geol 8:701–710

Engelder T (1984) The role of pore water circulation during the deformation of foreland fold and thrust belts. J Geophys Res 89:4319–4325

Engelder T, Marshak S (1985) Disjunctive cleavage formed at shallow depths in sedimentary rocks. J Struct Geol 7:327–344

England PC, Richardson SW (1977) The influence of erosion upon the mineral facies of rocks from different metamorphic environments. J Geol Soc Lond 134:201–213

England PC, Thompson AB (1984) Pressure-temperature-time paths of regional metamorphism 1. Heat transfer during the evolution of regions of thickened continental crust. J Petrol 25:894–928

Erskine BG, Heidelbach F, Wenk HR (1993) Lattice preferred orientations and microstructures of deformed Cordilleran marbles: correlation of shear indicators and determination of strain paths. J Struct Geol 15:1189–1206

Erslev EA (1988) Normalized center-to-center strain analysis of packed aggregates. J Struct Geol 10:201–210

Erslev E, Mann C (1984) Pressure solution shortening in the Martinsburg Formation, New Jersey Prov Pennsylvania. Acad Sci 58:84–88

Essene EJ (1989) The current status of thermobarometry in metamorphic rocks. In: Daly JS, Cliff RA, Yardley, BWD (eds) Evolution of metamorphic belts. Geol Soc Spec Publ 43:1–44, Blackwell, Oxford

Etchecopar A (1977) A plane kinematic model of progressive deformation in a ploycrystalline aggregate. Tectonophysics 39:121–139

Etchecopar A, Malavieille J (1987) Computer models of pressure shadows: a method for strain measurement and shear-sense determination. J Struct Geol 9:667–677

Etchecopar A, Vasseur G (1987) A 3-D kinematic model of fabric development in polycrystalline aggregates: comparisons with experimental and natural examples. J Struct Geol 9:705–718

Etheridge MA (1975) Deformation and recrystallization of orthopyroxene from the Giles complex, Central Australia. Tectonophysics 25:87–114

Etheridge MA (1983) Differential stress magnitudes during regional deformation and metamorphism: upper bound imposed by tensile fracturing. Geology 11:231–234

Etheridge MA, Oertel G (1979) Strain measurements from phyllosilicate preferred orientation – a precautionary note. Tectonophysics 60:107–120

Etheridge MA, Wilkie JC (1979) Grainsize reduction, grain boundary sliding and the flow strength of mylonites. Tectonophysics 58:159–178

Etheridge MA, Wilkie JC (1981) An assessment of dynamically recrystallized grainsize as a paleopiezometer in quartz-bearing mylonite zones. Tectonophysics 78:475–508

Etheridge MA, Paterson MS, Hobbs BE (1974) Experimentally produced preferred orientation in synthetic mica aggregates. Contrib Mineral Petrol 44:275–294

Etheridge MA, Wall VJ, Cox SF, Vernon RH (1983) The role of the fluid phase during regional metamorphism and deformation. J Metam Geol 1:205–226

Evans JP (1988) Deformation mechanisms in granitic rocks at shallow crustal levels. J Struct Geol 10:437–444

Evans JP (1990) Textures, deformation mechnisms and the role of fluids in the cataclastic deformation of granite rocks. Spec Publ Geol Soc Lond 54:29–39

Evans MA, Dunne WM (1991) Strain factorization and partitioning in the North Mountain thrust sheet, central Appalachians, USA. J Struct Geol 13:21–36

Farver JR, Yund RA (1991a) Oxygen diffusion in quartz: dependence on temperature and water fugacity. Chem Geol 90:55–70

Farver JR, Yund RA (1991b) Measurement of oxygen grain boundary diffusion in natural, fine-grained quartz aggregates. Geochim Cosmochim Acta 55:1597–1607

Ferguson CC (1980) Displacement of inert mineral grains by growing porphyroblasts: a volume balance constraint. Contrib Mineral Petrol 91:541–544

Ferguson CC (1981) A strain reversal method for estimating extension from fragmented rigid inclusions. Tectonophysics 79:T43–T52

Ferguson CC (1987) Fracture and deformation histories of stretched belemnites and other rigid-brittle inclusions in tectonites. Tectonophysics 139:255–273

Ferguson CC, Lloyd GE (1980) On the mechanical interaction between a growing porphyroblast and its surrounding matrix. Contrib Mineral Petrol 75:339–352

Fernandez A, Feybesse JR, Mezure JF (1883) Theoretical and experimental study of fabric development by different shaped markers in two-dimensional simple shear. Bull Soc Geol Fr 25:319–326

Ferrill DA (1991) Calcite twin widths and intensities as metamorphic indicators in natural low-temperature deformation of limestone. J Struct Geol 13:667–676

Fisher D, Bryne T (1990) The character and distribution of mineralized fractures in the Kodiak Formation, Alaska: implications for fluid flow in an underthrust sequence. J Geophys Res 95 (B6):9069–9080

Fisher DM (1990) Orientation history and rheology in slates, Kodiak and Afognak Islands, Alaska. J Struct Geol 12:483–498

Fisher DM, Anastasio DJ (1994) Kinematic analysis of a large-scale leading edge fold, Lost River Range, Idaho. J Struct Geol 16:337–354

FitzGerald JD, Stünitz H (1993) Deformation of granitoids at low metamorphic grade I: reactions and grain size reduction. Tectonophysics 221:299–324

FitzGerald JD, Etheridge MA, Vernon RH (1983) Dynamic recrystallization in a naturally deformed albite. Text Microstruct 5:219–237

Fleming PD, Offler R (1968) Pre-tectonic metamorphic crystallization in the Mt. Lofty Ranges, South Australia. Geol Mag 105:356–359

Fletscher RC, Pollard DD (1981) Anticrack model for pressure solution surfaces. Geology 9:419–424

Flood RH, Vernon RH (1988) Microstructural evidence of orders of crystallization in granitoid rocks. Lithos 21:237–245

Frejvald M (1970) The problem of platy quartz in rocks of crystalline basement. Acta Univ Carolina 2:95–103

Frondel C (1934) Selective incrustation of crystal forms. Am Mineral 19:316–329

Fry N (1979) Density distribution techniques and strained length methods for determination of finite strains. J Struct Geol 1:221–230

Gamond JF (1983) Displacement features associated with fault zones: a comparison between observed examples and experimental models. J Struct Geol 5:33–45

Gandais M, Willaime C (1984) Mechanical properties of feldspars. In: Brown WL (ed) Feldspars and feldspathoids. NATO Asi, Reidel, Dordrecht Ser C137:207–246

Gapais D (1989) Shear structures within deformed granites: mechanical and thermal indications. Geology 17:1144–1147

Gapais D, Brun JP (1981) A comparison of mineral grain fabrics and finite strain in amphibolites from eastern Finland. Can J Earth Sci 18:995–1003

Gapais D, White SH (1982) Ductile shear bands in a naturally deformed quartzite. Text Microstruct 5:1–17

Garcia Celma A (1982) Domainal and fabric heterogeneities in the Cap de Creus quartz mylonites. J Struct Geol 44:443–456

Garcia Celma A (1983) C-axis and shape-fabrics in quartz-mylonites of Cap de Creus (Spain); their properties and development. PhD Thesis, Utrecht Univ

Gates AE, Glover L (1989) Alleghanian tectono-thermal evolution of the dextral transcurrent hylas zone, Virginia Piedmont, USA. J Struct Geol 11:407–419

Gay NC (1968) Pure shear and simple shear deformation of inhomogeneous viscous fluids 1 Theory. Tectonophysics 5:211–234

Ghosh SK (1987) Measure of non-coaxiality. J Struct Geol 9:111–114

Ghosh SK, Ramberg H (1976) Reorientation of inclusions by combination of pure shear and simple shear. Tectonophysics 34:1–70

Gleason GC, Tullis JH, Heidelbach F (1993) The role of dynamic recrystallization in the development of lattice preferred orientations in experimentally deformed quartz aggregates. J Struct Geol 15:1145–1168

Goldstein AG (1988) Factors affecting the kinematic interpretation of asymmetric boudinage in shear zones. J Struct Geol 10:707–715

Goodwin LB, Wenk HR (1990) Intracrystalline folding and cataclasis in biotite of the Santa Rosa mylonite zone – HVEM and TEM observations. Tectonophysics 172:201–214

Gottstein G, Mecking H (1985) Recrystallization. In: Wenk HR (ed) Preferred orientation in deformed metals and rocks – an introduction to modern texture analysis. Academic Press, New York, pp 183–218

Gower RJW, Simpson C (1992) Phase boundary mobility in naturally deformed, high-grade quartzofeldspathic rocks: evidence for diffusional creep. J Struct Geol 14:301–314

Graham RH (1978) Quantitative deformation studies in the Permian rocks of Alpes-Maritimes. Goguel Symp, BRGM: 220–238

Grant PR, White SH (1978) Cathodoluminescence and microstructure of quartz overgrowths on quartz. Scanning Electron Microsc 1:789–794

Gray DR (1978) Cleavages in deformed psammitic rocks from Southeastern Australia: their nature and origin. Bull Geol Soc Am 89:577–590

Gray DR (1979) Microstructure of crenulation cleavages: an indicator of cleavage origin. Am J Sci 279:97–128

Gray DR (1981) Compound tectonic fabrics in singly folded rocks from SW Virginia, USA. Tectonophysics 78:229–248

Gray NH, Busa MD (1994) The three-dimensional geometry of simulated porphyroblast inclusion trails: inert-marker, viscous-flow models. J Metam Geol 12:575–587

Gray DR, Durney DW (1979a) Crenulation cleavage differentiation: implication of solution-deposition processes. J Struct Geol 1:73–80

Gray DR, Durney DW (1979b) Investigation on the mechanical significance of crenulation cleavage. Tectonophysics 58:35–79

Gray DR, Willman CE (1991) Thrust-related strain gradients and thrusting mechanisms in a chevron-folded sequence, southeastern Australia. J Struct Geol 13:691–710

Green HW, Griggs DT, Christie JM (1970) Syntectonic and annealing recrystallization of fine-grained quartz aggregates. In: Paulitsch P (ed) Experimental and natural rock deformation. Springer, Berlin Heidelberg New York, pp 272–335

Gregg WJ (1985) Microscopic deformation mechanisms associated with mica film formation in cleaved psammitic rocks. J Struct Geol 7:45–56

Gregg WJ (1986) Deformation of chlorite-mica aggregates in cleaved psammitic and pelitic rocks from Islesboro, Maine, USA. J Struct Geol 8:59–68

Griggs DT, Turner FJ, Heard HC (1960) Deformation of rocks at 500°–800°C. In: Griggs DT, Handin J (eds) Rock deformation. Mem Geol Soc Am 79:39–104

Grocott J (1977) The relationship between Precambrian shear belts and modern fault systems. J Geol Soc Lond 133:257–262

Grocott J (1981) Fracture geometry of pseudotachylite generation zones-a study of shear fractures formed during seismic events. J Struct Geol 3:169–179

Groshong RHJ (1988) Low temperature deformation mechanisms and their interpretation. Bull Geol Soc Am 100:1329–1360

Groshong RH, Pfiffner OA, Pringle LR (1984) Strain partitioning in the Helvetic thrust belt of eastern Switzerland from the leading edge to the internal zone. J Struct Geol 6:5–18

Gueguen Y, Boullier AM (1975) Evidence of superplasticity in mantle peridotites. NATO Petrophys Proc, Wiley & Academic Press, New York, pp 19–33

Guillopé M, Poirier JP (1979) Dynamic recrystallization during creep of single-crystalline halite: an experimental study. J Geophys Res 84:5557–5567

Hacker B, Yin A, Christie JM, Snoke AW (1990) Differential stress, strain rate, and temperatures of mylonitization in the Ruby Mountains, Nevada: implications for the rate and duration of uplift. J Geophys Res 95:8569–8580

Hacker B, Yin A, Christie JM, Davis GA (1992) Stress magnitude, strain rate, and rheology of extended middle continental crust inferred from quartz grain sizes in the Whipple Mountains, California. Tectonics 11:36–46

Hall MG, Lloyd GE (1981) The SEM examination of geological samples with a semiconductor back-scattered electron detector. Am Mineral 66:362–368

Handy MR (1989) Deformation regimes and the rheological evolution of fault zones in the lithosphere – the effects of pressure, temperature, grainsize and time. Tectonophysics 163:119–152

Handy MR (1992) Correction and addition to "The solid-state flow of polymineralic rocks". J Geophys Res 97:1897–1899

Hanmer S (1982) Microstructure and geochemistry of plagioclase and microcline in naturally deformed granite. J Struct Geol 4:197–213

Hanmer S (1984a) Strain-insensitive foliations in polymineralic rocks. Can J Earth Sci 21:1410–1414

Hanmer S (1984b) The potential use of planar and elliptical structures as indicators of strain regime and kinematics of tectonic flow. Geol Surv Can Pap 84:133–142

Hanmer S (1988) Great Slave Lake Shear Zone, Canadian Shield: reconstructed vertical profile of a crustal-scale fault zone. Tectonophysics 149:245–264

Hanmer S, Passchier CW (1991) Shear sense indicators: a review. Geol Surv Can Pap 90:1–71

Harley SL (1989) The origins of granulites: a metamorphic perspective. Geol Mag 126:215–247

Harris LB, Cobbold PR (1985) Development of conjugate shear bands during bulk simple shearing. J Struct Geol 7: 37–44

Harvey PK, Ferguson CC (1973) Spherically arranged inclusions in post-tectonic garnet porphyroblasts. Min Mag 39:85–88

Hedlund CA, Anastasio DJ, Fisher DM (1994) Kinematics of fault-related folding in a duplex, Lost River Range, Idaho, USA. J Struct Geol 16:571–584

Heilbronner – see also Panozzo

Heilbronner Panozzo R, Pauli C (1993) Integrated spatial and orientation analysis of quartz c-axes by computer-aided microscopy. J Struct Geol 15:369–382

Heilbronner Panozzo R, Pauli C (1994) Orientation and misorientation imaging: integration of microstructural and textural analysis. In: Bunge H J, Siegesmund S, Skrotzki W, Weber K (eds) Textures of geological materials. DGM Informationsges, Oberursel, pp 147–164

Helmstead H, Anderson OL, Gavasci AT (1972) Petrofabric studies of eclogite, spinel-websterite, and spinel-lherzolite xenoliths from kimberlite-bearing breccia pipes in southeastern Utah and northeastern Arizona. J Geophys Res 77:4350–4365

Henderson JR, Henderson MN, Wright TO (1990) Water-sill hypothesis for the origin of certain quartz veins in the Meguma Group, Nova Scotia, Canada. Geology 18: 654–657

Hippertt J F M (1993) 'V'-pull-apart microstructures: a new shear sense indicator. J Struct Geol 15: 1393–1404

Hirth G, Tullis J (1992) Dislocation creep regimes in quartz aggregates. J Struct Geol 14:145–159

Ho N, Peacor DR, van der Pluijm B A (1995) Reorientation mechanisms of phyllosilicates in the mudstone-to-slate transition at Lehigh Gap, Pennsylvania. J Struct Geol 17: 345–356

Hobbs BE (1985) The geological significance of microfabric. In: Wenk HR (ed) Preferred orientation in deformed metals and rocks. Academic Press, New York

Hobbs BE, Means WD, Williams PF (1976) An outline of structural geology. Wiley, New York

Hobbs BE, Means WD, Williams PF (1982) The relationship between foliation and strain: an experimental investigation. J Struct Geol 4:411–428

Hooper RJ, Hatcher RD (1988) Mylonites from the Towaliga fault zone, central Georgia: products of heterogeneous non-coaxial deformation. Tectonophysics 152:1–17

Houseknecht DW (1986) Intergranular pressure solution in four quartzose sandstones. J Sediment Petrol 58:228–246

Hull D (1975) Introduction to dislocations. Pergamon Press, Oxford

Hunter RH (1987) Textural equilibrium in layered igneous rocks. In: Parsons I (ed) Origins of igneous layering. Reidel, Dordrecht, pp 473–503

Hutton DHW (1982) A tectonic model for the emplacement of the Main Donegal granite, NW Ireland. J Geol Soc Lond 139:615–631

Ildefonse B, Mancktelow NS (1993) Deformation around rigid particles: the influence of slip at the particle/matrix interface. Tectonophysics 221:345–359

Ildefonse B, Lardeux JM, Caron JM (1990) The behaviour of shape-preferred orientations in metamorphic rocks: amphiboles and jadeites from the Monte Mucrone area, Sesia-Lanzo zone, Italian western Alps. J Struct Geol 12:1005–1012

Ishii K (1988) Grain-growth and re-orientation of phyllo-silicate minerals during the development of slaty cleavage in the South Kitakami Mountains, NE Japan. J Struct Geol 10:145–154

Jamieson RA, Vernon RH (1987) Timing of porphyroblast growth in the Fleur de Lys Supergroup, Newfoundland. J Metam Geol 5:273–288

Jamison WR, Spang JH (1976) Use of calcite twin lamellae to infer differential stress. Bull Geol Soc Am 87:868–872

Jeffrey G (1922) The motion of ellipsoidal particles immersed in a viscous fluid. Proc R Soc Lond A102:161–179

Jensen LN, Starkey J (1985) Plagioclase microfabrics in a ductile shear zone from the Jotun Nappe, Norway. J Struct Geol 7:527–541

Jessell MW (1986) Grain boundary migration and fabric development in experimentally deformed octachloropropane. J Struct Geol 8:527–542

Jessell MW (1987) Grain-boundary migration microstructures in a naturally deformed quartzite. J Struct Geol 9:1007–1014

Jessell MW (1988a) Simulation of fabric development in recrystallizing aggregates:1 Description of the model. J Struct Geol 10:771–778

Jessell MW (1988b) Simulation of fabric development in recrystallizing aggregates:2 Example model runs. J Struct Geol 10:779–793

Ji S, Mainprice D (1988) Naturally deformed fabrics of plagioclase: implications for slip systems and seismic anisotropy. Tectonophysics 147:145–163

Ji S, Martignole J (1994) Ductility of garnet as a indicator of extremely high temperature deformation. J Struct Geol 16:985–996

Ji S, Zhao P (1993) Location of tensile fracture within rigid-brittle inclusions in a ductile flowing matrix. Tectonophysics 220:23–31

Ji S, Zhao P (1994) Strength of two-phase rocks: a model based on fiber-loading theory. J Struct Geol 16:253–262

Joanny V, Villeurbanne R, van Roermund H, Lardeux JM (1991) The clinopyroxene/plagioclase symplectite in retrograde eclogites: a potential geothermobarometer. Geol Rdsch 80:303–320

Johnson SE (1993a) Unravelling the spirals: a serial thin-section study and three-dimensional computer-aided reconstruction of spiral-shaped inclusion trails in garnet porphyroblasts. J Metam Geol 11:621–634

Johnson SE (1993b) Testing models for the development of spiral-shaped inclusion trails in garnet porphyroblasts: to rotate or not to rotate, that is the question. J Metam Geol 11:635–659

Johnson TE (1991) Nomenclature and geometric classification of cleavage transected folds. J Struct Geol 13:261–274

Jordan PG (1987) The deformational behaviour of bimineralic limestone-halite aggregates. Tectonophysics 135:185–197

Jordan PG (1988) The rheology of polymineralic rocks – an approach. Geol Rdsch 77:285–294

Joy DC, Newbury DE, Davidson DL (1982) Electron channelling patterns in the scanning electron microscope. J Appl Phys 53:R82–R122

Kamb WB (1959) Theory of preferred orientation developed by crystallisation under stress. J Geol 67:153–170

Kanagawa K (1991) Change in dominant mechanisms for phyllosilicate preferred orientation during cleavage development in the Kitakami Slates of NE Japan. J Struct Geol 13:927–945

Kanaori Y (1986) A SEM cathodoluminescence study of quartz in mildly deformed granite from the region of the Atotsugawa fault, central Japan. Tectonophysics 131:133–146

Kanaori Y, Kawakami S, Yairi K (1991) Microstructure of deformed biotite defining foliation in cataclasite zones in granite, central Japan. J Struct Geol 13:777–786

Kano K, Sato H (1988) Foliated fault gouges: examples from the shear zones of the Sakai-Toge and Narai faults, central Japan. J Geol Soc Jpn 94:453–456

Karato SI (1984) Grain-size distribution and rheology of the upper mantle. Tectonophysics 104:155–176

Karato SI, Paterson MS, FitzGerald JD (1986) Rheology of synthetic olivine aggregates: influence of grain size and water. J Geophys Res 91:8151–8176

Killick AM (1990) Pseudotachylite generated as a result of a drilling "burn-in". Tectonophysics 171:221–227

Kirby SH, McCormick J (1984) Inelastic properties of rocks and minerals: strength and rheology. In: Carmichael RS (ed) CRC Handbook of physical properties of rocks, III. CRC Press, Boca Raton, pp 140–280

Knipe RJ (1979) Chemical changes during slaty cleavage development. Bull Minéral 102:206–210

Knipe RJ (1981) The interaction of deformation and metamorphism in slates. Tectonophysics 78:249–272

Knipe RJ (1989) Deformation mechanisms – recognition from natural tectonites. J Struct Geol 11:127–146

Koch PS (1983) Rheology and microstructures of experimentally deformed quartz aggregates. PhD Thesis, Univ of California, Los Angeles

Koch PS, Christie JM (1981) Spacing of deformation lamellae as a palaeopiezometer. Abstr Trans Am Geophys Un (EOS) 62:1030

Kreutzberger ME, Peacor DR (1988) Behaviour of illite and chlorite during pressure solution of shaly limestone of the Kalkberg Formation, Catskill, New York. J Struct Geol 10:803–812

Kriegsman LM (1993) Geodynamic evolution of the Pan-African lower crust in Sri Lanka. Geol Ultraject 114:208

Krohe A (1990) Local variations in quartz (c)-axis orientations in non-coaxial regimes and their significance for the mechanics of S-C fabrics. J Struct Geol 12:995–1004

Kronenberg AK, Shelton GL (1980) Deformation microstructures in experimentally deformed Maryland diabase. J Struct Geol 2:341–354

Kruhl JH (1987) Preferred orientations of plagioclase from amphibolite and greenstone facies rocks near the Insubric Line, Western Alps. Tectonophysics 135:233–242

Lacassin R, Mattauer M (1985) Kilometre scale sheath fold at Mattmark and implications for transport direction in the Alps. Nature 315:739–742

Lapworth C (1885) The highland controversy in British geology: its causes, course and consequences. Nature 32:558–559

Laurent P (1987) Shear-sense determination on striated faults from e twin lamellae in calcite. J Struct Geol 9:591–596

Laurent P, Bernard P, Vasseur G, Etchecopar A (1981) Stress tensor determination from the study of e twins in calcite: a linear programming method. Tectonophysics 78:651–660

Laurent P, Tourneret C, Laborde O (1990) Determining deviatoric stress tensors from calcite twins: applications to monophase synthetic and natural polycrystals. Tectonophysics 9:379–389

Law RD (1987) Heterogeneous deformation and quartz crystallographic fabric transitions: natural examples from the Moine Thrust zone at the Stack of Glencoul, northern Assynt. J Struct Geol 9:819–834

Law RD (1990) Crystallographic fabrics: a selective review of their applications to research in structural geology. In: Knipe RJ, Rutter EH (eds) Deformation mechanisms, rheology and tectonics. Geol Soc Spec Publ 54:335–352

Law RD, Knipe RJ, Dayan H (1984) Strain path partitioning within thrust sheets: microstructural and petrofabric evidence from the Moine Thrust zone at Loch Eriboll, northwest Scotland. J Struct Geol 6:477–497

Law RD, Casey M, Knipe RJ (1986) Kinematic and tectonic significance of microstructures and crystallographic fabrics within quartz mylonites from the Assynt and Eriboll regions of the Moine thrust zone, NW Scotland. Trans R Soc Edinb Earth Sci 77:99–125

Lawrence RD (1970) Stress analysis based on albite twinning of plagioclase feldspars. Bull Geol Soc Am 81:2507–2512

Lee JH, Peacor DR, Lewis DD, Wintsch RP (1984) Chlorite – illite/muscovite interlayered and interstratified crystals: a TEM / AEM study. Contrib Mineral Petrol 88:372–385

Lee JH, Peacor DR, Lewis DD, Wintsch RP (1986) Evidence for syntectonic crystallization for the mudstone to slate transition at Lehigh Gap, Pennsylvania, USA. J Struct Geol 8:767–780

Li G, Peacor DR, Merriman RJ, Roberts B, van der Pluijm BA (1994) TEM and AEM constraints on the origin and significance of chlorite-mica stacks in slates: an example from Central Wales, U.K. J Struct Geol 16:1339–1357

Lin A (1994) Glassy pseudotachylyte veins from the Fuyun fault zone, northwest China. J Struct Geol 16:71–84

Linker MF, Kirby JH (1981) Anisotropy in the rheology of hydrolytically weakened synthetic quartz crystals. In: Carter RL, Logan JM, Stearns DW (eds) Mechanical behaviour of crustal rocks. Am Geophys Un, Washington DC

Linker MF, Kirby SH, Ord A, Christie JM (1984) Effects of compression direction on the plasticity and rheology of hydrolytically weakened synthetic quartz crystals at atmospheric pressure. J Geophys Res 89:4241–4255

Lister GS (1977) Discussion: crossed-girdle c-axis fabrics in quartzites plastically deformed by plane strain and progressive simple shear. Tectonophysics 39:51–54

Lister GS, Dornsiepen UF (1982) Fabric transitions in the Saxony granulite terrain. J Struct Geol 41:81–92

Lister GS, Hobbs BE (1980) The simulation of fabric development during plastic deformation and its application to quartzite: the influence of deformation history. J Struct Geol 2:355–371

Lister GS, Paterson MS (1979) The simulation of fabric development during plastic deformation and its application to quartzite: fabric transitions. J Struct Geol 1:99–115

Lister GS, Price GP (1978) Fabric development in a quartz-feldspar mylonite. Tectonophysics 49:37–78

Lister GS, Snoke AW (1984) S-C Mylonites. J Struct Geol 6:617–638

Lister GS, Williams PF (1979) Fabric development in shear zones: theoretical controls and observed phenomena. J Struct Geol 1:283–297

Lister GS, Williams PF (1983) The partitioning of deformation in flowing rock masses. Tectonophysics 92:1–33

Lister GS, Paterson MS, Hobbs BE (1978) The simulation of fabric development in plastic deformation and its application to quartzite: the model. Tectonophysics 45:107–158

Lister GS, Boland JN, Zwart HJ (1986) Step-wise growth of biotite porphyroblasts in pelitic schists of the western Lys-Caillaouas massif (Pyrenees). J Struct Geol 8:543 –562

Lloyd GE (1987) Atomic number and crystallographic contrast images with the SEM: a review of backscattered electron techniques. Mineral Mag 51:3–19

Lloyd G (1994) An appreciation of the SEM electron channelling technique for petrofabric and microstructural analysis of geological materials. In: Bunge H J, Siegesmund S, Skrotzki W, Weber K (eds) Textures of geological materials. DGM Informationsges, Oberursel, pp 109–125

Lloyd GE, Ferguson CC (1981) Boudinage structures: some new interpretations based on elastic-plastic finite element simulations. J Struct Geol 3:117–128

Lloyd GE, Freeman B (1991) SEM electron channelling analysis of dynamic recrystallization in a quartz grain. J Struct Geol 13:945–954

Lloyd GE, Freeman B (1994) Dynamic recrystallization of quartz under greenschist facies conditions. J Struct Geol 16:867–881

Lloyd GE, Hall MG (1981) Application of scanning electron microscopy to the study of deformed rocks. Tectonophysics 78:687–698

Lloyd GE, Hall MG, Cockayne B, Jones DW (1981) Selected-area electron-channelling patterns from geological materials: specimen preparation, indexing and representation of patterns and applications. Can Mineral 19:505–518

Lloyd GE, Ferguson CC, Reading K (1982) A stress-transfer model for the development of extension fracture boudinage. J Struct Geol 43:355–372

Logan JM, Friedman M, Higgs NG, Dengo C, Shimamoto T (1979) Experimental studies of simulated gouge and their application to studies of natural fault zones. US Geol Surv Open-file Rep 79-1239:305–343

Maddock RH (1986) Partial melting of lithic porphyroclasts in fault-generated pseudotachylites. Neues Jahrb Miner Abh 155:1–14

Maddock RH, Grocott J, van Nes M (1987) Vesicles, amygdales and similar structures in fault-generated pseudotachylites. Lithos 20:419–432

Mainprice D, Nicolas A (1989) Development of shape and lattice preferred orientations: application to the seismic anisotropy of the lower crust. J Struct Geol 11:175–190

Mainprice D, Bouchez JL, Blumenfeld P, Tubia JM (1986) Dominant c-slip in naturally deformed quartz: implications for dramatic plastic softening at high temperature. Geology 14:819–822

Mainprice D, Lloyd GE, Casey M (1993) Individual orientation measurements in quartz polycrystals: advantages and limitations for texture and petrophysical property determinations. J Struct Geol 15:1169–1188

Malavieille J, Cobb F (1986) Cinématique des déformations ductiles dans trois massifs métamorphiques de l'Ouest des Etats-Unis: Albion (Idaho), Raft River et Grouse Creek (Utah). Bull Soc Geol France 2:885–898

Malavieille J, Etchecopar A, Burg J P (1982) Analyse de la géométrie des zones abritées: simulation et application à des examples naturels. CR Acad Sci Paris 294:279–284

Mancktelow NS (1994) On volume change and mass transport during the development of crenulation cleavage. J Struct Geol 16:1217–1232

Mancktelow NS, Abbassi MR (1992) Single layer buckle folding in non-linear materials II. Comparison between theory and experiment. J Struct Geol 14:105–120

March A (1932) Mathematische Theorie der Regelung nach der Korngestalt bei affiner Deformation. Z Krist 81:285–297

Mares VM, Kronenberg AK (1993) Experimental deformation of muscovite. J Struct Geol 15:1061–1076

Marjoribanks RW (1976) The relation between microfabric and strain in a progressively deformed quartzite sequence from central Australia. Tectonophysics 32:269–293

Marshak S, Mitra G (1988) Basic methods of structural geology. Prentice Hall, Englewood Cliffs, New Jersey

Marshall DJ (1988) Cathodoluminescence of geological materials. Unwin Hyman, Boston

Masuda T, Ando S (1988) Viscous flow around a rigid spherical body: a hydrodynamical approach. Tectonophysics 148:337–346

Masuda T, Fujimura A (1981) Microstructural development of fine-grained quartz aggregates by syntectonic recrystallisation. Tectonophysics 72:105–128

Masuda T, Kuriyama M (1988) Successive "mid-point" fracturing during microboudinage: an estimate of the stress-strain relation during a natural deformation. Tectonophysics 147:171–177

Masuda T, Mochizuki S (1989) Development of snowball structure: numerical simulation of inclusion trails during synkinematic porphyroblast growth in metamorphic rocks. Tectonophysics 170:141–150

Masuda T, Shibutani T, Igarashi T, Kuriyama M (1989) Microboudin structure of piedmontite in quartz schists: a proposal for a new indicator of relative palaeo-differential stress. Tectonophysics 163:169–180

Masuda T, Shibutani T, Kuriyama M, Igarashi T (1990) Development of microboudinage: an estimate of changing differential stress with increasing strain. Tectonophysics 178:379–387

Masuda T, Koike T, Yuko T, Morikawa T (1991) Discontinuous grain growth of quartz in metacherts: the influence of mica on a microstructural transition. J Metam Geol 9:389–402

Masuda T, Michibayashi, Ohta H (1995a) Shape preferred orientation of rigid particles in a viscous matrix; re-evaluation to determine kinematic parameters of ductile deformation. J Struct Geol 17:115–129

Masuda T, Mizuno N, Kobayashi M, Nam T N, Otoh S (1995b) Stress and strain estimates for Newtonian and non-Newtonian material in a rotational shear zone. J Struct Geol 17:451–454

Mawer CK, Williams PF (1991) Progressive folding and foliation development in a sheared coticule-bearing phyllite. J Struct Geol 13:539–557

Maxwell JC (1962) Origin of slaty and fracture cleavage in the Delaware Water Gap area, New Jersey and Pennsylvania. In: Engel AEJ, James HL, Leonard BF (eds) Petrological studies: a volume in honour of A F Buddington. Geol Soc Ame, Boulder, Colorado, pp 281–311

McCaig AM (1987) Deformation and fluid-rock interaction in metasomatic dilatant shear bands. Tectonophysics 135:121–132

McClay KR (1977) Pressure solution and Coble creep in rocks and minerals: a review. J Geol Soc Lond 134:57–70

McLaren AC, Etheridge MA (1976) A transmission electron microscope study of naturally deformed orthopyroxene I Slip mechanisms. Contrib Mineral Petrol 57:163–177

Means WD (1977) Experimental contributions to the study of foliations in rocks: a review of research since 1960. Tectonophysics 39:329–354

Means WD (1979) Stress and strain. Springer, Berlin Heidelberg New York

Means WD (1980) High-temperature simple shearing fabrics: a new experimental approach. J Struct Geol 2:197–202

Means WD (1981) The concept of steady – state foliation. Tectonophysics 78:179–199

Means WD (1982) An unfamiliar Mohr-circle construction for finite strain. Tectonophysics 89:T1–T6

Means WD (1983) Application of the Mohr-circle construction to problems of inhomogeneous deformation. J Struct Geol 5:279–286

Means WD (1989) Synkinematic microscopy of transparent polycrystals. J Struct Geol 11:163–174

Means WD (1994) Rotational quantities in homogeneous flow. J Struct Geol 16:437–445

Means WD, Jessell MW (1986) Accommodation migration of grain boundaries. Tectonophysics 127:67–86

Means WD, Ree JH (1988) Seven types of subgrain boundaries in octachloropropane. J Struct Geol 10:765–770

Means WD, Xia ZG (1981) Deformation of crystalline materials in thin section. Geology 9:538–543

Means WD, Hobbs BE, Lister GS, Williams PF (1980) Vorticity and non-coaxiality in progressive deformations. J Struct Geol 2:371–378

Means WD, Williams PF, Hobbs BE (1984) Incremental deformation and fabric development in a KCl – mica mixture. J Struct Geol 6:391–398

Mercier JCC (1985) Olivine and pyroxenes. In: Wenk HR (ed) Preferred orientation in deformed metals and rocks: an introduction to modern texture analysis. Academic Press, Orlando, pp 407–430

Mercier JC, Anderson DA, Carter NL (1977) Stress in the lithosphere: inferences from steady-state flow of rocks. Pure Appl Geophys 115:119–226

Michibayashi K (1993) Syntectonic development of a strain-independent steady-state grain size during mylonitization. Tectonophysics 222:151–164

Misch P (1969) Paracrystalline microboudinage of zoned grains and other criteria for synkinematic growth of metamorphic minerals. Am J Sci 267:43–63

Misch P (1970) Paracrystalline microboudinage in a metamorphic reaction sequence. Bull Geol Soc Am 81:2483–2486

Misch P (1971) Porphyroblasts and 'crystallisation force': some textural criteria. Bull Geol Soc Am 83:1203–1204

Mitra G (1978) Ductile deformation zones and mylonites: the mechanical processes involved in the deformation of crystalline basement rocks. Am J Sci 278:1057–1084

Mitra G, Yonkee WA (1985) Relationship of spaced cleavage to folds and thrusts in the Idaho-Utah-Wyoming thrust belt. J Struct Geol 7:361–374

Miyake A (1993) Rotation of biotite porphyroblasts in pelitic schist from the Nukata area, central Japan. J Struct Geol 15:1303–1313

Miyashiro A (1973) Metamorphism and metamorphic belts. Allen and Unwin, London

Montardi Y, Mainprice D (1987) A TEM study of the natural plastic deformation of calcic plagioclase (An 68–70). Bull Minéral 110:1–14

Moore AC (1970) Descriptive terminology for the textures of rocks in granulite facies terrains. Lithos 3:123–127

Mügge O (1930) Bewegungen von Porphyroblasten in Phylliten und ihre Messung. Neues Jahrb Mineral, Geol Paläontol 61:469–510

Narahara DK, Wiltschko DV (1986) Deformation in the hinge region of a chevron fold, Valley and Ridge Province, central Pennsylvania. J Struct Geol 8:157–168

Nazé L, Doukhan N, Doukhan JC, Latrons K (1987) A TEM study of lattice defects in naturally and experimentally deformed orthopyroxenes. Bull Minéral 110:497–512

Neurath C, Smith RB (1982) The effect of material properties on growth rates of folding and boudinage: experiments with wax models. J Struct Geol 4:215–229

Newman J (1994) The influence of grain size distribution on methods for estimating paleostress from twinning in carbonates. J Struct Geol 16:1589–1601

Nicolas A, Christensen NI (1987) Formation of anisotropy in upper mantle peridotites: a review. In: Fuchs K, Froidevaux C (eds) Composition, structure and dynamics of the lithosphere – asthenosphere system. Am Geophys Un Geodyn Ser 16:111–123

Nicolas A, Poirier JP (1976) Crystalline plasticity and solid state flow in metamorphic rocks. Wiley, New York

Norrell GT, Teixell A, Harper GD (1989) Microstructure of serpentinite mylonites from the Josephine ophiolite and serpentinitization in retrogressive shear zones, California. Bull Geol Soc Am 101:673–682

O'Brien DK, Wenk HR, Ratschbacher L, You Z (1987) Preferred orientation of phyllosilicates in phyllonites and ultramylonites. J Struct Geol 9:719–730

Oertel G (1970) Deformation of a slaty, lapillar tuff in the Lake district, England. Bull Geol Soc Am 81:1173–1188

Oertel G (1983) Construction of crossed girdles by superposing four subfabrics, each with a single maximum. Geol Rdsch 72:451–467

Oertel G (1985) Phyllosilicate textures in slates. In: Wenk HR (ed) Preferred orientation in deformed metals and rocks: an introduction to modern texture analysis. Academic Press, Orlando, pp 431–440

Olesen NO (1982) Heterogeneous strain of a phyllite as revealed by porphyroblast-matrix relationship. J Struct Geol 4:481–490

Olsen TS, Kohlstedt DL (1985) Natural deformation and recrystallization of some intermediate plagioclase feldspars. Tectonophysics 111:107–131

Olson JE, Pollard DD (1991) The initiation and growth of en échelon veins. J Struct Geol 13:595–608

Onasch CM, Davis TL (1988) Strain determination using cathodoluminescence of calcite overgrowths. J Struct Geol 10:301–304

Ord A, Christie JM (1984) Flow stresses from microstructures in mylonitic quartzites of the Moine thrust zone, Assynt area, Scotland. J Struct Geol 6:639–655

Ozawa K (1989) Stress-induced Al-Cr zoning of spinel in deformed peridotites. Nature 338:141–144

Panozzo R – see also Heilbronner

Panozzo R (1983) Two-dimensional analysis of shape fabric using projections of lines in a plane. Tectonophysics 95:279–294

Panozzo R (1984) Two-dimensional strain from the orientation of lines in a plane. J Struct Geol 6:215–222

Passchier CW (1982a) Mylonitic deformation in the Saint-Barthélemy Massif, French Pyrenees, with emphasis on the genetic relationship between ultramylonite and pseudotachylyte. GUA Pap Geol Ser 1 16:1–173

Passchier CW (1982b) Pseudotachylyte and the development of ultramylonite bands in the Saint-Barthélemy Massif, French Pyrenees. J Struct Geol 4:69–79

Passchier CW (1984) The generation of ductile and brittle shear bands in a low-angle mylonite zone. J Struct Geol 6:273–281

Passchier CW (1986a) Mylonites in the continental crust and their role as seismic reflectors. Geol Mijnb 65:167–176

Passchier CW (1986b) Flow in natural shear zones: the consequences of spinning flow regimes. Earth Plan et Sci Lett 77:70–80

Passchier CW (1987a) Efficient use of the velocity gradients tensor in flow modelling. Tectonophysics 136:159–163

Passchier CW (1987b) Stable positions of rigid objects in non-coaxial flow: a study in vorticity analysis. J Struct Geol 9:679–690

Passchier CW (1988a) Analysis of deformation paths in shear zones. Geol Rdsch 77:309–318

Passchier CW (1988b) The use of Mohr circles to describe non-coaxial progressive deformation. Tectonophysics 149: 323–338

Passchier CW (1990a) Reconstruction of deformation and flow parameters from deformed vein sets. Tectonophysics 180:185–199

Passchier CW (1990b) A Mohr circle construction to plot the stretch history of material lines. J Struct Geol 12:513–515

Passchier CW (1991a) The classification of dilatant flow types. J Struct Geol 13:101–104

Passchier CW (1991b) Geometric constraints on the development of shear bands in rocks. Geol Mijnb 70:203–211

Passchier CW (1994) Mixing in flow perturbations: a model for development of mantled porphyroclasts in mylonites. J Struct Geol 16:733–736

Passchier CW, Simpson C (1986) Porphyroclast systems as kinematic indicators. J Struct Geol 8:831–844

Passchier CW, Sokoutis D (1993) Experimental modelling of mantled porphyroclasts. J Struct Geol 15:895–910

Passchier CW, Speck PJHR (1994) The kinematic interpretation of obliquely-transected porphyroblasts: an example from the Trois Seigneurs Massif, France. J Struct Geol 16:971–984

Passchier CW, Urai JL (1988) Vorticity and strain analysis using Mohr diagrams. J Struct Geol 10:755–763

Passchier CW, Hoek JD, Bekendam RF, de Boorder H (1990a) Ductile reactivation of Proterozoic brittle fault rocks: an example from the Vestfold Hills. East Antarctica Prec Res 47:3–16

Passchier CW, Myers JS, Kröner A (1990b) Field geology of high-grade gneiss terrains. Springer, Berlin Heidelberg New York

Passchier CW, Trouw RAJ, Zwart HJ, Vissers RLM (1992) Porphyroblast rotation: eppur si muove? J Metam Geol 10:283–294

Passchier CW, ten Brink CE, Bons PD, Sokoutis D (1993) Delta-objects as a gauge for stress sensitivity of strain rate in mylonites. Earth Plan et Sci Lett 120:239–245

Passier ML (1991) Simple shear experimenten met het gesteente analoog paraffine was. Rep, Utrecht Univ (unpubl)

Paterson SR, Tobisch OT (1992) Rates of processes in magmatic arcs: implications for the timing and nature of pluton emplacement and wall rock deformation. J Struct Geol 14:291–300

Petit JP (1987) Criteria for the sense of movement on fault surfaces in brittle rocks. J Struct Geol 9:597–608

Pfiffner OA, Burkhard M (1987) Determination of paleo-stress axes orientations from fault, twin and earthquake data. Ann Tecton 1:48–57

Pfiffner OA, Ramsay JG (1982) Constraints on geological strain rates – arguments from finite strain states of naturally deformed rocks. J Geophys Res 87 B1:311–321

Philip H, Etchecopar A (1978) Exemple de variations de direction de cristallisation fibreuse dans un champ de contraintes unique. Bull Soc Géol Fr 20:263–268

Phillipot P, van Roermund HLM (1992) Deformation processes in eclogitic rocks: evidence for the rheological delamination of the oceanic crust in deeper levels of subduction zones. J Struct Geol 14:1059–1078

Phillips ER (1974) Myrmekite – one hundred years later. Lithos 7:181–194

Phillips GN (1980) Water activity changes across an amphibolite-granulite facies transition, Broken Hill, Australia. Contrib Mineral Petrol 75:377–386

Philpotts AR (1964) Origin of pseudotachylytes. Am J Sci 262:1008–1035

Platt JP (1984) Secondary cleavages in ductile shear zones. J Struct Geol 6:439–442

Platt JP, Behrmann JH (1986) Structures and fabrics in a crustal-scale shear zone, Betic Cordillera, SE Spain. J Struct Geol 8:15–33

Platt JP, Vissers RLM (1980) Extensional structures in anisotropic rocks. J Struct Geol 2:397–410

Poirier JP (1980) Shear localization and shear instability in materials in the ductile field. J Struct Geol 2:135–142

Poirier JP (1985) Creep of crystals: high-temperature deformation processes in metals, ceramics and minerals. Cambridge Univ Press, Cambridge

Post RL (1977) High-temperature creep of Mt Burnet dunite. Tectonophysics 42:75–110

Powell CMA (1979) A morphological classification of rock cleavage. Tectonophysics 58:21–34

Powell CMA, Vernon RH (1979) Growth and rotation history of garnet porphyroblasts with inclusion spirals in a Karakoram schist. Tectonophysics 54:25–43

Powell D, Treagus JE (1969) On the geometry of S-shaped inclusion trails in garnet porphyroblasts. Mineral Mag 36:453–456

Powell D, Treagus JE (1970) Rotational fabrics in metamorphic minerals. Mineral Mag 37:801–814

Price GP (1973) The photometric method in microstructural analysis. Am J Sci 273:523–537

Price GP (1980) The analysis of quartz c-axis fabrics by the photometric method. J Geol 88:181–195

Price NJ, Cosgrove JW (1990) Analysis of geological structures. Cambridge Univ Press, Cambridge

Prior DJ (1987) Syntectonic porphyroblast growth in phyllites: textures and processes. J Metam Geol 5:27–39

Pryer LL (1993) Microstructures in feldspars from a major crustal thrust zone: the Grenville Front, Ontario, Canada. J Struct Geol 15:21–36

Putnis A, McConnell JDC (1980) Principles of mineral behaviour. Blackwell, Elsevier, Oxford

Rajlich P (1991) Kinematics of crenulation cleavage development: example from the Upper Devonian rocks from northeast of the Bohemian Massif, Czechoslovakia. Tectonophysics 190:193–208

Raleigh CB (1965) Glide mechanisms in experimentally deformed minerals. Science 150:739–741

Raleigh CB, Talbot JL (1967) Mechanical twinning in naturally and experimentally deformed diopside. Am J Sci 265:151–165

Ramsay JG (1962) The geometry and mechanics of formation of "similar" type folds. J Geol 70:309–327

Ramsay JG (1967) Folding and fracturing of rocks. McGraw Hill, New York

Ramsay JG (1980a) Shear zone geometry: a review. J Struct Geol 2:83–101

Ramsay JG (1980b) The crack-seal mechanism of rock deformation. Nature 284:135–139

Ramsay JG (1981) Tectonics of the Helvetic nappes. In: McClay KR, Price NJ (eds) Thrust and nappe tectonics. Spec Publ Geol Soc Lond 9:293–309

Ramsay JG, Graham RH (1970) Strain variation in shear belts. Can J Earth Sci 7:786–813

Ramsay JG, Huber MI (1983) The techniques of modern structural geology, 1: Strain analysis. Academic Press, London

Ramsay JG, Huber MI (1987) The techniques of modern structural geology, 2: Folds and fractures. Academic Press, London

Ramsay JG, Wood DS (1973) The geometric effects of volume change during deformation processes. Tectonophysics 16:263–277

Ranalli G (1984) Grain size distribution and flow stress in tectonites. J Struct Geol 6:443–448

Ratschbacher L, Wenk HR, Sintubin M (1991) Calcite textures: examples from nappes with strain-path partitioning. J Struct Geol 13:369–384

Ray R (1982) Creep in polycrystalline aggregates by matter transport through a liquid phase. J Geophys Res 87:4731–4739

Ree JH (1990) High temperature deformation of octachloropropane – dynamic grain growth and lattice reorientation. Geol Soc Spec Publ 54:363–368

Ree JH (1991) An experimental steady-state foliation. J Struct Geol 13:1001–1011

Ree JH (1994) Grain boundary sliding and development of grain boundary openings in experimentally deformed octachloropropane. J Struct Geol 16:403–418

Reks IJ, Gray DR (1982) Pencil structure and strain in weakly deformed mudstone and siltstone. J Struct Geol 42:161–176

Reks IJ, Gray DR (1983) Strain patterns and shortening in a folded thrust sheet: an example from the southern Appalachians. Tectonophysics 93:99–128

Reynard B, Gillet P, Willaime C (1989) Deformation mechanisms in naturally deformed glaucophanes: a TEM and HREM study. Eur J Miner 1:611–624

Rice AHN, Mitchell JI (1991) Porphyroblast textural sector-zoning and matrix-displacement. Mineral Mag 55:379–396

Richter DK, Zinkernagel U (1981) Zur Anwendung der Kathodoluminiszenz in der Karbonatpetrographie. Geol Rdsch 70:1276–1302

Rickard MJ (1961) A note on crenulated rocks. Geol Mag 98:324–332

Roberts D, Strömgård KE (1972) A comparison of natural and experimental strain patterns around fold hinge zones. Tectonophysics 14:105–120

Robin PY (1979) Theory of metamorphic segregation and related processes. Geochim Cosmochim Acta 43:1587–1600

Roedder E (1984) Fluid inclusions. Rev Mineral Mineral Soc Am 12:108

Rosenfeld JL (1968) Garnet rotations due to major Paleozoic deformations in Southeast Vermont. In: Zen EA (ed) Studies of Appalachian Geology. Wiley, New York, pp 185–202

Rosenfeld JL (1970) Rotated garnets in metamorphic rocks. Geol Soc Am Spec Pap 129:102

Rosenfeld JL (1985) Schistosity. In: Wenk HR (ed) Preferred orientation in deformed metals and rocks: an introduction to modern texture analysis. Academic Press, Orlando, pp 441–461

Ross JV, Avé Lallement HG, Carter NL (1980) Stress-dependence of recrystallized-grain and subgrain size in olivine. Tectonophysics 70:39–61

Rousell DH (1981) Fabric and origin of gneissic layers in anorthositic rocks of the St Charles sill, Ontario. Can J Earth Sci 18:1681–1693

Rowe KJ, Rutter EH (1990) Paleostress estimation using calcite twinning: experimental calibration and application to nature. J Struct Geol 12:1–18

Roy AB (1978) Evolution of slaty cleavage in relation to diagenesis and metamorphism: a study from the Hunsrückschiefer. Bull Geol Soc Am 89:1775–1785

Rutter EH (1976) The kinetics of rock deformation by pressure solution. Phil Trans R Soc Lond A283:203–219

Rutter EH (1983) Pressure solution in nature, theory and experiment. J Geol Soc Lond 140:725–740

Rutter EH, Maddock RH, Hall SW, White SH (1986) Comparative microstructures of natural and experimentally produced clay-bearing fault gouges. Pure Appl Geophys 124:3–30

Rutter EH, Casey M, Burlini L (1994) Preferred crystallographic orientation development during the plastic and superplastic flow of calcite rocks. J Struct Geol 16:1431–1447

Saltzer SD, Hodges KV (1988) The Middle Mountain shear zone, southern Idaho: kinematic analysis of an early Tertiary high-temperature detachment. Bull Geol Soc Am 100:96–103

Sample JC, Fisher DM (1986) Duplex accretion and underplating in an ancient accretionary complex, Kodiak Islands, Alaska. Geology 14:160–163

Sander B (1950) Einführung in die Gefügekunde der geologischen Körper, Band II: Die Korngefüge. Springer, Wien Berlin Heidelberg

Schmid SM (1982) Microfabric studies as indicators of deformation mechanisms and flow laws operative in mountain building. In: Hsu KJ (ed) Mountain building processes. Academic Press, London, pp 95–110

Schmid SM (1994) Textures of geological materials: computer model predictions versus empirical interpretations based on rock deformation experiments and field studies. In: Bunge H J, Siegesmund S, Skrotzki W, Weber K (eds) Textures of geological materials. DGM Informationsges, Oberursel, pp 279–301

Schmid SM, Casey M (1986) Complete fabric analysis of some commonly observed quartz C-axis patterns. Geophys Monogr 36:263–286

Schmid SM, Boland JN, Paterson MS (1977) Superplastic flow in fine grained limestone. Tectonophysics 43:257–291

Schmid SM, Paterson MS, Boland JN (1980) High temperature flow and dynamic recrystallization in Carrara Marble. Tectonophysics 65:245–280

Schmid SM, Casey M, Starkey J (1981) The microfabric of calcite tectonites from the Helvetic nappes (Swiss Alps). In: McClay KR, Price NJ (eds) Thrust and nappe tectonics. Spec Publ Geol Soc Lond 9:151–158

Schmid SM, Zingg A, Handy M (1987) The kinematics of movements along the Insubric Line and the emplacement of the Ivrea Zone. Tectonophysics 135:47–66

Scholz CH (1988) The brittle-plastic transition and the depth of seismic faulting. Geol Rdsch 77:319–328

Schoneveld C (1977) A study of some typical inclusion patterns in strongly paracrystalline rotated garnets. Tectonophysics 39:453–471

Schoneveld C (1979) The geometry and the significance of inclusion patterns in syntectonic porphyroblasts. PhD Thesis, Leiden State Univ

Schweitzer J, Simpson C (1986) Cleavage development in dolomite of the Elbrook formation, southwest Virginia. Bull Geol Soc Am 97:778–786

Sedgwick A (1835) Remarks on the structure of large mineral masses, and especially on the chemical changes produced in the aggregation of stratified rocks during different periods after their deposition. Trans Geol Soc Lond 2nd Ser 3:416–486

Seifert KE (1964) The genesis of plagioclase twinning in the Nonewang granite. Am Mineral 49:297–320

Sellars CM (1978) Recrystallization of metals during hot deformation. Phil Trans R Soc Lond A288:147–158

Shaosheng J, Mainprice D (1988) Natural deformation fabrics of plagioclase: implications for slip systems and seismic anisotropy. Tectonophysics 147:145–163

Shelley D (1979) Plagioclase preferred orientation, Foreshore Group metasediments, Bluff, New Zealand. Tectonophysics 58:279–290

Shelley D (1989) Plagioclase and quartz preferred orientations in a low-grade schist: the roles of primary growth and plastic deformation. J Struct Geol 11:1029–1038

Shelley D (1992) Calcite twinning and determination of paleostress orientations: three methods compared. Tectonophysics 206:193–201

Shelley D (1993) Igneous and metamorphic rocks under the microscope. Chapman and Hall, London

Shelley D (1994) Spider texture and amphibolite preferred orientations. J Struct Geol 16:709–717

Shewmon PG (1969) Transformations in metals. McGraw-Hill, New York

Shimamoto T, Kanaori Y, Asai K (1991) Cathodoluminiscence observations on low-temperature mylonites: potential for detection of solution-precipitation microstructures. J Struct Geol 13:967–973

Sibson RH (1975) Generation of pseudotachylyte by ancient seismic faulting. Geophys J R Astr Soc 43:775–794

Sibson RH (1977a) Kinetic shear resistance, fluid pressures and radiation efficiency during seismic faulting. Pure Appl Geophys 115:387–399

Sibson RH (1977b) Fault rocks and fault mechanisms. J Geol Soc Lond 133:191–213

Sibson RH (1980) Transient discontinuities in ductile shear zones. J Struct Geol 2:165–171

Sibson RH (1983) Continental fault structure and the shallow earthquake source. J Geol Soc Lond 140:741–769

Siddans AWB (1972) Slaty cleavage – a review of research since 1815. Earth Sci Rev 8:205–232

Siddans AWB (1977) The development of slaty cleavage in part of the French Alps. Tectonophysics 39:533–557

Siegesmund S, Helming K, Kruse R (1994) Complete texture analysis of a deformed amphibolite: comparison between neutron diffraction and U-stage data. J Struct Geol 16:131–142

Simpson C (1985) Deformation of granitic rocks across the brittle-ductile transition. J Struct Geol 7:503–511

Simpson C, Schmid SM (1983) An evaluation of criteria to determine the sense of movement in sheared rocks. Bull Geol Soc Am 94:1281–1288

Simpson C, Wintsch RP (1989) Evidence for deformation-induced K-feldspar replacement by myrmekite. J Metam Geol 7:261–275

Skrotzki W (1992) Defect structure and deformation mechanisms in naturally deformed hornblende. Phys Stat Sol 131:605–624

Skrotzki W (1994) Mechanisms of texture development in rocks. In: Bunge H J, Siegesmund S, Skrotzki W, Weber K (eds) Textures of geological materials. DGM Informationsges, Oberursel, pp 167–186

Slack JF, Palmer MR, Stevens BPJ, Barnes RG (1993) Origin and significance of tourmaline rich rocks in the Broken Hill district, Australia. Econ Geol 88:505–541

Smith CS, Guttman L (1953) Measurement of internal boundaries in three-dimensional structures by random sectioning. Trans Am Inst Min Engng J Metals 197:81–87

Smith JV (1974) Feldspar minerals, 2 vols. Springer, Berlin Heidelberg New York

Smith JV, Brown WL (1988) Feldspar minerals, vol 1. Springer, Berlin Heidelberg New York

Solomon SF (1989) The early diagenetic origin of lower Carboniferous mottled limestones (pseudobreccias). Sedimentology 36:399–418

Sorby HC (1853) On the origin of slaty cleavage. Edinb New Philos J 55:137–148

Sosman RB (1927) The properties of silica. Am Chem Soc Monogr Ser, Chemical Catalog Company, New York

Southwick DL (1987) Bundled slaty cleavage in laminated argillite, North-Central Minnesota. J Struct Geol 9:985–993

Spear FS, Selverstone J (1983) Quantitative P-T paths from zoned minerals: theory and tectonic applications. Contrib Mineral Petrol 83:348–357

Spear FS, Kohn MJ, Florence FP (1990) A model for garnet and plagioclase growth in pelitic schists: implications for thermobarometry and P-T path determinations. J Metam Geol 8:683–696

Spiers CJ, Schutjens PMTM, Brzesowsky RH, Peach CJ, Liezenberg JL, Zwart HJ (1990) Experimental determination of constitutive parameters governing creep of rocksalt by pressure solution. Geol Soc Spec Publ 54:215–227

Spray JG (1987) Artificial generation of pseudotachylite using friction welding apparatus: simulation of melting on a fault plane. J Struct Geol 9:49–60

Spray JG (1992) A physical basis for the frictional melting of some rock-forming minerals. Tectonophysics 204:205–221

Spry A (1969) Metamorphic textures. Pergamon Press, Oxford

Stel H (1981) Crystal growth in cataclasites: diagnostic microstructures and implications. Tectonophysics 78:585–600

Stesky RM (1978) Mechanisms of high temperature frictional sliding in Westerly granite. Can J Earth Sci 15:361–375

Stesky RM, Brace WF, Riley DK, Robin PYF (1974) Friction in faulted rock at high temperature and pressure. Tectonophysics 23:177–203

Stoffel G (1976) Het vervaardigen van slijpplaatjes van ongeconsolideerde sedimenten. Museologia 6:12–16

Strating EHH, Vissers RLM (1994) Structures in natural serpentinite gouges. J Struct Geol 16:1205–1215

Strehlau J (1986) A discussion of the depth extent of rupture in large continental earthquakes. Earthquake Source Mechanics. Geophys Monogr 37:131–146

Stünitz H, FitzGerald JD (1993) Deformation of granitoids at low metamorphic grade II: granular flow in albite-rich mylonites. Tectonophysics 221:269–297

Suhr G (1993) Evaluation of upper mantle microstructures in the Table Mountain massif (Bay of Islands ophiolite). J Struct Geol 15:1273–1292

Takeshita T, Tomé C, Wenk HR, Kocks UF (1987) Single-crystal yield surface for trigonal lattices: application to texture transitions in calcite polycrystals. J Geophys Res 92:12917–12930

Talbot CJ (1970) The minimum strain ellipsoid using deformed quartz veins. Tectonophysics 9:47–76

Talbot GL (1965) Crenulation cleavage in the Hunsrückschiefer of the Middle Moselle region. Geol Rdsch 54:1026–1043

Tanaka H (1992) Cataclastic lineations. J Struct Geol 14: 1239–1252

Tapp B, Wickham J (1987) Relationships of rock cleavage fabrics to incremental and acccumulated strain in the Conococheague Formation, USA. J Struct Geol 9:457–472

Ten Brink CE, Passchier CW (1995) Modelling of mantled porphyroclasts using rock analogue materials. J Struct Geol 17:131–146

Ten Have T, Heynen WMM (1985) Cathodoluminiscence activation and zonation in carbonate rocks: an experimental approach. Geol Mijnb 64:297–310

Thompson AB, England PC (1984) Pressure-temperature-time paths of regional metamorphism, II. Their inference and interpretation using mineral assemblages in metamorphic rocks. J Petrol 25:928–955

Treagus SH (1983) A theory of finite strain variation through contrasting layers and its bearing on cleavage refraction. J Struct Geol 5:351–368

Treagus SH (1985) The relationship between foliation and strain: an experimental investigation: discussion. J Struct Geol 7:119–122

Trepied L, Doukhan JC, Paquet J (1980) Subgrain boundaries in quartz: theoretical analysis and microscopic observations. Phys Chem Miner 5:201–218

Trouw RAJ (1973) Structural geology of the Marsfjällen area, Caledonides of Västerbotten, Sweden. Sver Geol Unders Ser C 689:1–115

Tucillo M E, Essene E J, van der Pluijm B A (1990) Growth and retrograde zoning in garnets from high grade metapelites: implications for pressure-temperature paths. Geology 18:839–842

Tullis J (1977) Preferred orientation of quartz produced by slip during plane strain. Tectonophysics 39:87–102

Tullis J (1983) Deformation of feldspars. In: Ribbe PH (ed) Feldspar mineralogy. Mineral Soc Am Rev Mineral 2:297–323

Tullis J, Yund RA (1977) Experimental deformation of dry Westerly Granite. J Geophys Res 82:5705–5718

Tullis J, Yund RA (1980) Hydrolitic weakening of experimentally deformed Westerly granite and Hale albite rock. J Struct Geol 2:439–451

Tullis J, Yund RA (1985) Dynamic recrystallisation of feldspar: a mechanism for ductile shear zone formation. Geology 13:238–241

Tullis J, Yund RA (1987) Transition from cataclastic flow to dislocation creep of feldspar: mechanisms and microstructures. Geology 15:606–609

Tullis J, Yund RA (1991) Diffusion creep in feldspar aggregates: experimental evidence. J Struct Geol 13:987–1000

Tullis J, Christie JM, Griggs DT (1973) Microstructures and preferred orientations of experimentally deformed quartzites. Bull Geol Soc Am 84:297–314

Tullis J, Dell'Angelo L, Yund RA (1990) Ductile shear zones from brittle precursors in feldspathic rocks: the role of dynamic recrystallization. In: Hobbs BE, Heard HC (eds) Mineral and rock deformation: laboratory studies. AGU, Geophys Monogr 56:67–81

Tullis JT, Snoke AW, Todd VR (1982) Significance of petrogenesis of mylonitic rocks. Geology 10:227–230

Tullis TE (1976) Experiments on the origin of slaty cleavage and schistosity. Bull Geol Soc Am 87:745–753

Tullis TE, Wood DS (1975) Correlation of finite strain from both reduction bodies and preferred orientation of mica in slate from Wales. Bull Geol Soc Am 86:632–638

Tungatt PD, Humphreys FJ (1981a) An in situ optical investigation of the deformation behaviour of sodium nitrate – an analogue of calcite. Tectonophysics 78:661–676

Tungatt PD, Humphreys FJ (1981b) Transparent analogue materials as an aid to understanding high-temperature polycrystalline plasticity. In: Horsewell A, Leffers T, Lilholt H (eds) Deformation of polycrystals: mechanisms and microstructures. Riso Nat Lab, Roskilde, pp 393–398

Turner FJ (1953) Nature and dynamic interpretation of deformation lamellae in calcite of three marbles. Am J Sci 251:276–298

Turner FJ (1968) Metamorphic petrology, mineralogical and field aspects. McGraw Hill, New York, 403 pp

Turner FJ, Weiss LE (1963) Structural analysis of metamorphic tectonites. McGraw Hill, New York

Turner FJ, Griggs DT, Heard HC (1954) Experimental deformation of calcite crystals. Bull Geol Soc Am 65:883–934

Twiss RJ (1986) Variable sensitivity piezometric equations for dislocation density and subgrain diameter and their relevance to olivine and quartz. In: Heard HC, Hobbs BE (eds) Mineral and rock deformation: laboratory studies, the Paterson volume. Geophys Monogr 36:247–261, Am Geophys Union, Washington DC

Twiss RJ, Moores EM (1992) Structural geology. Freeman, New York

Ullemeyer K, Helming K, Siegesmund S (1994) Quantitative texture analysis of plagioclase. In: Bunge HJ, Siegesmund S, Skrotzki W, Weber K (eds) Textures of geological materials. DGM Informationsges, Oberursel, pp 83–92

Urai J, Means WD, Lister GS (1986) Dynamic recrystallization of minerals. In: Heard HC, Hobbs BE (eds) Mineral and rock deformation: laboratory studies, the Paterson volume. Geophys Monogr 36:161–200, Am Geophys Union, Washington DC

Urai JL (1983) Water assisted dynamic recrystallization and weakening in polycrystalline bischofite. Tectonophysics 96:125–157

Urai JL, Humphreys FJ (1981) The development of shear zones in polycrystalline camphor. Tectonophysics 78:677–685

Urai JL, Humphreys FJ, Burrows SE (1980) In-situ studies of the deformation and dynamic recrystallization of rhombohedral camphor. J Materials Sci 15:1231–1240

Urai JL, Williams PF, van Roermund HLM (1991) Kinematics of crystal growth in syntectonic fibrous veins. J Struct Geol 13:823–836

Van den Driessche J, Brun JP (1987) Rolling structures at large shear strain. J Struct Geol 9:691–704

Van der Pluijm BA (1984) An unusual 'crack-seal' vein geometry. J Struct Geol 6:593–597

Van der Pluijm BA (1991) Marble mylonites in the Bancroft shear zone, Ontario, Canada: microstructures and deformation mechanisms. J Struct Geol 13:1125–1136

Van der Pluijm BA, Kaars-Sijpesteijn CH (1984) Chlorite-mica aggregates: morphology, orientation, development and bearing on cleavage formation in very-low-grade rocks. J Struct Geol 6:399–408

Van der Pluijm BA, Ho NC, Peacor DR (1994) High-resolution X-ray texture goniometry. J Struct Geol 16:1029–1032

Van der Wal D, Vissers RMD, Drury M R (1992) Oblique fabrics in porphyroclastic Alpine peridotites: a shear sense indicator for upper mantle flow. J Struct Geol 14:839–846

Van Roermund HLN (1983) Petrofabrics and microstructures of omphacites in a high temperature eclogite from the Swedish Caledonides. Bull Minéral 106:709–713

Van Roermund HLM (1992) Thermal and deformation induced omphacite microstructures from eclogites; implications for the formation and uplift of HP metamorphic terrains. Trends Miner 1:117–151

Van Roermund HLM, Boland JN (1981) The dislocation substructures of naturally deformed omphacites. Tectonophysics 78:403–418

Van Roermund HLM, Boland JN (1983) Retrograde P-T trajectories of high-temperature eclogites deduced from omphacite exsolution microstructures. Bull Minéral 106:723–726

Vernon RH (1965) Plagioclase twins in some mafic gneisses from Broken Hill, Australia. Miner Mag 35:488–507

Vernon RH (1975) Deformation and recrystallizaton of a plagioclase grain. Am Mineral 60:884–888

Vernon RH (1976) Metamorphic processes. Allen and Unwin, London

Vernon RH (1981) Optical microstructure of partly recrystallized calcite in some naturally deformed marbles. Tectonophysics 78:601–612

Vernon RH (1988) Microstructural evidence of rotation and non-rotation of mica porphyroblasts. J Metam Geol 6:595–601

Vernon RH (1989) Porphyroblast-matrix microstructural relationships – recent approaches and problems. In: Daly JS, Cliff RA, Yardley BWD (eds) Evolution of metamorphic belts. Geol Soc London, Spec Publ 43:83–102

Vernon RH, Flood RH (1987) Contrasting deformation and metamorphism of S and I type granitoids in the Lachlan Fold Belt, Eastern Australia. Tectonophysics 147:127–143

Vernon RH, Williams VA, D'Arcy WF (1983) Grain-size reduction and foliation development in a deformed granitoid batholith. Tectonophysics 92:123–145

Vernon RH, Collins WJ, Paterson SR (1993a) Pre-foliation metamorphism in low-pressure/high-temperature terrains. Tectonophysics 219:241–256

Vernon RH, Paterson SR, Foster D (1993b) Growth and deformation of porphyroblasts in the Foothills terrane, central Sierra Nevada, California: negotiating a microstructural minefield. J Metam Geol II, 203–222

Vidal JL, Kubin L, Debat P, Soula JL (1980) Deformation and dynamic recrystallisation of K-feldspar augen in orthogneiss from Montagne Noir, Occitana. Lithos 13:247–257

Visser P, Mancktelow NS (1992) The rotation of garnet porphyroblasts around a single fold, Lukmanier Pass, Central Alps. J Struct Geol 14:1193–1202

Vissers RLM (1989) Asymmetric quartz c-axis fabrics and flow vorticity: a study using rotated garnets. J Struct Geol 11:231–244

Wagner F, Wenk HR, Kern V, van Houtte P, Esling C (1982) Development of preferred orientaion in plane strain deformed limestone, experiment and theory. Contrib Mineral Petrol 80:132–139

Waldron HM, Sandiford M (1988) Deformation volume and cleavage development in metasedimentary rocks from the Ballarat slate belt. J Struct Geol 10:53–62

Wallis SR (1992a) Vorticity analysis in a metachert from the Sanbagawa belt , SW Japan. J Struct Geol 14:271–280

Wallis SR (1992b) Do smoothly curved, spiral-shaped inclusion trails signify porphyroblast rotation? Geology 20:1054–1056

Weber K (1976) Gefügeuntersuchungen an transversalgeschieferten Gesteinen aus dem östlichen Rheinischen Schiefergebirge Geol Jahrb Reihe D 15:1–99

Weber K (1981) Kinematic and metamorphic aspects of cleavage formation in very low grade metamorphic slates. Tectonophysics 78:291–306

Wenk HR (1985) Carbonates. In: Wenk HR (ed) Preferred orientation in deformed metals and rocks: an introduction to modern texture analysis. Academic Press, Orlando, pp 11–47

Wenk HR, Takeshita T, van Houtte P, Wagner F (1986a) Plastic anisotropy and texture development in calcite polycrystals. J Geophys Res 91:3861–3869

Wenk HR, Bunge HJ, Jansen E, Pannetier J (1986b) Preferred orientation of plagioclase-neutron diffraction and U-stage data. Tectonophysics 126:271–284

Wenk HR, Takeshita T, Bechler E, Erskine BG, Matthies S (1987) Pure shear and simple shear calcite textures. Comparison of experimental, theoretical and natural data. J Struct Geol 9:731–746

Wheeler J (1987a) The significance of grain-scale stresses in the kinetics of metamorphism. Contrib Miner Petrol 17:397–404

Wheeler J (1987b) The determination of true shear senses from the deflection of passive markers in shear zones. J Geol Soc Lond 144:73–77

White JC, Barnett RL (1990) Microstructural signatures and glide twins in microcline, Hemlo, Ontario. Can Miner 28:757–769

White JC, Mawer CK (1988) Dynamic recrystallisation and associated exsolution in perthites: evidence of deep crystal thrusting. J Geophys Res 93:325–337

White SH (1976) The role of dislocation processes during tectonic deformation with special reference to quartz. In: Strens RJ (ed) The physics and chemistry of minerals and rocks. Wiley, London, pp 75–91

White SH (1979a) Grain and sub-grain size variations across a mylonite zone. Contrib Mineral Petrol 70:193–202

White SH (1979b) Large strain deformation: report on a tectonic studies group discussion meeting held at Imperial College, London; introduction. J Struct Geol 4:333–339

White SH, Johnston DC (1981) A microstructural and microchemical study of cleavage lamellae in a slate. J Struct Geol 3:279–290

White SH, Knipe RJ (1978) Microstructure and cleavage development in selected slates. Contrib Mineral Petrol 66:165–174

White SH, Burrows SE, Carreras J, Shaw ND, Humphreys FJ (1980) On mylonites in ductile shear zones. J Struct Geol 2:175–187

Wickham J, Anthony M (1977) Strain paths and folding of carbonate rocks near Blue Ridge, central Appalachians. Bull Geol Soc Am 88:920–924

Wickham JS (1973) An estimate of strain increments in a naturally deformed carbonate rock. Am J Sci 273:23–47

Wilcox RE, Harding TP, Seely DR (1973) Basic wrench tectonics. Am Assoc Petrol Geol Bull 57:74–96

Williams H, Turner FJ, Gilbert CM (1954) Petrography – an introduction to the study of rocks in thin sections, 1st edn. Freeman, IMC, San Francisco

Williams H, Turner FJ, Gilbert CM (1982) Petrography – an introduction to the study of rocks in thin sections, 2nd edn. Freeman, IMC, San Francisco

Williams ML, Burr JL (1994) Preservation and evolution of quartz phenocrysts in deformed rhyolites from the Proterozoic of southwestern North America. J Struct Geol 16:203–222

Williams PF (1972a) Development of metamorphic layering and cleavage in low grade metamorphic rocks at Bermagui, Australia. Am J Sci 272:1–47

Williams PF (1972b) 'Pressure shadow' structures in foliated rocks from Bermagui, New South Wales. J Geol Soc Aust 18:371–377

Williams PF (1985) Multiply deformed terrains – problems of correlation. J Struct Geol 7:269–280

Williams PF, Urai JL (1989) Curved vein fibres – an alternative explanation. Tectonophysics 158:311–333

Willis DG (1977) A kinematic model of preferred orientation. Bull Geol Soc Am 88:883–894

Wilson CJL (1975) Preferred orientation in quartz ribbon mylonites. Bull Geol Soc Am 86:968–974

Wilson CJL (1980) Shear zones in a pegmatite: a study of albite-mica-quartz deformation. J Struct Geol 2:203–209

Wilson CJL (1982) Texture and grain growth during the annealing of ice. Text Microstruct 5:19–31

Wilson CJL (1984) Shear bands, crenulations and differentiated layering in ice-mica models. J Struct Geol 6:303–320

Wilson CJL (1994) Crystal growth during a single-stage opening event and its implications for syntectonic veins. J Struct Geol 16:1283–1296

Wilson CJL, Burg JP, Mitchell JC (1986) The origin of kinks in polycrystalline ice. Tectonophysics 127:27–48

Wilson CJR, Zhang Y (1994) Comparison between experiment and computer modelling of plane-strain simple-shear ice deformation. J Glaciol 40:48–55

Wilson RW (1971) On syntectonic porphyroblast growth. Tectonophysics 11:239–260

Wintsch RP (1986) The possible effects of deformation on chemical processes in metamorphic fault zones. In: Thompson AB, Rubie DC (eds) Metamorphic reactions, kinetics textures and deformation. Springer, Berlin Heidelberg New York, pp 251–268

Wintsch RP, Kvale CM, Kisch HD (1991) Open system constant volume development of slaty cleavage, and strain induced replacement reactions in the Martinsburg Formation, Lehigh Gap, Pennsylvania. Bull Geol Soc Am 103:916–927

Wood DS (1974) Current views of the development of slaty cleavage. Annu Rev Earth Sci 2:1–35

Wood DS, Oertel G (1980) Deformation in the Cambrian slate belt of Wales. J Geol 88:309–326

Wood DS, Oertel G, Singh J, Bennett HF (1976) Strain and anisotropy in deformed rocks. Phil Trans R Soc Lond A283:27–42

Woodland BG (1982) Gradational development of domainal slaty cleavage, its origin and relation to chlorite porphyroblasts in the Martinsburg Formation, eastern Pennsylvania. Tectonophysics 82:89–124

Woodland BG (1985) Relationship of concretions and chlorite-muscovite porphyroblasts to the development of domainal cleavage in low-grade metamorphic deformed rocks from north-central Wales, Great Britain. J Struct Geol 7:205–216

Wright TO, Henderson JR (1992) Volume loss during cleavage formation in the Meguma Group, Nova Scotia, Canada. J Struct Geol 14:281–290

Wright TO, Platt LB (1982) Pressure dissolution and cleavage in the Martinsburg shale. Am J Sci 282:122–135

Yardley BWC (1989) An introduction to metamorphic petrology. Longman Earth Sci Series, Wiley, New York

Yardley BWD, MacKenzie WS, Guilford C (1990) Atlas of metamorphic rocks and their textures. Longman, New York

Yund RA, Tullis J (1991) Compositional changes of minerals associated with dynamic recrystallisation. Contrib Mineral Petrol 108:346–355

Zeuch DH (1982) Ductile faulting, dynamic recrystallization, and grain size sensitive flow of olivine. Tectonophysics 83:293–308

Zhang J, Dirks PHGM, Passchier CW (1994) Extensional collapse and uplift in a polymetamorphic granulite terrain in the Archaean and Palaeoproterozoic of north China. Precambrian Res 67:37–57

Zwart HJ (1960) The chronological succession of folding and metamorphism in the central Pyrenees. Geol Rdsch 50:203–218

Zwart HJ (1962) On the determination of polymetamorphic mineral associations, and its application to the Bosost area (central Pyrenees). Geol Rdsch 52:38–65

Zwart HJ, Calon T (1977) Chloritoid crystals from Curaglia: growth during flattening or pushing aside. Tectonophysics 39:477–486

Zwart HJ, Oele JA (1966) Rotated magnetite crystals from the Rocroi Massif (Ardennes). Geol Mijnb 45:70–74

Index